GROUPS
AND
FIELDS

*A Programmed Unit
in Modern Mathematics*

BOYD EARL
Department of Mathematics
Bucknell University

Program Editors

J. WILLIAM MOORE
Department of Education
Bucknell University

WENDELL I. SMITH
Department of Psychology
Bucknell University

GROUPS
A Programmed Unit

McGRAW-HILL BOOK COMPANY, INC.

AND FIELDS

in Modern Mathematics

New York   San Francisco   Toronto   London

GROUPS AND FIELDS: A Programmed Unit in Modern Mathematics

Library of Congress Catalog Card Number: 63-10837

Preface

In a sense, the century in which we live has been, and is, a century of revolution—in particular, of revolutions in knowledge. Mathematics has been centrally involved in the revolutions in the sciences—in both the social and natural sciences. Of equal importance to its participation in the scientific revolutions is the revolution within mathematics itself. Teachers of mathematics rapidly are becoming aware of the changing views of the appropriate content for courses in mathematics, courses bearing such familiar titles as algebra, geometry, trigonometry, and calculus. Through the impetus provided by the work of the School Mathematics Study Group, the Commission on Mathematics of the College Entrance Examination Board, the University of Illinois Committee on School Mathematics, and similar groups, text material in *modern mathematics* for secondary schools and college curricula has been developed in the past half-dozen years.

What is "modern" mathematics? How does it differ from traditional mathematics? Why should we study it? What can be done with it? These are questions which are raised frequently by both teachers and students of the traditional mathematics. They deserve an explanation, although it is not an easy task to provide specific answers to such general questions. Much of modern mathematics is not new. Little of it has been developed recently; in fact, many of the most important ideas in modern mathematics, e.g., the concepts of set, relationship, and function, probably antedate man's recorded history. Further, the formal development and introduction of many of the concepts into mathematics during the nineteenth and twentieth centuries was preceded by some three hundred years of research. To mortal man, "modern" does not mean anything as old as a sixteenth-, seventeenth-, or eighteenth-century invention! The "new" mathematics is modern largely in the sense that its importance has become generally recognized by mathematicians only during this century. The great significance of the "new" mathematics has been widely recognized as a result of (1) the tremendous amount of research in mathematics and science which has been done in this century and (2) the technological revolution which goes on around us unabated.

The chief task of the creative mathematician is the development of theorems and the construction of proofs for them. While pursuing the research necessary for attaining this goal, the need for more languages which permit precise definition of terms became apparent. Increasingly in the recent history of mathematics the importance of formal logic has been recognized. The use of axioms, theorems, and proofs has been extended to all mathematics, not restricted simply to Euclid's geometry.

The extension of the logical system to the algebras has been particularly fruitful, since it has brought more attention to the *structure* of algebras and has helped to decrease the emphasis on an algebra as a means only of solving equations—with the accompanying decrease in the overemphasis on the development of manipulative skills. This is not to imply that solving equations and manipulating a number system with skill are unimportant. On the contrary, the ability to solve and the ability to manipulate have great utility *providing that they are done with understanding*. Without understanding, one manipulates numbers and solves problems as though mathematics were a bag of tricks. The important developments in the mathematics underlying the technological revolution which has produced automation and the digital computer were not new "tricks." The increasing number of applications of mathematics in economics, biology, sociology, and psychology are not the result of transplanting old "tricks" to new subject matter.

Many concepts have been developed formally and applied to the revolution mentioned in the preceding paragraphs. In *Prelude to Mathematics*[1] W.W. Sawyer states, "At one time mathematicians felt groups were the key to the secret of the universe, and one can hardly blame them." The French mathematician, Evariste Galois, first reported in 1832 an extensive study of groups. His interest was in a problem which had troubled mathematicians for nearly three hundred years, *viz.*, the solvability of the equation of the fifth degree by algebraic methods. Galois was able to show that any algebraic equation is connected with a group and that by examining the group, one could determine whether the equations could be reduced to something simpler. The assumptions involved are few; yet it is surprising how much theory has been built on these few assumptions and into how wide a range of mathematics this theory has entered.

The reader will find little difficulty in following the presentation, since he already has had extensive experience with one or more systems which have this type of structure, e.g., the system of integers. As with many topics in modern mathematics, however, the student may feel that the usefulness of this topic is small. It may be helpful to keep in mind that such concepts as set, group, ring, and field have helped immensely in clarifying and unifying many topics in "traditional" mathematics. The concept of group, for example, has been useful in clarifying certain relationships between geometry and algebra, relationships which were once considered quite distant. Further, these same concepts must be considered as part of the language required for applying mathematics to an increasing range of problems, including problems in the social sciences and psychology.

Some applications of the concepts of groups and fields will be found in the References.

---

[1] Penguin Books, Inc., Baltimore, 1955, p. 102.

Prerequisites

In order to read this material with profit, you should have had at least one
year of high school algebra and some work in geometry. The examples used
have been chosen from algebra and geometry. Further, you should be familiar with the concept of a set and with the elementary relations (equality,
inclusion) between sets and the elementary operations (union, intersection)
on sets. Naturally, this includes a knowledge of the symbolism used to indicate each. If you find that you are not entirely familiar with the symbolism
and operations for sets, you will discover that you can acquire the knowledge
you need by spending a few hours with an elementary treatment of sets, such
as *Sets, Relations, and Functions: A Programmed Unit in Modern Mathematics*,[1] *Modern Mathematics: Topics and Problems*,[2] or *Principles of
Mathematics*.[3]

How to Use This Text

The material presented to you in this text is in the form of a program for
self-instruction. The subject matter covered in this program has been bro-
ken into items, or frames, which permit you to learn efficiently by studying
and answering each step or frame separately.

The material in this text will be arranged in this manner:

1   To assist the student to learn mathematics more efficiently, a self-
    instruction program provides units of new information in separate
    frames. The information is broken down into separate question-and-
    answer frames to make it easier for you to _____.

    learn

2   Thus each program item, or _____, provides new information
    which you will read carefully and for which you provide an answer
    in writing. You will then be able to compare your answer with the
    correct one given below each question frame.

    frame

Usually a student will find that the most effective way to study a program
for self-instruction is to read and study each frame carefully, covering with
a sheet of paper or an index card all of the material on the page below the

[1]Myra McFadden, McGraw-Hill Book Company, Inc., New York, 1962.
[2]D. J. Aiken and C. A. Beseman, McGraw-Hill Book Company, Inc., New York,
1959.
[3]C. B. Allendoerfer and C. O. Oakley, McGraw-Hill Book Company, Inc., New
York, 1955.

frame he is studying. It is best to study definitions and formulas thoroughly as you go along so that you will be able to acquire new information, step by step, as you go through this self-instruction course.

After you have studied a question frame, write out your answer fully on a separate piece of paper. Then move the sheet of paper down the page until you uncover the correct answer below the question frame. Compare your answer with the answer given in the text. Since later topics in the program build on the material covered in earlier sections, you will find it desirable to study again each question on which you make an error and to correct your first answer to that question.

IMPORTANT THINGS TO REMEMBER

1. Always read the question frame first.
2. Write your answer out in complete form.
3. Compare your answer with the answer given in the answer frame of the text.
4. If you make an error, correct your answer before going to the next question frame.
5. Learning is an *active* process. You must *do* something; i.e., you must *respond* to each question by writing your answer *before* you read the answer provided.

Review

To enable you to review the material in a programmed text, the author has made three provisions: (1) At regular intervals, *criterion frames* have been prepared. Each of these will be recognized by the symbol • preceding the frame number. If you are unable to answer a criterion frame correctly, you should reread the teaching frames immediately preceding it to be certain that you have acquired the information before proceeding to the next set of teaching frames. (2) Self-test problems have been provided at intervals. The answers to these test problems are given at the end of the program. It is advisable to work through each test problem before proceeding to the next section. If you find that you are not able to answer most of the questions correctly, you should reread the teaching frames which contain the information needed to answer correctly any question upon which you have not succeeded. (3) An Index to the teaching frames in which key concepts are presented is provided at the back of the book.

Panels

At several points in the text, you will be asked to refer by number to one of thirteen panels, each of which contains information required for solving and understanding problems. These panels are located at the end of the book, following the Index. If you find that reference to the panels is more convenient with the panel pages out of the book, you may remove them from the book at the inner margins.

The Development and Testing of a Self-instructional Program

Unlike nearly all textbooks, a self-instructional program is developed in a manner which maximizes its ability to teach. If the program has been properly constructed, the reader who carefully *follows the directions* for its use will be able to learn its contents with no other help.

Groups and Fields has been tested on more than four hundred students in several high schools and colleges throughout the country. The students' answers to the question frames have guided the author through three revisions of the original draft of the program. In a sense, a programmed text is written by students—or what is written in the final form is determined by the students on whom the program was tested.

Our "student authors" were drawn from several sources:

1. High school mathematics teachers, enrolled in a summer institute to learn some modern algebra
2. High school students enrolled in college preparatory programs
3. High school students enrolled in an enrichment program in which two hours were devoted to working with programmed mathematics once each week
4. Beginning mathematics majors in colleges
5. College students enrolled in courses in general mathematics

How long will it take a reader to complete the total program? The time required by students in the trials varied from fifteen to thirty-nine hours, with the average about twenty-six hours. These times include the completion of all review questions.

In the table below, the mean gain in achievement based on five tests and the mean per cent of errors committed on the program are presented for three high school populations and two college freshman populations.

Type of population	Mean gain in achievement, %	Mean per cent of errors
1. Rural high school junior and senior volunteers	80	2.2
2. Metropolitan high school seniors enrolled in "modern mathematics"	72	5.3
3. Metropolitan high school seniors enrolled in "advanced algebra"	75	4.8
4. Public college freshmen	82	4.4
5. Private liberal arts college freshmen	81	2.0

Since very few of these students had ever heard of group or field before working through the programmed text, these data indicate that the program was a reasonably effective teacher.

Acknowledgements

The original draft of the program was written by Boyd Earl; each of the succeeding revisions was prepared by Mary Haupt Smith with the assistance of William Hauck. Without their contributions, publication of the program would not have been possible.

We, also, are indebted to all the students and teachers who volunteered to work through the program to improve its instructional value and to McGraw-Hill Book Co., Inc. for its sincere efforts to test the program widely before its publication.

Wendell I. Smith
J. William Moore

References

Adler, Irving: *The New Mathematics*, The John Day Company, Inc., New York, 1958. For an elementary treatment of binary operations and groups see chaps. 1, 2, and 3.

Allendoerfer, C. B., and C. O. Oakley: *Principles of Mathematics*, McGraw-Hill Book Company, Inc., New York, 1955. For a brief treatment of groups, see pp. 80-81; for fields, see pp. 83-91.

Andree, R. V.: *Selections from Modern Abstract Algebra*, Holt, Rinehart and Winston, Inc., New York, 1958. For relations see pp. 36-43; for groups see pp. 78-85.

Eves, Howard, and C. V. New Som: *An Introduction to the Foundations and Fundamental Concepts of Mathematics*, Holt, Rinehart and Winston, Inc., New York, 1958. For relations see pp. 139-142.

Felix, Lucien: *The Modern Aspects of Mathematics*, Basic Books, Inc., New York, 1960.

School Mathematics Study Group: *Mathematics for High School: Intermediate Mathematics; Part II*, rev. ed., Yale University Press, New Haven, Conn., 1961. For a general introduction for high school students to groups and fields, see chap. 15.

Stoll, R. R.: *Sets, Logic, and Axiomatic Theories*, W. H. Freeman and Company, San Francisco, 1961. For relations see pp. 25-37.

Weiss, Marie: *Higher Algebra for the Undergraduate*, John Wiley & Sons, Inc., New York, 1949. For groups see chap. 3.

Contents

	Frame	Page
Preface		v
References		x

Part One BINARY RELATIONS   1

	Frame	Page
I. Sets and Ordered Pairs	1	2
II. Cartesian Products	28	7
Self-test I		14
III. Binary Relations	68	15
Self-test II		35
IV. Properties of a Binary Relation		35
a. Reflexive	163	35
Self-test III		50
b. Symmetric	242	51
c. Transitive	301	61
V. Equivalence Relation	361	71
VI. Partition of a Set and Equivalence Classes	403	79
VII. Review Test for Part One		88
Criterion Frames 8, 13, 20, 22, 23, 29, 40, 45, 46, 74, 105, 198, 206, 207, 212, 213, 222, 232, 233, 252, 269, 270, 309, 332-334, 339, 366, 367, 373, 379, 385, 417, 428, 437, 442		

Part Two BINARY OPERATIONS ON A SET   93

	Frame	Page
I. Functions and Mapping	448	94
II. Permutations of Degree N	475	100
Self-test IV		113
III. Permutation Multiplication	541	117
IV. Binary Operations on a Set	580	126
V. Properties of a Binary Operation		136
a. Commutative	623	136
b. Associative	656	143
c. Identity Element	685	149
Self-test V		154
d. Inverse	710	155

	Frame	*Page*
VI. Review Test for Part Two		163
Criterion Frames 449, 456, 457, 460, 469, 473, 480-486, 489, 506, 507, 508, 520, 528, 543, 554-556, 563, 583, 597, 598, 616, 632, 633, 653-655, 664-667, 672, 689, 707, 739-743		

Part Three   GROUPS   165

	Frame	Page
I. Symmetries of an Equilateral Triangle	744	165
II. Group	768	174
III. Proofs of Some Theorems on Groups	809	183
Self-test VI		198
IV. Mappings and Transformations	874	199
V. Transformation Group	1024	236
VI. Review Test for Part Three		249
Criterion Frames 783, 797, 810, 820, 821, 828, 838, 851, 873, 896, 925, 926, 939, 960, 971, 972, 990, 992		

Part Four   FIELDS   251

	Frame	Page
I. Review of Binary Relations and Properties	1074	251
II. Review of Binary Operations and Properties	1089	252
III. Example of Sets with Two Binary Operations	1130	263
IV. Fields	1192	274
V. Proofs of Some Theorems of Fields	1265	288
VI. Review Test for Part Four		302
Criterion Frames 1096, 1097, 1099, 1103, 1106, 1109, 1120, 1160, 1164, 1193, 1197, 1284, 1287, 1288		

Appendix A   An Arbitrary Equivalence Relation   303

Appendix B   Elementary Set Theory   305

Answers to Test Questions	311
Index	321

Part One   BINARY RELATIONS

Recall for a moment your previous study of mathematics and consider some typical mathematical statements from these studies. You will soon notice that, almost invariably, such statements do *not* involve a single object by itself, but they concern conditions or relationships holding (or failing to hold) between two or more objects. For example, consider the following:

1. Line m is perpendicular to line n
2. $2x = 4$
3. $a < b$
4. $A \not\subset B$ (A is not a subset of B)
5. Lines m, n, p are concurrent

In example 1 there is a relationship (perpendicularity) existing between line m and line n, in that order.

In example 2 there is a condition (equality) existing between the two quantities, $2x$ and 4, in that order.

In example 3 there is a condition ("less than") existing between the two quantities a and b, in that order.

In example 4 there is a condition (inclusion) which does not exist between the set A and the set B, in that order.

In example 5 there is a condition (concurrency) existing between three lines m, n, p, in that order.

Even a simpler statement such as:

6. $\triangle ABC$ is isosceles

which at first glance seems to concern an object ($\triangle ABC$) in isolation, is equivalent to a statement involving a relationship existing between two objects, namely, the relationship of equality existing between the lengths of two of the sides of the triangle.

7. "8 is an even integer" is equivalent to the statement "2 is a divisor of 8"; thus we have a relationship ("is a divisor of") existing between two integers 2 and 8, in that order.

The simplest relationships in mathematics are those between two elements, and in examining some specific examples, we soon discover some striking similarities between seemingly dissimilar objects and relationships. For example, consider the following:

1

I. In the set of real numbers R with the relationship "less than or equal" ($\leq$):

   a. If a is an element of R, then $a \leq a$.

   b. If a, b, c are elements of R and $a \leq b$ and $b \leq c$, then $a \leq c$.

   c. If a, b are elements of R and $a \leq b$ and $b \leq a$, then $a = b$.

II. In the set of all subsets of a given set S with the relation "is a subset of" ($\subset$):

   a. If A is a subset of S, then $A \subset A$.

   b. If A, B, C are subsets of S and $A \subset B$ and $B \subset C$, then $A \subset C$.

   c. If A, B are subsets of S and $A \subset B$ and $B \subset A$, then $A = B$.

There are also differences, of course. For example, in II there is a special set ϕ (the empty set) and: If A is a subset of S, then $\phi \subset A$. There is no special element x of the real numbers satisfying a similar statement in example I (that is, if a is an element of R, then $x \leq a$).

In Part One of the program we will abstract the concept of a relationship between two elements and consider some important properties which such relationships may or may not have. Eventually we will discover the characteristic properties of a very important class of relationships between two elements, the class which includes the relationships of equality of numbers, similarity of triangles, and congruency of triangles, among others.

I. Sets and Ordered Pairs

1 Let A be a set having exactly two members, p and q. We may write $A = \{p, q\}$. Since the equality of sets is not affected by the order in which the members are written, we may also write $A = $ ____ .

$\{q, p\}$

2 Let S be a set having two members, x and y.

(1) $S = $ _____ or $S = $ _____

(2) We may do this because the equality of sets is *not* affected by the _____ in which the members appear.

(1) $\{x, y\}$, $\{y, x\}$ (2) order

3 When we consider relationships or conditions which may hold between objects, order often *is* important. Consider the relationship "is a subset of" ($\subset$) between the sets $A = \{a, b, c\}$, $B = \{b, c\}$. We have (1) _____ $\subset$ _____ . But (2) _____ $\not\subset$ _____ .

(1) $B \subset A$ or $\{b, c\} \subset \{a, b, c\}$
(2) $A \not\subset B$ or $\{a, b, c\} \not\subset \{b, c\}$

4 Let $S = \{1, 2, 3, 4\}$ and the condition be "is a divisor of." We might propose to list the set of subsets of S for which the condition "is a divisor of" holds. Since 2 is a divisor of 4, $\{2, 4\}$ would be an element.

However, since the _____ of the elements of a set is *not* important, $\{2, 4\} = \{$ ___ , ___ $\}$, and ____ is not a divisor of ___ .

order, $\{4, 2\}$,   4,   2

5 If we wish to consider a pair of elements in a specified order, say with p first and q second, we write the *ordered pair* (___ , ___). If we wish to consider the same pair of elements with q first and p second, we write the _____ pair (___ , ___).

(p,q),   ordered, (q,p)

6 (1)   A set is indicated by enclosing its members in _____ .
  (2)   The _____ of the elements is not important.
  (3)   An *ordered* _____ is indicated by enclosing the elements in parentheses.
  (4)   The _____ of the elements is important.

(1)   braces
(2)   order
(3)   pair
(4)   order

7 The braces in $\{a, b\}$ indicate that $\{a, b\}$ is a set. The order of the elements of $\{a, b\}$ is not important.
  (1)   The _____ in (a,b) indicate that (a,b) is a(n) _____ .
  (2)   The _____ of the elements of (a,b) _____ (is or is not) important.

(1)   parentheses,   ordered pair
(2)   order,   is

•8 Write the ordered pair having p as the first element and q as the second element.

(p,q)
Note that the parentheses and the specified order are necessary for the correct answer.

9 A set having exactly two elements, p and q, is written
(1) _____ or (2) _____. An ordered pair with p considered as the first element and q considered as the second element is written
(3) _____. A *different* ordered pair is obtained when q is considered as the first element and p considered as the second element. It is written (4) _____.

(1) $\{p, q\}$ (2) $\{q, p\}$ (3) (p,q) (4) (q,p)

COMMENT

If you continue your study of mathematics, you will find that an ordered pair can be defined in terms of sets; however, we will define the properties of ordered pairs which would result from the definition to which we referred above.

10 The element in the first position of an ordered pair is called the *first coordinate* of the ordered pair. The element in the second position is called the *second coordinate* of the ordered pair.
Thus (1) _____ is the first _____ of the _____ (p,q)
(2) ___ is the _____ of the _____ (p,q)

(1) p,   coordinate,   ordered pair
(2) q,   second coordinate,   ordered pair

11 Write the ordered pair having the first coordinate y and the second coordinate x.

(y,x)

12 p is the _____ of the ordered pair (q,p).

second coordinate

•13 In the _____ (a,b), a is the _____ of (a,b) and b is
     the _____ of (a,b).

ordered pair,   first coordinate,   second coordinate

14 (5,6) is a(n) _____ . The first coordinate of (5,6) is _____ and
     the second coordinate of (5,6) is _____ .

ordered pair,   5,   6

15 Definition (equality of ordered pairs): If (a,b) and (c,d) are ordered
     pairs, $(a,b) = (c,d)$ if and only if $a = c$ and $b = d$. Thus
     (5,3) _____ (= or $\neq$) (3,5).

$\neq$

16 Since the function of ordered pairs is to designate the order of the
     elements, we define two ordered pairs as equal if and only if they
     have equal coordinates arranged in the same order. That is,
     $(a,b) = (c,d)$ if and only if _____ = _____ and _____ = _____ .

$a = c,$ $b = d$

17 A similar definition is used in the complex number system. The
     complex number $p + qi$ is equal to the complex number $x + yi$ if and
     only if _____ = _____ and _____ = _____ .

$p = x,$ $q = y$

18 In addition to acquiring order, we have also gained another new prop-
     erty not held by a two-element set. $\{a, a\} = \{\_\_\_\}$, so $\{a, a\}$ is *not*
     a two-element set, but (a,a) *is* a(n) _____ .

$\{a\},$ ordered pair

19 $(a,b) = (5,-2)$ if and only if _____ and _____ .

$a = 5,$ $b = -2$

•20 If (a,b) and (c,d) are ordered pairs, $(a,b) = (c,d)$ if and only if
     _____ .

$a = c$ and $b = d$

21 (1)   Does $\{5, 7\} = \{7, 5\}$?
   (2)   Does $(5,7) = (7,5)$?

(1)   yes   Note that these are sets.
(2)   no   Note that these are ordered pairs.
If you miss either frame 22 or frame 23, you should review frames 1 to 21.

•22 (1) (x,y) is a(n) _____ .
   (2) x is the _____ of (x,y).
   (3) y is the _____ of (x,y).

(1)   ordered pair
(2)   first coordinate
(3)   second coordinate

•23 If (x,y) and (p,q) are ordered pairs, $(x,y) = (p,q)$ if and only if
_____ .

$x = p$ and $y = q$

24 Let $A = \{(1,4), (a,b), (p,q)\}$.
   (1) A is a(n) _____ having _____ (how many) members.
   (2)   Each of its members is a(n) _____ .

(1)   set,   three   (2)   ordered pair

25 Let $S = \{(a,b), (1,2)\}$. Since S is a set, the (1) _____ of the elements of S is not important. We might have written
   (2) $S = \{$_____ $\}$.

(1)   order
(2) $\{(1,2), (a,b)\}$ Note that the elements themselves are ordered pairs. The ordering of the coordinates of an ordered pair is fixed.

26 For what value of y will the ordered pairs $(-2,y)$ and $(-2,\pi)$ be equal ?

$y = \pi$

27 Let $S = \{0, 1, 2\}$ and $T = \{p, q\}$. $(0,q)$ is a(n) _____whose first coordinate is an element of ____ and whose second coordinate is an element of ____ .

ordered pair, S, T

II. Cartesian Products

28 Let $S = \{0, 1, 2\}$ and $T = \{p, q\}$. Write in tabulated or roster form the set of all ordered pairs that can be formed with the first coordinate a member of S and the second coordinate a member of T.
$\{(\_\_,\_\_), (\_\_,\_\_), (\_\_,\_\_), (\_\_,\_\_), (\_\_,\_\_), (\_\_,\_\_)\}$

$\{(0,p), (0,q), (1,p), (1,q), (2,p), (2,q)\}$
Note: Since this is a set, you may have the elements (ordered pairs) arranged in different order. Within each ordered pair the coordinates may not be rearranged.

•29 Let $S = \{a, b, c\}$ and $T = \{c, d\}$. Write in roster or tabulated form the set of all ordered pairs which can be formed with the first coordinate from S and the second coordinate from T.

$\{(a,c), (a,d), (b,c), (b,d), (c,c), (c,d)\}$

30 Let $S = \{a, b, c\}$ and $T = \{1, 2\}$. Write in roster form the set of the ordered pairs of the form (x,y) such that $x \in S$ and $y \in T$. The new set formed is usually denoted by $S \times T$, and read "S cross T."

$S \times T = \{(a,1), (a,2), (b,1), (b,2), (c,1), (c,2)\}$

31 Let $S = \{a, b\}$. Write in roster form the set of all ordered pairs of the form (x,y) such that $x \in S$ and $y \in S$. This set is denoted by $S \times S$, and read "S cross S."

$S \times S = \{(a,a), (a,b), (b,a), (b,b)\}$

32 Let $S = \{a, b, c\}$. Write in roster form the set of all ordered pairs
    (x,y) such that $x \in S$ and $y \in S$.
    $S \times S =$ _____

$\{(a,a), (a,b), (a,c), (b,a), (b,b), (b,c), (c,a), (c,b), (c,c)\}$

---

33 Let $S = \{a, b\}$ and $T = \{1\}$. The ordered pairs of the form (x,y)
    such that $x \in S$ and $y \in T$ form a new set $\{(a,1), (b,1)\}$.
    (1)   Each element of this new set is a(n) _____.
    (2)   The set $\{(a,1), (b,1)\}$ has how many elements ?

---

(1)   ordered pair   (2)   two

---

34 (1) $\{(a,1), (b,2), (a,3)\}$ is a(n) _____.
    (2)   Each of its elements is a(n) _____.

---

(1)   set   (2)   ordered pair

---

35 The set $\{(1,1), (0,-4), (a,b)\}$ contains three elements. Each element
    is an ordered pair.
    (1)   The set $\{(1,1), (2,1), (a,b), (b,1)\}$ contains _____ elements.
    (2)   Each element is a(n) _____.

---

(1)   four   (2)   ordered pair

---

36 Let $S = \{a, b\}$ and $T = \{1, 2\}$.
    (1)   Tabulate the set of the ordered pairs of the form (x,y) such that
          $x \in S$ and $y \in T$.
    (2)   Your answer is a set of _____.
    (3)   How is the set denoted ?

---

(1) $\{(a,1), (a,2), (b,1), (b,2)\}$ (2)   ordered pairs   (3) $S \times T$

---

37 Let $S = \{1, 2, 3\}$ and $T = \{a, b\}$. The notation used to describe the
    set of ordered pairs such as you have been constructing is
    $S \times T = \{(x,y) \mid x \in S$ and $y \in T\}$. This is read, "$S \times T$ equals the
    set of all ordered pairs (x,y) such that x is an element of S and y
    is an element of T." Write $S \times T$ in roster form.

$S \times T = \{(1,a), (1,b), (2,a), (2,b), (3,a), (3,b)\}$

38 Let $S = \{a, b\}$. Consider $S \times S = \{(x,y) \mid x \in S$ and $y \in S\}$. $S \times S$ is the set of all **(1)** _____ of the form **(2)** _____ such that x is an element of **(3)** _____ and y is an element of **(4)** _____.

(1) ordered pairs   **(2)** (x,y)
(3) S **(4)** S

39 Let $S = \{a, b\}$ and $S \times S = \{(x,y) \mid x \in S$ and $y \in S\}$. Then $S \times S = \{(a,a), (a,b),$ _____ , _____ $\}$.

(b,b), (b,a)

•40 Let $S = \{0, 1, 2\}$. If $S \times S = \{(x,y) \mid x \in S$ and $y \in S\}$, write $S \times S$ in roster form.

$S \times S = \{(0,0), (0,1), (0,2), (1,0), (1,1), (1,2), (2,0), (2,1), (2,2)\}$

41 The set of ordered pairs which can be formed from two sets in a fixed order, say A and B, is called the "cartesian product" or "cross product" of A and B. It is denoted by **(1)** _____ and sometimes read "A cross B." Let $S = \{1, 2\}$ and $T = \{1, 2, 3\}$.
(2) Write $S \times T$ in roster form.

(1) $A \times B$ **(2)** $S \times T = \{(1,1), (1,2), (1,3), (2,1), (2,2), (2,3)\}$

42 *Definition*: Given the sets S and T, the cartesian product (or cross product) of S and T is given by $S \times T = \{(x,y) \mid x \in S$ and $y \in T\}$.
Let $A = \{a, b\}$ and $B = \{1, 2, 3\}$.
(1) Write $A \times B$ in roster form
(2) $A \times B$ is called the _____ of A and B.

(1) $\{(a,1), (a,2), (a,3), (b,1), (b,2), (b,3)\}$
(2) cartesian product or cross product

43 If S or T is an empty set, there is no element which can be chosen from that set in order to form an ordered pair; therefore there are no ordered pairs. Then $S \times T$ is the **(1)** _____ set. If A and B are nonempty sets, then $S \times T$ is a(n) **(2)** _____ set, each of whose members is a(n) **(3)** _____.

(1) empty or null
(2) nonempty
(3) ordered pair

44 Given the sets A and B, the set of all ordered pairs which can be formed with the first coordinate an element of A and the second coordinate an element of B is called the **(1)** _____ of A and B. It is denoted by **(2)** $A \times B = \{$ ____ $| x \in A$ and $y \in B\}$.

(1) cartesian product or cross product   **(2)** (x,y)

•45 Given the sets S and T, $S \times T \{(x,y) | x \in S$ and $y \in T\}$ and
$T \times S \{(x,y) | x \in T$ and $y \in S\}$.
Let $A = \{1\}$ and $B = \{a, b\}$.
(1) Write $A \times B$ in roster form.
(2) Write $B \times A$ in roster form.
(3) $A \times B$ is called the _____ of A and B.

(1) $\{(1,a), (1,b)\}$
(2) $\{(a,1), (b,1)\}$ (Note that in this case $A \times B \neq B \times A$.)
(3) cartesian product or cross product

•46 Often only one set, say S, is involved. In this case the cartesian product is the set of all ordered pairs which can be formed with the first coordinate an element of S, and the second coordinate an element of S; i.e., $S \times S \{(x,y) | x \in S$ and $y \in S\}$. Let $S = \{a, b, c\}$. Write $S \times S$ in roster form.

$\{(a,a), (a,b), (a,c), (b,a), (b,b), (b,c), (c,a), (c,b), (c,c)\}$

47 Given the sets A and B, $A \times B$ is called the _____ of A and B and is denoted by $A \times B = \{(x,y) |$ ____ $\}$.

cartesian product or cross product
$x \in A$ and $y \in B$

48 Let S and T be sets. $S \times T =$ _____

$\{(x,y) | x \in S$ and $y \in T\}$ (You may use symbols other than x and y.)

49 $S \times T = \{(a,1), (a,2), (b,1), (b,2), (c,1), (c,2)\}$ where $S = \{$ ____ $\}$ and $T = \{$ ____ $\}$

$\{a, b, c\}$,
$\{1, 2\}$

50 Let $S = \{\phi, \{p\}, \{p,q\}\}$ and $T = \{\phi, \{a\}\}$. Write $S \times T$ in roster form.

$S \times T = \{(\phi,\phi), (\phi,\{a\}), (\{p\},\phi), (\{p\},\{a\}), (\{p,q\},\phi), (\{p,q\},\{a\})\}$.

51 A handy device for representing the cartesian product of two sets, say S and T, can be made as follows:

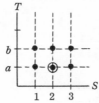

Let $S = \{1, 2, 3\}$
$T = \{a, b\}$

Notice the six points of intersection of the dotted lines. These six points correspond to the six ordered pairs of $S \times T$. The point circled corresponds to the ordered pair $(2,a)$. Make a similar drawing and circle the point that corresponds to the ordered pair $(3,b)$.

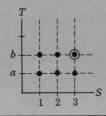

52 Let $S = \{1, 2, 3\}$. $S \times S$ is represented by:

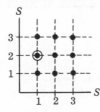

The point circled represents the ordered pair $(1,2)$. Notice that the first coordinate comes from the horizontal line. Make a similar sketch and circle the point that corresponds to the ordered pair $(3,1)$.

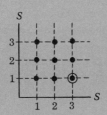

53 Let $S = \{a, b, c\}$. Represent $S \times S$ graphically and label the point representing the ordered pair (b,c). Unless otherwise stated, it is understood that the first coordinate is represented by a point along the horizontal line and the second coordinate is represented by a point along the vertical line.

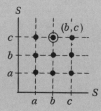

54 Let S be the set of positive integers.
    (1) $S \times S = \{(x,y) \mid$ _____ $\}$.
    (2) Is $(1,3) \in S \times S$?
    (3) Is $(3,1) \in S \times S$?
    (4) Is $(3,1) = (1,3)$?

    (1) $x \in S$ and $y \in S$ or x is a positive integer and y is a positive integer
    (2) yes   **(3)** yes   **(4)** no

55 Let $S = \{0, 1\}$ and $T = \{1, 2, 3\}$. $S \times T = \{$ __ , __ , __ , __ , __ , __ $\}$

$(0,1)$, $(0,2)$, $(0,3)$, $(1,1)$, $(1,2)$, $(1,3)$
If your answer is correct, omit frames 56 to 60.

56 Let $S = \{a, b, c\}$. $S \times S = \{$ __ , __ , __ , __ , __ , $\cdots \}$

(a,a), (a,b), (a,c), (b,a), (b,b), (b,c), (c,a), (c,b), (c,c)

57 Given a set S, the cross product $S \times S$ is a set each of whose elements is a(n) _____ .

ordered pair

58 Given sets S and T, $S \times T$ is called the _____ of S and T.

cartesian product or cross product

59 Let $S = \{1, 2, 3\}$ and $T = \{a, b\}$. Write $S \times T$ in roster form.

$\{(1,a), (1,b), (2,a), (2,b), (3,a), (3,b)\}$

60 Suppose $S \times T = \{(a,1), (a,3), (b,1), (b,3)\}$. Then $S = \{a, b\}$ and $T =$ _____.

$\{1, 3\}$

61 Let $W = \{(1,a), (2,b)\}$.
   (1) *If there were* two sets S and T such that $W = S \times T$, then
       $S =$ _____ and $T =$ _____.
   (2) Write $S \times T$ in roster form.
   (3) Does $W = S \times T$?
   (4) Is $W \subset S \times T$ (W a subset of $S \times T$)?

   (1) $\{1, 2\}$, $\{a, b\}$ **(2)** $\{(1,a), (1,b), (2,a), (2,b)\}$
   (3) No.
   (4) yes

62 Suppose $W = \{(a,1), (a,2), (b,3)\}$. Then if W is to be the cross product of some sets, say S and T, S would have to have a and b as members.
   (1) T would have to have 1, 2, and _____ as members.
   (2) $S = \{a, b\}$ and $T = \{1, 2,$ _____ $\}$.
   (3) Write $S \times T$ in roster form.
   (4) Does $W = S \times T$?
   (5) W is a(n) _____ of $S \times T$.

   (1) 3
   (2) 3
   (3) $\{(a,1), (a,2), (a,3), (b,1), (b,2), (b,3)\}$
   (4) no
   (5) subset

63 Given any set W of ordered pairs, you can find sets S and T such that every member of W is a member of $S \times T$; but it is not necessarily true that every member of $S \times T$ is a member of W. The most that can be guaranteed is that W is a(n) _____ of $S \times T$
(W _____ $S \times T$).

subset, $\subset$

64 Thus, given a set W of ordered pairs, S and T exist such that W is a subset of $S \times T$. Simply let S be any set such that the set of all first coordinates of elements of W are members of S. Let T be any set such that the set of all second coordinates of elements of W are members of T. Then $W \subset S \times T$. For example, let $W = \{(0,1), (1,a), (3,5), (0,5), (0,a)\}$. The *minimal* choice of S and T would be $S =$ _____ and $T =$ _____ .
Note: By minimal, we mean the set containing as few members as possible.

$\{0, 1, 3\}$, $\{1, a, 5\}$

65 Let $W = \{(a,0), (0,1), (b,3), (b,4)\}$. The minimal S and T such that $W \subset S \times T$ is $S =$ _____ and $T =$ _____ .

$\{a, 0, b\}$, $\{0, 1, 3, 4\}$

66 Given two sets S and T, $S \times T$, $S \times S$, $T \times T$, and $T \times S$ are new
(1) _____ whose elements are (2) _____ .
(3) $S \times S = \{(x,y)\, |$ _____ $\}$
(4) $S \times T = \{(x,y)\, |$ _____ $\}$
(5) $T \times T = \{(x,y)\, |$ _____ $\}$
(6) $T \times S = \{(x,y)\, |$ _____ $\}$

(1)   sets   (2)   ordered pairs   (3) $x \in S$ and $y \in S$
(4) $x \in S$ and $y \in T$ (5) $x \in T$ and $y \in T$ (6) $x \in T$ and $y \in S$

67 Let $S = \{1, 2, 3\}$ and $T = \{a, b\}$.
(1)   Write $S \times T$ in roster form.
(2)   Write $T \times S$ in roster form.
(3)   Does $S \times T = T \times S$?

(1) $\{(1,a), (1,b), (2,a), (2,b), (3,a), (3,b)\}$
(2) $\{(a,1), (a,2), (a,3), (b,1), (b,2), (b,3)\}$
(3)   no, not in this case

Self-test I (Answers to Self-test I appear on page 311)

1   (p,q) is a(n) _____ .

2   In the ordered pair (x,y), x is called the _____ and y is called the _____ .

3 If (a,b) and (c,d) are ordered pairs, $(a,b) = (c,d)$ if and only if _____.

4 Let S and T be sets. $S \times T$ is called the **(1)** _____ and is defined as follows (symbolically): **(2)** $S \times T =$ _____

5 Let $S = \{a, b\}$ and $T = \{1, 2, 3\}$. Write $S \times T$ in roster form.

6 Let $A = \{1, 2\}$. Write $A \times A$ in roster form.

III. Binary Relations

68 Let $S = \{1, 2, 3, 4\}$.
   (1) Write the cross product $S \times S$ in roster form.
   (2) Consider the condition "is a divisor of" (with remainder 0). For each ordered pair in $S \times S$, say (x,y), decide whether "x is a divisor of y" is true. Write in roster form the set R of ordered pairs for which the statement is true. Consider $(1,3)$. "1 is a divisor of 3" is true, so $(1,3) \in R$. Consider $(4,3)$. "4 is a divisor of 3" is not true, so $(4,3) \notin R$. Consider $(2,3)$. "2 is a divisor of 3" is not true, so $(2,3) \notin R$.

   (1) $\{(1,1), (1,2), (1,3), (1,4), (2,1), (2,2), (2,3), (2,4), (3,1), (3,2), (3,3), (3,4), (4,1), (4,2), (4,3), (4,4)\}$
   (2) $R = \{(1,1), (1,2), (1,3), (1,4), (2,2), (2,4), (3,3), (4,4)\}$

69 Let $S = \{1, 2, 3\}$.
   (1) Write the cross product $S \times S$ in roster form.
   (2) Consider the condition "is equal to" ($=$). Let R be the subset of $S \times S$ containing those ordered pairs for which the condition "$=$" is satisfied. Write R in roster form.

   (1) $S \times S = \{(1,1), (1,2), (1,3), (2,1), (2,2), (2,3), (3,1), (3,2), (3,3)\}$
   (2) $R = \{(1,1), (2,2), (3,3)\}$

70 Let $S = \{\phi, \{p, q\}, \{p\}\}$.
   (1) Write the cross product $S \times S$ in roster form.
   (2) For each ordered pair of $S \times S$, determine whether the condition "$\subset$" holds. Write those ordered pairs for which "$\subset$" holds in roster form.

   (1) $S \times S = \{(\phi,\phi), (\phi,\{p, q\}), (\phi,\{p\}), (\{p, q\},\phi), (\{p, q\},\{p, q\}), (\{p, q\},\{p\}), (\{p\},\phi), (\{p\},\{p, q\}), (\{p\},\{p\})\}$
   (2) $\{(\phi,\phi), (\phi,\{p\}), (\phi,\{p, q\}), (\{p, q\},\{p, q\}), (\{p\},\{p, q\}), (\{p\},\{p\})\}$

71 Let $S = \{0, 1, 2\}$ and $T = \{1, 2\}$.
    (1) Write the cross product $S \times T$ in roster form.
    (2) Consider the condition "is less than" (<). Let R be the subset
         of $S \times T$ for which the condition holds. Write R in roster form.

    (1) $S \times T = \{(0,1), (0,2), (1,1), (1,2), (2,1), (2,2)\}$
    (2) $R = \{(0,1), (0,2), (1,2)\}$

72 Let S and T be sets.
    (1) $S \times T$ is called the _____ and consists of *all* _____
         of the form (x,y) such that _____ .
    (2) Symbolically, $S \times T =$ _____ .

    (1) cartesian or cross product of S and T,   ordered pairs,
         $x \in S$ and $y \in T$
    (2) $\{(x,y) \mid x \in S$ and $y \in T\}$.

73 Let $S = \{1, 2, 3\}$ and $T = \{3, 4\}$.
    (1) Write $S \times T$ in roster form.
    (2) Consider the condition "$x + y$ is an even integer." Instead of
         writing: let R be the subset of $S \times T$ containing those ordered
         pairs satisfying the condition above, we could write:
         $R = \{(x,y) \mid x \in S, \ y \in T, \ \text{and} \ x + y \ \text{is an even integer}\}$. List R
         in roster form.

    (1) $S \times T = \{(1,3), (1,4), (2,3), (2,4), (3,3), (3,4)\}$
    (2) $R = \{(1,3), (2,4), (3,3)\}$

•74 Let $S = \{-1, 0, 1\}$.
    (1) Write $S \times S$ in roster form.
    (2) Consider the condition "$x \cdot y > 0$." ($x \cdot y$ is a positive number.)
         Let $R = \{(x,y) \mid x \in S, \ y \in S, \ \text{and} \ x \cdot y > 0\}$. List R in roster
         form.

    (1) $S \times S = \{(-1,-1), (-1,0), (-1,1), (0,-1), (0,0), (0,1), (1,-1), (1,0),$
         $(1,1)\}$
    (2) $R = \{(-1,-1), (1,1)\}$

75 Given the condition "$<$," we have been interested in those ordered
    pairs (x,y) for which the statement "$x < y$" is true. Given the con-
    dition "is a divisor of," we have been interested in those ordered
    pairs (x,y) for which the statement "x _____ y" is true.

    is a divisor of

76 Given the condition "$\subset$" ("is a subset of" or "is contained in"), we have been interested in those ordered pairs (A,B) for which the statement ____ holds.

$A \subset B$

77 If we designate any such condition between two elements x and y by "$\Re$" then we are interested in those ordered pairs (x,y) for which the statement x ____ y is true.

$\Re$

78 Then the problems in frames 68 to 77 could be characterized in the following way:
1. Let S and T be sets. (We have $S \times T$.)
2. Let $\Re$ be a condition between two elements x, y where $x \in S$ and $y \in T$. Then we are interested in the *subset R* of $S \times T$ for which the statement ____ holds.

$x \; \Re \; y$

79 To distinguish between the condition $\Re$ and the subset R, we denote the condition by _____ $\Re$ and the subset by R.

script

80 Let S and T be given sets.
   (1) $S \times T =$ _____.
   (2) Let $\Re$ be a condition or relationship between pairs of elements from S and T. The condition $\Re$ determines a subset of $S \times T$, given by:
   $R = \{(x,y) \mid x \in S, \; y \in T, \; \text{and} \; \text{_____}\}$.

   (1) $\{(x,y) \mid x \in S, \; y \in T\}$
   (2) $x \; \Re \; y$ (note script $\Re$)

81 Let $S = \{1, 2, 3\}$.
    (1) Write $S \times S$ in roster form.
    (2) $S \times S$ is called the _____.
    (3) Let $R = \{(x,y) \mid x \in S, \ y \in T, \text{ and } x \le y\}$. (Note that $\le$ means is less than or equal to.) List R in roster form.
    (4) How are R and $S \times S$ related?

    (1) $S \times S = \{(1,1), (1,2), (1,3), (2,1), (2,2), (2,3), (3,1), (3,2), (3,3)\}$
    (2) cartesian or cross product of S and S
    (3) $R = \{(1,1), (1,2), (1,3), (2,2), (2,3), (3,3)\}$
    (4) $R \subset S \times S$

82 Let S and T be sets.
    (1) $S \times T$ is a set. Each element of $S \times T$ is a(n) _____.
    (2) $S \times T$ is called _____.
    (3) Define $S \times T$ symbolically.
    (4) Define $T \times S$ symbolically.
    (5) Under what condition will $S \times T = T \times S$?

    (1) ordered pair
    (2) the cross or cartesian product of S and T
    (3) $S \times T = \{(x,y) \mid x \in S \text{ and } y \in T\}$
    (4) $T \times S = \{(x,y) \mid x \in T \text{ and } y \in S\}$
    (5) If $S = T$, then $S \times T = T \times S$.

83 Let S and T be sets. Given a condition $\Re$ between two elements x, y, where $x \in S$ and $y \in T$, $\Re$ determines a set, R.
    (1) $R =$ _____ (symbolically)
    (2) How are R and $S \times T$ related?

    (1) $\{(x,y) \mid x \in S, \ y \in T, \text{ and } x \ \Re \ y\}$
    (2) $R \subset S \times T$

84 Let $S = \{2, 3, 4\}$.
    (1) Write $S \times S$ in roster form.
    (2) Let $R = \{(x,y) \mid x \in S, \ y \in S, \text{ and } x \text{ is a divisor of } y\}$. Write R in roster form.
    (3) Let R' be the set of elements of $S \times S$ which are *not* in R. (Recall that R' is called the complement of R in $S \times S$.) Write R' in roster form.
    (4) R' is the subset of $S \times S$ containing those _____ (x,y)

▼

where $x \in S$, $y \in S$, and the statement x _____ y is not true.

(5) $R \cup R' =$ _____ .

---

(1) $S \times S = \{(2,2), (2,3), (2,4), (3,2), (3,3), (3,4), (4,2), (4,3), (4,4)\}$
(2) $R = \{(2,2), (2,4), (3,3), (4,4)\}$
(3) $R' = \{(2,3), (3,2), (4,2), (4,3), (3,4)\}$
(4) ordered pairs,   is a divisor of
(5) $S \times S$

COMMENT

We began by studying relationships between two elements (such as $<$, $\subset$, $=$, "is a divisor of," etc.) where the elements were members of two sets in a given order. We now see that such conditions or relationships determine a subset of the cross product. That subset contains those ordered pairs for which the relationship holds (is true). The remaining elements of $S \times S$ are those ordered pairs for which the relationship does not hold.

In order to study the relationships such as those listed above ($<$, $=$, etc.), we used a technique common in mathematics; that is, *we studied the subset of $S \times T$ determined by the relationship*. We found that a condition $\Re$ which can hold between two elements in a given order determines a subset of $S \times T$, namely:

$$R = \{(x,y) \mid x \in S, \; y \in T, \text{ and } x \; \Re \; y\}$$

Now we will focus our attention on R, not on the condition determining R.

Thus our problem in the next section of the program is to study arbitrary subsets of $S \times T$ and to find properties which can be used to characterize these subsets. Then, given any condition $\Re$ ($\leq$, $\subset$, $=$, etc.), we will describe this condition $\Re$ by describing the subset of $S \times T$ determined by $\Re$.

---

85 Let $S = \{1, 3, 5\}$.
(1) Write $S \times S$ in roster form.
(2) Let $R = \{(x,y) \mid x \in S, \; y \in S, \text{ and } x + y \text{ is an odd integer}\}$. Write R in roster form.

---

(1) $S \times S = \{(1,1), (1,3), (1,5), (3,1), (3,3), (3,5), (5,1), (5,3), (5,5)\}$
(2) $R = \phi$

86 Let $S = \{1, 2, 3\}$.
   (1) Write $S \times S$ in roster form.
   (2) Let $R = \{(x,y) \mid x \in S, \; y \in S,$ and $2xy$ is an even integer$\}$. How are R and $S \times S$ related?

   (1) $S \times S = \{(1,1), (1,2), (1,3), (2,1), (2,2), (2,3), (3,1), (3,2), (3,3)\}$
   (2) $R = S \times S$

87 In frames 85 and 86 you saw the extremes of the subsets of cross products. In one case, the empty set was the result because *no* ordered pair satisfied the condition.
   (1) Is $\phi \subset S \times S$?
   In the second case, the entire cross product was determined because *every* ordered pair in the cross product satisfied the condition.
   (2) Is $S \times S \subset S \times S$?

   (1) Yes, recall that the empty set is a subset of any set.
   (2) Yes, recall that any set is a subset of itself.

88 Given sets S and T: a relationship $\Re$ determines a subset R of $S \times T$. $R = \underline{\hspace{2cm}}$(symbolically)

   $\{(x,y) \mid x \in S, \; y \in T,$ and $x \, \Re \, y\}$

89 We have seen examples of relationships $\Re$ which determine subsets of $S \times T$ ranging from the $\underline{\hspace{2cm}}$ set to $\underline{\hspace{1cm}}$ itself.

   empty, $S \times T$
   If you do not understand this answer, review frames 85 and 86.

90 Let $A = \{p, q, r\}$. List the subsets of A. There are eight.

   $\{p, q, r\}, \{p, q\}, \{p, r\}, \{q, r\}, \{p\}, \{q\}, \{r\}, \phi$

91 If you had frame 90 entirely correct, you may omit this frame. Consider the set $A = \{1, 2, 0\}$. Remember that if $C \subset A$, then all members of C must be in A.
   (1) Suppose $C = \{1, 2\}$. Is $C \subset A$?
   (2) Suppose $D = \{1, 0\}$. Is $D \subset A$?
   (3) Suppose $E = \{2, 0\}$. Is $E \subset A$?
   (4) Suppose $F = \{1\}$. Is $F \subset A$?

   (1) yes   (2) yes   (3) yes   (4) yes

▼

Now answer these questions.
(5) Is $\{2\} \subset A$?   (7) Is $\{0, 1, 2\} \subset A$?
(6) Is $\{0\} \subset A$?   (8) Is $\phi \subset A$?

---

(5) yes   (6) yes   (7) yes   (8) yes

---

(9) Thus we see that A has _____ (how many) members and
     from it we were able to form _____ subsets.

---

(9) three,   eight

---

92 If A is a set having n members, there are 2^n subsets of A. Thus
    the set $S = \{a, b, c, d, e\}$ has _____ subsets.

2^5 or 32

---

93 Let $S = \{x, y, z\}$, $T = \{1\}$.
    (1) Write $S \times T$ in roster form.
    (2) List all the subsets of $S \times T$. There are eight.

---

(1) $S \times T = \{(x,1), (y,1), (z,1)\}$
(2) $R_1 = S \times T$ or $\{(x,1), (y,1), (z,1)\}$
     $R_2 = \{(x,1), (y,1)\}$
     $R_3 = \{(x,1), (z,1)\}$
     $R_4 = \{(y,1), (z,1)\}$
     $R_5 = \{(x,1)\}$
     $R_6 = \{(y,1)\}$
     $R_7 = \{(z,1)\}$
     $R_8 = \phi$
Only the order of the coordinates within each ordered pair is fixed.

---

94 Given the sets S and T, $S \times T$ is determined.
    (1) A condition $\Re$ (such as $<$, $\subset$, $=$, $\cong$, etc.) determines a subset R
         of _____, namely,
    (2) $R =$ _____ (symbolically)

---

(1) $S \times T$
(2) $\{(x,y) \mid x \in S,\ y \in T,\ \text{and}\ x \Re y\}$

---

95 Since any subset R of $S \times T$ can be thought of as having been deter-
    mined by some condition $\Re$ between two elements, we are interested
    in the subsets of $S \times T$. Hence we give these subsets a name.

▼

Definition: A subset R of $S \times T$ is called a *binary relation in $S \times T$*.
Example: Let $S \times T = \{(x,-1), (x,0), (x,1), (y,-1), (y,0), (y,1)\}$. Let
$R = \{(x,0), (y,0)\}$. R is a(n) _____ of $S \times T$, so R is a(n)
_____ .

---

subset,   binary relation in $S \times T$

---

96 A subset of $S \times S$ is called a *binary relation in S*. *Example*: Let
$S = \{1, 2, 3\}$.
(1) Write $S \times S$ in roster form.
(2) Consider the relationship "$\leq$." This condition determines a
subset of $S \times S$, namely,
$R = \{(x,y) \mid x \in S, \ y \in S, \text{ and } x \leq y\}$
Write R in roster form.
(3) R is a subset of $S \times S$, so R is called a(n) _____ .

---

(1) $S \times S = \{(1,1), (1,2), (1,3), (2,1), (2,2), (2,3), (3,1), (3,2), (3,3)\}$
(2) $R = \{(1,1), (1,2), (1,3), (2,2), (2,3), (3,3)\}$
(3) binary relation in S

---

97 (1) Define a binary relation in $S \times T$.
(2) Define a binary relation in S.

---

(1) A binary relation in $S \times T$ is a subset of $S \times T$.   or R is a binary relation in $S \times T$ if R is a subset of $S \times T$.
(2) A binary relation in S is a subset of $S \times S$.   or R is a binary relation in S if R is a subset of $S \times S$.

---

98 Given a condition $\Re$ and two sets S and T, then $\Re$ determines the subset:
$R = \{(x,y) \mid x \in S, \ y \in T, \text{ and } x \ \Re \ y\}$
R is a subset of $S \times T$, so R is called a(n) _____ .

---

binary relation in $S \times T$

---

99 Given sets S and T, then a condition $\Re$ determines a subset R of
$S \times T$. The subset consists of those ordered pairs (x,y) of $S \times T$ that
satisfy that condition. R is a *binary relation* in $S \times T$ because
_____ .

R is a subset of $S \times T$

100 **(1)** Any subset of $S \times S$ is called a(n) _____ in ___.
    (2) Let $S = \{1, a\}$. $S \times S = \{(1,1), (1,a), \overline{(a,1), (a,a)}\}$. Suppose $R = \{(1,1), (a,1)\}$. R is a subset of $S \times S$, so R is a(n) _____ in ___.

---

(1) binary relation, S **(2)** binary relation, S
You are not wrong if you wrote "in $S \times S$" but "in S" is better form.

---

101 Let $S = \{1, 2, 3\}$. $S \times S = \{(1,1), (1,2), (1,3), (2,1), (2,2), (2,3), (3,1), (3,2), (3,3)\}$.
Suppose $R = \{(1,2), (2,2), (2,3)\}$. R is a subset of $S \times S$, so R is a(n) _____.

---

binary relation in S

---

102 Let $S = \{a, b\}$. Then $S \times S = \{(a,a), (a,b), (b,a), (b,b)\}$. Let $R = S \times S$.
    (1) Is R a subset of $S \times S$?
    (2) R _____(is or is not) a binary relation in S.

---

(1) Yes, recall that given any set A, $A \subset A$.
(2) is, since *any* subset of $S \times S$ is a binary relation in S

---

103 Let $S = \{1, 2\}$. $S \times S = \{(1,1), (1,2), (2,1), (2,2)\}$. Let $R = \phi$.
    (1) Is R a subset of $S \times S$?
    (2) ϕ _____(is or is not) a binary relation in S.

---

(1) Yes, recall that if A is any set, $\phi \subset A$.
(2) is (Note that we have defined *any* subset of $S \times T$ to be a binary relation in $S \times T$.)

---

104 Let $S = \{a, x\}$. $S \times S = \{(a,a), (a,x), (x,a), (x,x)\}$. Any subset of $S \times S$ is a binary relation in S. In this example there are sixteen distinct binary relations which could be chosen. Among them are:

$R_1 = \{(a,a), (a,x), (x,a), (x,x)\}$ $R_6 = \{(a,a), (a,x)\}$
$R_2 = \{(a,a), (a,x), (x,a)\}$ $R_7 = \{(a,a), (x,a)\}$
$R_3 = \{(a,a), (a,x), (x,x)\}$ $R_8 = \{(a,a), (x,x)\}$
$R_4 = \{(a,a), (x,a), (x,x)\}$ $R_9 = \{(a,x), (x,a)\}$
$R_5 = \{(a,x), (x,a), (x,x)\}$ $R_{10} = \{(a,x), (x,x)\}$

List the other six.

---

subset
$R_{11} = \{(x,a), (x,x)\}$ $R_{14} = \{(x,a)\}$
$R_{12} = \{(a,a)\}$ $R_{15} = \{(x,x)\}$
$R_{13} = \{(a,x)\}$ $R_{16} = \phi$

●105 Let $S = \{1, 2\}$.
(1) List $S \times S$.
(2) List all of the binary relations in S.

Answer is on Panel 3.

---

106 In fact, as shown earlier, given any set of ordered pairs, R, we can construct sets S and T so that R is a subset of $S \times T$; so any set of ordered pairs can be considered to be a(n) _____ relation. For example, Let $R = \{(a,3), (2,b), (\sqrt{2},13)\}$; R is a subset of $S \times T$ where $S = \{ \_\_ , \_\_ , \_\_ \}$ and $T = \{ \_\_ , \_\_ , \_\_ \}$. Therefore R is a(n) _____ in _____.

---

binary, $\{a, 2, \sqrt{2}\}$, $\{3, b, 13\}$,   binary relation, $S \times T$

---

107 Suppose $R = \{(a,2), (x,1), (a,17)\}$. R is a binary relation in $S \times T$ where S is any superset of $\{ \_\_ , \_\_ \}$ and T is any superset of $\{ \_\_ , \_\_ , \_\_ \}$.
Note: If $A \subset B$, A is a subset of B, and B is a superset of A.

$\{a, x\}$, $\{1, 2, 17\}$

---

108 Given sets S and T, $S \times T$ is the set of all ordered pairs (x,y) such that x is an element of S and y is an element of T.
(1) Any subset of $S \times T$ is called a(n) _____ in $S \times T$.
Let $S = \{1, 2, 3, 4\}$ and $T = \{a, b, c\}$.
Suppose $R = \{(1,a), (1,b), (4,b)\}$.
(2) R is a subset of $S \times T$, so R is a(n) _____ in _____.

---

(1) binary relation
(2) binary relation, $S \times T$

---

109 Let $S = \{a, b\}$ and $T = \{1, 2\}$. $S \times T = \{(a,1), (a,2), (b,1), (b,2)\}$.
There are sixteen distinct subsets of $S \times T$.

1. $\{(a,1)\}$ 5. $\{(a,1), (a,2)\}$ 9. $\{(a,2), (b,2)\}$
2. $\{(a,2)\}$ 6. $\{(a,1), (b,1)\}$ 10. $\{(b,1), (b,2)\}$
3. $\{(b,1)\}$ 7. $\{(a,1), (b,2)\}$ 11. $\{(a,1), (a,2), (b,1)\}$
4. $\{(b,2)\}$ 8. $\{(a,2), (b,1)\}$ 12. $\{(a,1), (a,2), (b,2)\}$
(1) List the other four.
(2) Each of these subsets of $S \times T$ is called a(n) _____.

---

(1) $\{(a,1), (b,1), (b,2)\}$ (2) binary relation in $S \times T$.
     $\{(a,2), (b,1), (b,2)\}$
     $\{(a,1), (a,2), (b,1), (b,2)\}$
      ϕ

110 A binary relation in $S \times S$ is often called simply a binary relation in S. For example, let $S = \{1, 2, 3\}$. Suppose $R = \{(1,2), (1,3), (2,3)\}$. R is a subset of $S \times S$, so R is a(n) _____ .

binary relation in S

111 Remember, a binary relation is a set. It is a set of ordered pairs. The word "binary" refers to the pair. The word "relation" is used in the following sense. Suppose $S = \{1, 2, 3\}$.
$S \times S = \{(1,1), (1,2), (1,3), (2,1), (2,2), (2,3), (3,1), (3,2), (3,3)\}$. If some subset of $S \times S$ is chosen, certain of these ordered pairs are singled out for attention. A pair is chosen because its coordinates satisfy some condition; another pair is not chosen because its elements do not satisfy the special condition. The coordinates of a chosen pair are "related" with respect to this condition. For example, choose from $S \times S$ the set of all ordered pairs (x,y) such that x is less than y.

(1,2), (1,3), (2,3)

112 Let $S = \{1, 2, 3\}$.
$S \times S = \{(1,1), (1,2), (1,3), (2,1), (2,2), (2,3), (3,1), (3,2), (3,3)\}$.
(1) Pick out from $S \times S$ all of the ordered pairs (x,y) such that $x + y = 4$.
(2) This set just picked out is a subset of $S \times S$, so it is a(n) _____ .

(1) (1,3), (2,2), (3,1)
(2) binary relation in S

113 Let $S = \{1, 2, 3\}$ and $T = \{\alpha\}$. $S \times T = \{(1,\alpha), (2,\alpha), (3,\alpha)\}$. List the subsets of $S \times T$.

$\{(1,\alpha)\}$, $\{(2,\alpha)\}$, $\{(3,\alpha)\}$
$\{(1,\alpha), (2,\alpha)\}$, $\{(1,\alpha), (3,\alpha)\}$, $\{(2,\alpha), (3,\alpha)\}$
$\{(1,\alpha), (2,\alpha), (3,\alpha)\}$
ϕ

114 From your previous study of sets, you may recall that, if $S \times T$ is a finite set containing n elements (each an ordered pair), then there are 2^n subsets of $S \times T$. Each of these subsets is a(n) _____ in ____ .

binary relation, $S \times T$

115   Given sets S and T, the elements of R are often determined by some condition imposed upon the coordinates. For example, let $V = \{-3, 1, 5\}$.
    (1)   Write $V \times V$ in roster form.
    (2)   Suppose R is the subset of $V \times V$ containing exactly those ordered pairs (x,y) for which $x \cdot y > 0$. Write R in roster form.

    (1) $V \times V = \{(-3,-3), (-3,1), (-3,5), (1,-3), (1,1), (1,5), (5,-3),$
           $(5,1), (5,5)\}$
    (2) $R = \{(-3,-3), (1,1), (1,5), (5,1), (5,5)\}$

116   In frame 115 we could have indicated R as follows:
$R = \{(x,y) \mid x \in S, \ y \in S, \text{ and } xy > 0\}$.
Similarly, if $T = \{1, 2, 3\}$ and $R_1 = \{(x,y) \mid x \in T, \ y \in T, \text{ and } x < y\}$, this notation indicates that R_1 is a binary relation containing exactly the ordered pairs (x,y) such that $x \in T$, $y \in T$, and $x < y$.
    (1)   Write $T \times T$ in roster form.
    (2)   Write R_1 in roster form.

    (1) $T \times T = \{(1,1), (1,2), (1,3), (2,1), (2,2), (2,3), (3,1), (3,2), (3,3)\}$
    (2) $R_1 = \{(1,2), (1,3), (2,3)\}$

117   Let $S = \{1, 2, 3\}$ and $R = \{(x,y) \mid x \in S, \ y \in S, \text{ and } x + y = 4\}$.
$S \times S = \{(1,1), (1,2), (1,3), (2,1), (2,2), (2,3), (3,1), (3,2), (3,3)\}$.
    (1)   Write R in roster form.
    (2) R is a subset of $S \times S$, so R is a(n) _____ .

    (1) $\{(1,3), (2,2), (3,1)\}$ (2)   binary relation in S

118   Let $S = \{1, 3, 5\}$.
    (1)   List $S \times S$ in roster form.
    (2)   Let $R = \{(x,y) \mid x \in S, \ y \in S, \text{ and } x + y = 11\}$. Write R in roster form.

    (1) $S \times S = \{(1,1), (1,3), (1,5), (3,1), (3,3), (3,5), (5,1), (5,3), (5,5)\}$
    (2) $R = \phi$

119   Given J the set of integers: Let $R = \{(x,y) \mid x \in J, \ y \in J, \text{ and } x = y + 2\}$.
Then $(-5,-7) \in R$ since $-5 \in J$, $-7 \in J$, and $-5 = -7 + 2$.
$(3,1) \in R$ since $3 \in J$, $1 \in J$, and $3 = 1 + 2$.
$(7,8) \notin R$ since _____ .

$7 \neq 8 + 2$

120 Let $S = \{1, 2, 3\}$. Let $R = \{(x,y) \mid x \in S, \ y \in S, \ \text{and} \ x + y \neq 3\}$.
   (1) $R = \{$ ____ , ____ , ____ , ____ , ____ , ____ , ____ $\}$.
   (2) R is a subset of $S \times S$, so R is a(n) _____.

   (1) (1,1), (1,3), (2,2), (2,3), (3,1), (3,2), (3,3)
   (2) binary relation in S

121 Let $S = \{1, 2, 3, 4\}$ and $R = \{(x,y) \mid x \in S, \ y \in S, \ \text{and} \ x - y \ \text{is divisible}$ by $3\}$.
   (1) Write R in roster form.
   (2) R is a binary relation in S because _____.
Note: "Is divisible by 3" means "has a remainder of 0 when divided by 3."

   (1) $R = \{(1,1), (2,2), (3,3), (4,4), (1,4), (4,1)\}$
   (2) R is a subset of $S \times S$

122 Let $S = \{1, 2, 3\}$ and let $R = \{(x,y) \mid x \in S, \ y \in S, \ \text{and} \ x + y = 7\}$.
   (1) Then $R = $ ____.
   (2) R is a subset of $S \times S$, so R is a(n) _____.

   (1) φ
   (2) binary relation in S

123 (1) A binary relation R in a set S is a set of _____. A set of ordered pairs might be chosen arbitrarily (at random) and then $(x,y) \in R$ simply because it was chosen. Usually, however, there is given some relationship which must exist between the coordinates of any member of R. For example, the condition "x is less than or equal to y" in $S \times S$, where S is the set of integers, defines the set of ordered pairs R; and R is a binary relation in S.
   (2) Is $(5,3) \in R$? Why?
   (3) Is $(-3,5) \in R$? Why?
   (4) Is $(2,2) \in R$? Why?

   (1) ordered pairs   (2) no, $5 \not\leq 3$
   (3) yes, $-3 \leq 5$ (4) yes, $2 \leq 2$

124 Let $S = \{1, 2, 3, 4\}$ and consider $R = \{(x,y) \mid x \in S, \ y \in S, \ \text{and} \ x = 2y\}$.
Write R in roster form.

   $\{(2,1), (4,2)\}$

125   Let $S = \{a, b, c\}$ where a, b, and c are straight lines in a plane as shown in the drawing, with right angles as shown.

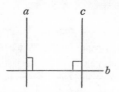

Let $R = \{(x,y) \mid x \in S,\ y \in S,$ and x is perpendicular to $y\}$. Write R in roster form.

$R = \{(a,b),\ (b,a),\ (b,c),\ (c,b)\}$

126   Let $S = \{1, 2, 3\}$.
   (1)   Write $S \times S$ in roster form.
   (2)   Let $R = \{(x,y) \mid x \in S,\ y \in S,$ and $x = y\}$. Write R in roster form.
   (3) R is a subset of $S \times S$, so R is a(n) _____ .
   (4)   The condition "$=$" is so commonly used that we often refer to the $=$ relation (equals relation) in S. Keep in mind that the binary relation is *not* the *condition* ($=$, $<$, $\cong$, etc.), but rather it is the _____ .

   (1) $S \times S = \{(1,1),\ (1,2),\ (1,3),\ (2,1),\ (2,2),\ (2,3),\ (3,1),\ (3,2),\ (3,3)\}$
   (2) $R = \{(1,1),\ (2,2),\ (3,3)\}$
   (3)   binary relation in S
   (4)   subset of $S \times S$ determined by the condition, in this case R

127   Let S be a nonempty set of real numbers. Let $R = \{(x,y) \mid x \in S,\ y \in S,$ and $x < y\}$.
   (1) R is a subset of $S \times S$ and so R is _____ .
   (2)   Note that R is completely determined in S by the condition "$<$." Here again the condition is so commonly used that it has a special symbol ($<$). We often refer to R as the "$<$ relation" in S. Keep in mind, however, that the binary relation *is* the _____ , *not* the symbol $<$.

   (1)   a binary relation in S
   (2)   subset of $S \times S$ (in this case R) determined by the condition (in this case $<$).

128   Let S be a set and suppose "$\Re$" is some condition (such as "is less than," "is the father of") which may or may not hold between an ordered pair of elements of S, and $R = \{(x,y) \mid x \in S, y \in S, \text{ and } x \Re y\}$ is the binary relation made up of exactly those elements of $S \times S$ for which the condition $\Re$ holds. Then note that R contains *all* of the elements and only the elements for which $x \Re y$. That is,

   if $x, y \in S$ and

   if $(x,y) \in R$, then x is in the relation $\Re$ to y,

   if $(x,y) \notin R$, then x is not in the relation $\Re$ to y,

(1)   if x is in the relation $\Re$ to y, then ____ $\in R$.

(2)   if x is not in the relation $\Re$ to y, then ____ $\notin R$.

(1) (x,y) (2) (x,y)

129   Suppose S is the set of all humans and $R = \{(x,y) \mid x \in S, y \in S, \text{ and } x \text{ is the father of } y\}$. R is a binary relation in S containing *all* of the elements and *only* the elements (x,y) for which x is the father of y. Therefore,

   if $(\text{John,Mary}) \in R$, John is the father of Mary,

   if $(\text{John,Jane}) \notin R$, John is not the father of Jane,

(1)   if Joe is the father of Margaret, then _____ $\in R$,

(2)   if Bob is not the father of Peggy, then _____ $\notin R$.

(1)   (Joe,Margaret)
(2)   (Bob,Peggy)

130   Given a set S and $R = \{(x,y) \mid x \in S, y \in S, \text{ and } x + y = 1\}$: Suppose $a, b \in S$ and $a + b = 1$. Which is true (if either), $(a,b) \in R$ or $(a,b) \notin R$?

$(a,b) \in R$

131   Given a set S and $R = \{(x,y) \mid x \in S, y \in S, \text{ and } x + y = 1\}$: Suppose $a, b \in S$ and $a + b \neq 1$. Which of the following is true (if either), $(a,b) \in R$ or $(a,b) \notin R$?

$(a,b) \notin R$

132   Given a set S and $R = \{(x,y) \mid x \in S, y \in S, \text{ and } x < y\}$: Suppose $a, b \in S$ and $(a,b) \in R$. What valid relationship holds between a and b?

$a < b$

133   Given a set S and $R = \{(x,y) \mid x \in S,\ y \in S,\ \text{and}\ x < y\}$: Suppose a, $b \in S$ and $(a,b) \notin R$. What valid relationship holds between a and b?

$a \nless b$ (or $a \geq b$)

134   Given a set S and $R_1 = \{(x,y) \mid x \in S,\ y \in S,\ \text{and}\ x < y\}$,
$R_2 = \{(x,y) \mid x \in S,\ y \in S,\ \text{and}\ x = y\}$,
$R_3 = \{(x,y) \mid x \in S,\ y \in S,\ \text{and}\ x > y\}$:
(1)   Suppose a, $b \in S$ and $a = b$; then $(a,b) \in$ _____ .
(2)   Suppose a, $b \in S$ and $a \neq b$; then $(a,b) \in$ _____ .
(3)   Suppose $(a,b) \in R_3$; write a valid relationship existing between a and b.

(1) R_2
(2) R_1 or R_3 (or $R_1 \cup R_3$)
(3) $a > b$

135   Given a set S and $R = \{(X,Y) \mid X \in S,\ Y \in S,\ \text{and}\ X \subset Y\}$: Suppose A, $B \in S$ and $B \subset A$; then which of the following is true (if either), $(A,B) \in R$ or $(B,A) \in R$?

$(B,A) \in R$

136   Given a set S and $R = \{(X,Y) \mid X \in S,\ Y \in S,\ \text{and}\ X \subset Y\}$: Suppose $A \in S$ and A is a set.
(1)   Is $A \subset A$?
(2)   Which of the following is true (if either), $(A,A) \in R$ or $(A,A) \notin R$?

(1)   yes   (2) $(A,A) \in R$

137   Let $S = \{0, 1, 2\}$ and $R = \{(x,y) \mid x \in S,\ y \in S,\ \text{and}\ x = y^2\}$. Is $(2,1) \in R$? Why?

No, $2 \neq 1^2$.

138   Let $S = \{0, 1, 2\}$ and $R = \{(x,y) \mid x \in S,\ y \in S,\ \text{and}\ x = y^2\}$.
(1)   Is $(9,3) \in R$? Why?
(2)   Is $(1,1) \in R$? Why?

(1)   No, $9 \notin S$, $3 \notin S$ (even though $9 = 3^2$).
(2)   Yes, $1 \in S$, $1 \in S$, and $1 = 1^2$.

139 Let $S = \{0, 1, 2\}$ and $R = \{(x,y) \mid x \in S, y \in S,$ and $x = y^2\}$. Is $(4,2) \in R$? Why?

No, $4 \notin S$ or $(4,2) \notin S \times S$.

140 Let $S = \{a, b, c, d\}$ and $R = \{(x,y) \mid x \in S, y \in S,$ and $x = y^2\}$. If $a^2 = b$, name one element of R.

(b,a)

141 Let $S = \{a, b, c, d\}$ and $R = \{(x,y) \mid x \in S, y \in S,$ and $x = y^2\}$. If $b^2 \neq d$, name one element of $S \times S$ which is *not* an element of R.

(d,b)

142 Let $S = \{a, b, c, d\}$ and $R = \{(x,y) \mid x \in S, y \in S,$ and $x = y^2\}$. Suppose $(c,a) \in R$. State a valid equality involving a and c.

$c = a^2$

143 Let $S = \{a, b, c, d\}$ and $R = \{(x,y) \mid x \in S, y \in S,$ and $x = y^2\}$. Suppose $(b,d) \notin R$; then b _____ d^2.

$\neq$

144 Let S be the set of humans and $R = \{(x,y) \mid x \in S, y \in S,$ and x is the father of $y\}$.
 (1) If $(a,b) \in R$, then _____ is the father of _____.
 (2) If $a, b \in S$ and a is the father of b, then _____.
 (3) If $a, b \in S$ and $(a,b) \notin R$, then _____ is not the father of _____.
 (4) If $a, b \in S$ and a is not the father of b, then _____.

(1) a, b (2) $(a,b) \in R$ (3) a, b (4) $(a,b) \notin R$

145 Let S be the set of human beings. Let $R = \{(x,y) \mid x \in S, y \in S,$ and x is the husband of $y\}$. R is a subset of $S \times S$.
 (1) Therefore R is a(n) _____. If Joe Zilch is the husband of Mary Zilch, then (Joe Zilch, Mary Zilch) $\in R$.
 (2) For every ordered pair $(x,y) \in R$, the statement _____ is true.

(1) binary relation in S
(2) x is the husband of y

146   The point is, given a set S and some condition $\Re$ (such as "less
      than," "is the father of," "$\cong$") which defines a binary relation
      R in S, that is, $R = \{(x,y) \mid x \in S,\ y \in S,\ \text{and}\ x \Re y\}$.
      1. if $(a,b) \in R$, then $a \Re b$,
      2. if $a,\ b \in S$ and $a \Re b$, then $(a,b) \in R$,
      3. if $a,\ b \in S$ and $(a,b) \notin R$, then a is not related by $\Re$ to b,
      4. if $a,\ b \in S$ and a is not related by the condition $\Re$ to b, then
          $(a,b) \notin R$.

No answer is required.

147   Let $S = \{a,\ b\}$ and $T = \{c,\ d,\ e\}$. Suppose $R = \{(a,c),\ (a,e),\ (b,d)\}$.
      (1) R is a(n) _____ . It is a common convention to indicate
           membership in a relation in the following manner: $(a,c) \in R$
           is written $a\ R\ c$ and is read "a is R-related to c." Similarly,
           $(b,c) \notin R$ is written $b\ \not{R}\ c$ and is read "b is not R-related to c."
      (2) $(a,e) \in R$ or _____.
      (3) $(a,d) \notin R$ or _____.
      (4) _____ or $b\ R\ d$.
      (5) _____ or $b\ \not{R}\ c$.

(1)   binary relation in $S \times T$
(2) $a\ R\ e$ (3) $a\ \not{R}\ d$ (4) $(b,d) \in R$ (5) $(b,c) \notin R$

148   Suppose $S = \{-1,\ 0,\ 1,\ 2\}$ and $R = \{(x,y) \mid x \in S,\ y \in S,\ \text{and}\ x^2 \le y\}$.
      Then $(-1,1) \in R$ or $-1\ R\ 1$. Similarly,
      (1) $(0,1) \in R$ or _____.
      (2) $(1,0) \notin R$ or _____.
      (3) _____ or $1\ R\ 1$

(1) $0\ R\ 1$
(2) $1\ \not{R}\ 0$
(3) $(1,1) \in R$

149   Suppose $S = \{5,\ 6,\ 7\}$ and $R = \{(x,y) \mid x \in S,\ y \in S,\ \text{and}\ x$ and y have
                                  the same remainder when divided by $2\}$.
      Both notations, $(7,5) \in R$ and $7\ R\ 5$, are acceptable and mean exactly
      the same thing. The first notation emphasizes the binary relation as
      a set, while the second notation emphasizes the condition existing
      between the coordinates of an element of the binary relation. The
      way in which the two notations are read illustrates this distinction.
      "The ordered pair $(7,5)$ is a member of R" indicates the importance
      of the relation as a set. "7 is R-related to 5" indicates an empha-
      sis on the condition existing between the coordinates, that is, that 7
      and 5 when divided by 2 have the same remainder.

▼

(1)   Write $S \times S$ in roster form.
(2)   Write R in roster form.

---

(1) $S \times S = \{(5,5), (5,6), (5,7), (6,5), (6,6), (6,7), (7,5), (7,6), (7,7)\}$
(2) $R = \{(5,5), (5,7), (6,6), (7,5), (7,7)\}$

---

150   Given sets S and T, the set of ordered pairs (x,y) with $x \in S$ and
$y \in T$ is called the **(1)** _____and is denoted by
(2) $S \times T = \{$ _____ $\}$.
Any subset of $S \times T$ (including all of $S \times T$ or the empty set) is
called, **(3)** a(n) _____.

---

(1)   cartesian (or cross) product of S and T
(2) $\{(x,y) \mid x \in S$ and $y \in T\}$
(3)   binary relation in $S \times T$

---

151   Let $S = \{1, 2, 3\}$ and $R = \{(x,y) \mid x \in S,\ y \in S,$ and $x > y\}$.
Note: $>$ means greater than.
Which of the following are true ?
$(1,1) \in R$ $(2,1) \in R$ $(3,2) \in R$

$(2,1) \in R,$ $(3,2) \in R$

---

152   Let $S = \{1, 2, 3\}$. Let $R = \{(x,y) \mid x \in S,\ y \in S,$ and $x > y\}$. Which of
the following are true ?
$2\ R\ 1$ $3\ R\ 1$ $2\ R\ 2$ $2\ R\ 3$

$2\ R\ 1,$ $3\ R\ 1$

---

153   Sometimes a condition which defines a binary relation R is so useful that it is given a special name and symbol. For example, let S
be the set of real numbers and
$R = \{(x,y) \mid x \in S,\ y \in S,$ and x is less than $y\}$.
"Is less than" is represented by $<$, and instead of writing $x\ R\ y$ we
replace R by $<$ and get ____.

$x < y$

---

154   Similarly, let S be the set of all lines in a given plane and let
$R = \{(p,q) \mid p \in S,\ q \in S,$ and p is perpendicular to $q\}$. "Is perpendicular to" is represented by $\perp$, and instead of writing $p\ R\ q$ we replace R by this special symbol and get ____.

$p \perp q$

155　Again let S be the set of real numbers and
$R = \{(x,y) \mid x \in S, \; y \in S, \text{ and } x \text{ is equal to } y\}$.
"Is equal to" is represented by $=$, and instead of writing $x \, R \, y$ we
write ＿＿＿ .

$x = y$

156　Let S be the set of all triangles and let
$R = \{(x,y) \mid x \in S, \; y \in S, \text{ and } x \text{ is congruent to } y\}$.
Instead of writing $x \, R \, y$ in this case, we usually use the symbol for
"is congruent to" and write ＿＿＿ .

$x \cong y$

157　Let S be the set of all straight lines and
$R = \{(x,y) \mid x \in S, \; y \in S, \text{ and } x \text{ is parallel to } y\}$.
$x \, R \, y$ would be written instead as ＿＿＿ .

$x \parallel y$

158　Let S be a set each of whose elements is a set.
Let $R = \{(A,B) \mid A \in S, \; B \in S, \text{ and } A \text{ is a subset of } B\}$.
Then, if $(A,B) \in R$, instead of writing $A \, R \, B$ we write ＿＿＿ .

$A \subset B$

159　So, if a special symbol exists for a condition defining a binary relation R in a set S and $(X,Y) \in R$, then instead of writing $X \, R \, Y$ the
R is replaced by that symbol. Similarly, if $(x,y) \notin R$, instead of
writing $x \, \not{R} \, y$ the $\not{R}$ is usually replaced by that special symbol with
a slash through it. For example, let $R = \{(x,y) \mid x \text{ and } y \text{ are integers}$
and $x < y\}$. $(5,2) \notin R$ or $5 \, \not{R} \, 2$ is written ＿＿＿ .

$5 \not< 2$

160　Similarly, suppose $R = \{(x,y) \mid x \text{ and } y \text{ are straight lines and } x \perp y\}$.
If $(a,b) \in R$, $a \, R \, b$ is written $a \perp b$. If $(c,d) \notin R$, $c \, \not{R} \, d$ is written
＿＿＿ .

$c \not\perp d$

161 Thus you see that you are already familiar with, and the notation is consistent with, many special conditions represented by such symbols as $>$, $<$, $\le$, $\ge$, $=$ for numbers, $\cong$, $=$, $\sim$ for triangles. Each of these symbols represents a condition which "picks out" a subset from a cartesian product, that is, determines a(n) _____ in S. In such familiar cases, we often refer to the "equals relation," the "less than relation," etc.

binary relation

162 We have found a theme underlying all of these familiar concepts—each of these binary relations is a(n) _____ of a cartesian product. Now we wish to find distinguishing characteristics of binary relations in order to classify them according to these properties, just as, for example, we classify triangles in terms of certain distinguishing properties (isosceles, scalene, right, equilateral, etc.).

subset

Self-test II   (Answers to Self-test II appear on page 311)

1 Our original purpose was to study relations as defined in the following typical problem: let $S = \{0, 1, 2\}$ and consider "____ $\le$ ____."
   (1) Write $S \times S$ in roster form.
   (2) Let $R = \{(x,y) \mid x \in S, y \in S, \text{ and } x \le y\}$. Write R in roster form.
   (3) R is a subset of $S \times S$, so R is a(n) _____.

2 Define a binary relation in $S \times T$.

3 If R is a binary relation in S, R is a set of ordered pairs of $S \times S$. Suppose $(x,y) \in R$; an alternative way of expressing $(x,y) \in R$ is _____.

IV. Properties of a Binary Relation

a. Reflexive

We are now going to attempt to find characteristic properties of binary relations in S, rather than in $S \times T$. We do this because the majority of applications with which we shall be concerned (such as $=$, $\cong$, $<$, etc.) will involve elements from a single set S.

163   Let $S = \{1, 2, 3\}$.
    (1)   Write $S \times S$ in roster form.
    (2)   Consider the relationship of equality ($=$). This relationship de-
    termines a binary relation: $R = \{(x,y) \mid x \in S,\ y \in S,\ \text{and}\ x = y\}$.
    Write R in roster form.

    (1) $S \times S = \{(1,1),\ (1,2),\ (1,3),\ (2,1),\ (2,2),\ (2,3),\ (3,1),\ (3,2),\ (3,3)\}$
    (2) $R = \{(1,1),\ (2,2),\ (3,3)\}$

164   Let $S = \{1, 2, 3, 4, 5, 6, 7, 8, 9\}$.
    Do not write $S \times S$ in tabular form unless you find that you need it
    for your answer. (After all, there are eighty-one members of $S \times S$.)

    Let $R = \{(x,y) \mid x \in S,\ y \in S,\ \text{and}\ x = y\}$. Write R in roster form.

    $R = \{(1,1),\ (2,2),\ (3,3),\ (4,4),\ (5,5),\ (6,6),\ (7,7),\ (8,8),\ (9,9)\}$

165   Let I be the set of integers, that is,
    $I = \{\ldots, -4, -3, -2, -1, 0, 1, 2, 3, 4, \ldots\}$. (The dots indicate
    missing elements.) $I \times I = \{(x,y) \mid x \in I\ \text{and}\ y \in I\}$. $I \times I$ contains all
    ordered pairs of integers. For example, $(-50,10)$, $(1,15)$, $(4,-2)$,
    $(3,3)$, $(-5,150)$, etc., are all elements of $I \times I$. Let
    $R = \{(x,y) \mid x \in I,\ y \in I,\ \text{and}\ x = y\}$. List some typical elements of R.

    $(-5,-5)$, $(-4,-4)$, $(50,50)$, $(0,0)$, $(1,1)$, $(1000,1000)$, etc. Any ordered
    pair of the form (x,x), where x is an integer.

166   Let $S = \{a, b, c\}$. Let $R = \{(x,y) \mid x \in S,\ y \in S,\ \text{and}\ x = y\}$. Write R
    in roster form.

    $R = \{(a,a),\ (b,b),\ (c,c)\}$

167   Note the similarity of the last three answers. We see that for every
    $x \in S$, (____ , ____) $\in R$.

    $(x,x) \in R$

168   Let $S = \{\{p\},\ \{q,\ r\},\ \{a,\ b\}\}$.
    (1)   Write $S \times S$ in roster form.
    (2)   Let $R = \{(A,B) \mid A \in S,\ B \in S,\ \text{and}\ A \subset B\}$. Write R in roster
    form.

▼

(3)   Here again, for every $x \in S$, _____ $\in R$.

---

(1) $S \times S = \{(\{p\},\{p\}), (\{p\},\{q, r\}), (\{p\},\{a, b\}), (\{q, r\},\{p\}),$
        $(\{q, r\},\{q, r\}), (\{q, r\},\{a, b\}), (\{a, b\},\{p\}), (\{a, b\},\{q, r\}),$
        $(\{a, b\},\{a, b\})\}$
(2) $R = \{(\{p\},\{p\}), (\{q, r\},\{q, r\}), (\{a, b\},\{a, b\})\}$
(3) $(x,x) \in R$

---

169   Let $S = \{3, 4, 5\}$.
(1)   Write $S \times S$ in roster form.
(2)   Let $R = \{(x,y) \mid x \in S, \ y \in S, \text{ and } x + y \text{ is an even integer}\}$.
        Write R in roster form.
(3)   Does the condition, for every $x \in S$, $(x,x) \in R$, hold in this case?

---

(1) $S \times S = \{(3,3), (3,4), (3,5), (4,3), (4,4), (4,5), (5,3), (5,4), (5,5)\}$
(2) $R = \{(3,3), (3,5), (4,4), (5,3), (5,5)\}$
(3)   yes   Note: $3 \in S$, $(3,3) \in R$, $4 \in S$, $(4,4) \in R$, $5 \in S$, $(5,5) \in R$

---

170   Let $S = \{2, 3, 4, 5\}$. Let $R = \{(x,y) \mid x \in S, \ y \in S, \text{ and } x \leq y\}$. Which
of the following are members of R? $(2,2)$, $(3,3)$, $(4,4)$, $(5,5)$, $(5,3)$,
$(4,2)$, $(3,2)$, $(2,3)$

$(2,2)$, $(3,3)$, $(4,4)$, $(5,5)$, $(2,3)$ R has other members such as $(3,5)$

---

171   Let $S = \{T_1, T_2, T_3\}$. T_1, T_2, T_3 are triangles.
Let $R = \{(A,B) \mid A \in S, \ B \in S, \text{ and } A \cong B\}$. ($\cong$ means is congruent to,
and a triangle is always congruent to itself.) Which of the following
are members of R? (T_1,T_1), (T_2,T_2), (T_3,T_3)

All of them. There *may* be other members of R, but we are *certain*
that these are members.

---

172   Let N be the set of positive integers; then $N = \{1, 2, 3, 4, 5, \ldots\}$.
Let $R = \{(x,y) \mid x \in N, \ y \in N, \text{ and } x \text{ is a divisor of } y\}$. Which of the
following members of $S \times S$ are members of R? $(1,1)$, $(2,2)$, $(3,7)$,
$(5,38)$, $(16,16)$, $(16,4)$, $(100,3)$, $(20,20)$

$(1,1)$, $(2,2)$, $(16,16)$, $(20,20)$
There are other ordered pairs in R, such as $(5,10)$.

---

173   In frames 164 to 172, there was a property common to each of the
binary relations; namely, that (1) _____ $\in R$ for every $x \in S$. For
example, let $S = \{-2, -1, 0, 1, 2\}$.
Let $R = \{(x,y) \mid x \in S, \ y \in S, \text{ and } x \cdot y \geq 0\}$.

▼

(2) Although there are other elements of $S \times S$, determine whether $(-2,-2)$, $(-1,-1)$, $(0,0)$, $(1,1)$, $(2,2)$ are elements of R.

(1) (x,x)
Note: This does not hold for every binary relation in R; examples will come later.
(2) yes, in each case

---

174 Let $S = \{p, q, r\}$, where p, q, and r are points on a line as shown. The distance between p and q is 1 inch and the distance between q and r is 2 inches.

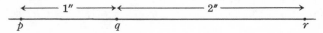

(1) Write $S \times S$ in roster form.
(2) Let $R = \{(x,y) \mid x \in S,\ y \in S,\ \text{and the distance between } x \text{ and } y \text{ is less than 2 inches}\}$. Write R in roster form.
(3) Are (p,p), (q,q), and (r,r) members of R?

(1) $\{(p,p),\ (p,q),\ (p,r),\ (q,p),\ (q,q),\ (q,r),\ (r,p),\ (r,q),\ (r,r)\}$
(2) $\{(p,p),\ (p,q),\ (q,p),\ (q,q),\ (r,r)\}$
(3) yes

---

175 Let $S = \{0, 1, 2\}$.
(1) Write $S \times S$ in roster form.
(2) Let $R = \{(x,y) \mid x \in S,\ y \in S,\ \text{and } x \cdot y > 0\}$. Write R in roster form.
(3) Does this binary relation R have the property that we have been discussing; namely, that $(0,0)$, $(1,1)$, $(2,2)$ are members of R?

(1) $S \times S = \{(0,0),\ (0,1),\ (0,2),\ (1,0),\ (1,1),\ (1,2),\ (2,0),\ (2,1),\ (2,2)\}$
(2) $R = \{(1,1),\ (1,2),\ (2,1),\ (2,2)\}$
(3) No, $(0,0) \notin R$.
This is an example of where the condition $(x,x) \in R$ for *every* $x \in S$ does not hold, because $0 \in S$, but $(0,0) \notin R$.

---

176 Any binary relation R in S that has the property that ____ $\in R$ for every ____ $\in S$, is said to be *reflexive in S*.

(x,x), x

---

177 Let S be a set.
Definition: A binary relation R in S is said to be _____ if and only if $(x,x) \in R$ for *every* $x \in S$.

reflexive in S

178 Let S be a set. A(n) _____ R in S is said to be _____ if
and only if $(x,x) \in R$ for _____ $x \in S$.

binary relation,   reflexive,   every (or each)

179 Let S be a set. A binary relation R in S is said to be reflexive in S
if and only if _____ .

$(x,x) \in R$ for every $x \in S$

180 Let S be a set. Let R be a(n) _____ in S, such that
_____ . Then R is said to be in reflexive in S.

binary relation, $(x,x) \in R$ for every $x \in S$

181 Define a reflexive binary relation R in a set S.

A binary relation R in a set S is said to be reflexive if and only if
$(x,x) \in R$ for every $x \in S$ (or if and only if $x \, R \, x$ for every $x \in S$).

COMMENT

1. When there is no chance for confusion about the set with which we
   are working, we often say simply that "R is reflexive" or "R
   has the reflexive property" rather than "R is a reflexive binary
   relation in the set S" or "R has the reflexive property in S."
2. When a binary relation R has a special symbol, such as "$=$,"
   "$\subset$," "$\leq$," "$\cong$," "$\perp$," we usually use that special symbol and
   name to refer to the binary relation. Thus we speak of "the $=$
   relation" (read "the equals relation"), or "the $<$ relation" (read
   "the less than relation"), or "the $\cong$ relation" (read "the congruence relation"), etc.
3. Since $(x,y) \in R$ has the same meaning as $x \, R \, y$, it is a matter of
   personal taste whether you write

$$(x,x) \in R \text{ for every } x \in S$$

   or

$$.x \, R \, x \text{ for every } x \in S$$

   For those binary relations mentioned above, having special symbols attached, it seems more appropriate to write, for example,
   "$x \leq x$ for every $x \in S$" rather than "$(x,x) \in R$ for every $x \in S$"
   (where it is understood that R is the subset of $S \times S$ determined
   by "$\leq$").
4. No attempt is being made to force you to write a definition

in the exact order or form in which it is written in an answer.
For example, the definition of a reflexive binary relation in S has
been given as:

a. A binary relation R in a set S is reflexive in S if and only if
$(x,x) \in R$ for every $x \in S$. As noted above, $(x,y) \in R$ has the
same meaning as $x \, R \, y$. So the definition could have been
written equally well as:

b. A binary relation R in a set S is reflexive in S if and only if
$x \, R \, x$ for every $x \in S$.

Also, as a matter of personal taste, you might prefer to invert
the word order and write:

c. A binary relation R in a set S is reflexive in S if and only if
for every $x \in S$ it follows that $(x,x) \in R$.

Or:

d. A binary relation R in a set S is reflexive in S if and only if
for every $x \in S$ it follows that $x \, R \, x$.

You might also prefer to invert the order of the entire clause and
say:

e. If a binary relation R in a set S is such that $(x,x) \in R$ for
every $x \in S$, then R is said to be reflexive in S.

You might prefer to use the words "for each" rather than "for
every."

The five definitions listed above are equivalent, and there are other
variations which you might write. Only one form will be given in the
answer, but if your answer contains the distinguishing characteristics of whatever is being defined, and your answer differs only in
sentence structure or in equivalent symbolism (such as $(x,x) \in R$ instead of $x \, R \, x$), your answer is correct.

---

182 Let $S = \{1, 2, 3, 4, 5\}$.
$R = \{(1,1), (2,2), (2,4), (3,3), (4,4), (4,2), (5,1), (5,5)\}$.
(1) Is it true that $(x,x) \in R$ for *every* $x \in S$?
(2) Therefore R _____ (is or is not) reflexive in S.

(1) yes *Note:* $1 \in S$ and $(1,1) \in R$; $2 \in S$ and $(2,2) \in R$; $3 \in S$ and
$(3,3) \in R$; $4 \in S$ and $(4,4) \in R$; $5 \in S$ and $(5,5) \in R$.
(2) is

---

183 Let $S = \{1, 2, 3, 4, 5\}$.
$R = \{(1,1), (2,2), (4,3), (4,4), (5,5)\}$.
(1) Is it true that $(x,x) \in R$ for *every* $x \in S$?
(2) Therefore R _____ (is or is not) reflexive in S.

(1) no   *Note:* $3 \in S$ but $(3,3) \notin R$.
(2) is not Note that the definition of reflexivity requires $(x,x) \in R$
for *every* $x \in S$.

184   Let $S = \{1, 2, 3\}$ and $R = \{(1,1),\ (1,2),\ (2,2),\ (2,3),\ (3,3)\}$.
    (1)   Is it true that $x\,R\,x$ for every $x \in S$?
    (2)   Therefore R _____(is or is not) reflexive.

(1) yes   (2) is

185   Let $S = \{a,\ b,\ c\}$.
    (1)   Write $S \times S$ in roster form.
    (2)   Consider $\{(x,x) \mid x \in S\}$. This set is a subset of $S \times S$. Write the
        set in roster form.

(1) $S \times S = \{(a,a),\ (a,b),\ (a,c),\ (b,a),\ (b,b),\ (b,c),\ (c,a),\ (c,b),\ (c,c)\}$
(2) $\{(a,a),\ (b,b),\ (c,c)\}$

186   Let S be a set. The *diagonal set* in $S \times S$ is denoted by Δ (delta) and
    is given by:
    $\Delta = \{(x,x) \mid x \in S\}$
    Let $S = \{a,\ b,\ c,\ d,\ e\}$.
    (1)   Write Δ in roster form.
    (2)   Represent $S \times S$ graphically.
    (3)   Circle the points that represent the members of Δ.
    (4)   You should now see why Δ is called the _____set in $S \times S$.

(1) $\Delta = \{(a,a),\ (b,b),\ (c,c),\ (d,d),\ (e,e)\}$
(2) and (3)

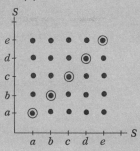

(4) diagonal

187   Using the concept of the diagonal set Δ, construct an *alternative* def-
    inition of reflexivity in S. That is, complete the following by speci-
    fying a relationship between Δ and R: A binary relation R in a set S
    is reflexive in S if and only if _____.

$\Delta \subset R$
Note: If Δ is a subset of R, then $(x,x) \in R$ for every $x \in S$. The con-
verse is also true. We will not use this definition, but the ideas involved are descriptive and should help you remember the concept of
reflexivity.

188 Let S be the set of integers, that is:
$S = \{\ldots, -3, -2, -1, 0, 1, 2, 3, \ldots\}$
Let $R = \{(x,y) \mid x \in S,\ y \in S,\ \text{and}\ x \le y\}$.
(1) Because we have a special symbol ($\le$) for the condition defining R, it would be more meaningful to use this symbol. Instead of saying "Is it true that $(x,x) \in R$ for every $x \in S$?" we say "Is it true that $x \le x$ for every $x \in S$?" Answer this question.
(2) The "$\le$ relation" _____(is or is not) reflexive in S.

(1) Yes, any integer is less than or equal to itself.
(2) is

189 Let S be the set of integers. Consider the $<$ relation in S.
(1) Is it true that $x < x$ for every $x \in S$?
(2) Therefore the "$<$ relation" _____(is or is not) reflexive in S.

(1) No, a number cannot be less than itself.
(2) is not

190 A distinguishing characteristic between the $<$ relation and the $\le$ relation, in the set of integers, is that the ____ relation *is* reflexive, but the ____ relation *is not* reflexive. This holds for any nonempty set of real numbers.

$\le$, $<$

191 Let S be a nonempty set of real numbers. Consider the "$\ge$" relation."
(1) Is it true that $x \ge x$ for every $x \in S$?
(2) Therefore the "$\ge$ relation" _____(is or is not) reflexive in S.

(1) Yes, any real number is greater than or equal to itself.
(2) is

192 Let S be a nonempty set of real numbers. Consider the "$>$ relation."
(1) Is it true that $x > x$ for every $x \in S$?
(2) Therefore the "$>$ relation" _____(is or is not) reflexive in S.

(1) No, a real number is greater than itself.
(2) is not

193 We have just seen a distinguishing feature, in the set of integers, between the "$\geq$ relation" and the "$>$ relation." It is true that ____ is reflexive, but ____ is not reflexive.

$\geq$, $>$

194 Let S be a nonempty collection of sets. Consider the "$\subset$ relation."
(1) Is it true that $A \subset A$ for every $A \in S$?
(2) Therefore the "$\subset$ relation" _____ (is or is not) reflexive in S.

(1) Yes, any set is a subset of itself.
(2) is

195 Let S be the set of positive integers. Let $R = \{(x,y) \mid x \in S,\ y \in S$, and x is a divisor of $y\}$. This is called "the divisibility relation."
(1) Is it true that x divides x for every $x \in S$ (in other words $x\,R\,x$ for every $x \in S$, or $(x,x) \in R$ for every $x \in S$)?
(2) Therefore the divisibility relation on the set of positive integers _____ (is or is not) reflexive.

(1) Yes, any positive integer divides into itself with a remainder of zero.
(2) is

196 Let S be the set of integers; then
$S = \{\dots,\,-5,\,-4,\,-3,\,-2,\,-1,\,0,\,1,\,2,\,3,\,4,\,\dots\}$
Consider the divisibility relation in S.
$R = \{(x,y) \mid x \in S,\ y \in S$, and x is a divisor of $y\}$.
(1) Is it true that x divides x for every $x \in S$?
(2) Therefore the "divisibility relation" in the set of integers _____ (is or is not) reflexive.

(1) No, there is one member of S for which the relation does not hold, namely, 0. Division by zero is not defined, so $(0,0) \notin R$.
(2) is not, because $(0,0) \notin R$.

197 We can remedy the problem in frame 196 by doing the following: Let T be the set of nonzero integers; then
$T = \{\dots,\,-2,\,-1,\,1,\,2,\,3,\,\dots\}$
Now consider the divisibility relation in T, i.e.,
$R = \{(x,y) \mid x \in T,\ y \in T$, and x is a divisor of $y\}$
(1) Is it true that for *every* $x \in S$, x divides x?

▼

(2)   The divisibility relation in the set of nonzero integers _____ (is or is not) reflexive.

(1)   yes
(2)   is

•198   Define a reflexive binary relation R in a set S.

A binary relation R in a set S is reflexive if and only if $(x,x) \in R$ for every $x \in S$.

(If you have $x \, R \, x$ instead of $(x,x) \in R$, or different word order, you still may have a good definition. Have you specified that the relation must hold for *every* $x \in S$?)

199   (1)   To show that a binary relation R in a set S *is* reflexive, you must show that _____ for _____ $x \in S$.
       (2)   To show that a binary relation R in a set S *is not* reflexive, you need to show only one $x \in S$ for which _____.

(1) $(x,x) \in R$ (or $x \, R \, x$),   every (or each)
(2) $(x,x) \notin R$ (or $x \, R\!\!\!/ \, x$)

200   This situation is one of the few places in mathematics in which a single example is used as proof. You can prove that a binary relation R _____ (is or is not) reflexive in a set S, if you can find *one* example of an element x which is in S, but for which $(x,x) \notin R$. There may be others, but one example will do. This is true because the definition of reflexivity requires that $(x,x) \in R$ for _____ $x \in S$.

is not,   each (or every)

201   Let $S = \{0, 1, 2, 3\}$ and $R = \{(0,0), (0,1), (1,2), (3,3)\}$.
       Is R reflexive in S? Why?

No, $1 \in S$, but $(1,1) \notin R$ or $2 \in S$, but $(2,2) \notin R$. You need show only one.
Note: It is not enough to say that $(1,1) \notin R$ or $(2,2) \notin R$. After all, $(10,10) \notin R$ either, but then $10 \notin S$. You must have $1 \in S$ and $\underline{(1,1) \notin R}$ to be correct.

202   Let $S = \{1, 2, 3, 4\}$ and $R = \{(1,1), (1,2), (2,2), (3,3), (3,1), (4,1), (4,4)\}$.
       Is R reflexive? Why?

Yes, $(x,x) \in R$ for every $x \in S$.

203 Look at Panel 2. Does R_1 have the reflexive property in S? Why?

No, $a \in S$, but $(a,a) \notin R_1$ (or $a \not\mathrel{R_1} a$).

204 Look at Panel 2. Does R_2 have the reflexive property in S? Why?

Yes, $(x,x) \in R_2$ for every $x \in S$.
Note: You need not use x; any symbol except a, b, or c is correct.

205 A binary relation R is reflexive in S if and only if $(x,x) \in S$ for
every $x \in S$. Let S be the set of all triangles, and $R = \{(x,y) \mid x \in S,$
$y \in S$, and $x \cong y\}$. A triangle is always congruent to itself, so for all
$x \in S$, $x \mathrel{R} x$. Therefore R satisfies the _____ in S.

reflexive property

•206 A binary relation R in S is reflexive if and only if _____ .

$x \mathrel{R} x$ or $(x,x) \in R$ for every $x \in S$

•207 A binary relation R in S is not reflexive if there exists an $x \in S$
such that _____ .

$(x,x) \notin R$ or $x \not\mathrel{R} x$

208 Let $S = \{a, 1, d\}$ and $R = \{(a,1), (a,a), (1,a), (1,1), (1,d), (d,1), (a,d)\}$.
R is not reflexive since _____ .

$d \in S$ but $(d,d) \notin R$

209 Let $S = \{1, 2, a, g\}$. If you were to pick out elements of $S \times S$ to
form a binary relation R in S and you want R to be reflexive, name
four elements which must be included in R.

$(1,1)$, $(2,2)$, (a,a), (g,g)

210 Let $S = \{0, 1, a, b\}$ and $R = \{(0,0), (0,1), (1,0), (a,a), (b,b), (a,1)\}$.
R is not reflexive in S because _____ .

$1 \in S$, but $(1,1) \notin R$

211 Let $S = \{1, 2, 17, z\}$. Fill in the blank so that R is reflexive.
$R = \{(1,1), (1,2), (z,2), (17,17), (z,1), (z,z), \underline{\hspace{1cm}}\}$

(2,2)

•212 Let $S = \{1, 38, a, x\}$ and
$R = \{(a,x), (a,a), (38,38), (1,38), (1,1), (x,a), (x,38), (x,x), (1,x)\}$.
Is R reflexive? Why?

Yes, for all $y \in S$, it follows that $(y,y) \in R$.

•213 Let $S = \{a, c, 11\}$ and $R = \{(a,c), (c,a), (a,a), (11,c), (11,11)\}$.
Is R reflexive? Why?

No, $c \in S$ but $(c,c) \notin R$.

214 Let $S = \{a, 2, 13, b, 25\}$. A binary relation R in S, if it is to be reflexive, would have to contain at least $\underline{\hspace{1cm}}$ (how many) elements
(although it could contain more)?

five

215 Let $S = \{a, b, c\}$. Let R be a binary relation in S which is reflexive.
R must contain *at least* $\underline{\hspace{1cm}}$ (how many) elements?

three $[R$ must contain $(a,a), (b,b), (c,c)]$

216 Let $S = \{a, b, c\}$ and suppose R is a binary relation in S such that
R is reflexive. Is $(a,a) \in R$? (That is, is $a R a$?)

yes

217 Let $S = \{1, a\}$ and $R = \{(1,1)\}$. Is R reflexive? Why?

No, $a \in S$, but $(a,a) \notin R$.

218 Let $S = \{1, 2, 3\}$ and $R = \left\{(x,y) \mid x \in S, \ y \in S, \ \text{and} \ \dfrac{x}{y} = 1\right\}$.
Is R reflexive in S? Why?

Yes, if $x \in S$, $\dfrac{x}{x} = 1$, so $(x,x) \in R$.

219 Let $S = \{0, 1, 2\}$ and $R = (x,y)\,|\,x \in S,\ y \in S,$ and $\frac{x}{y} = 1$.
Is R reflexive in S? Why?

No, $0 \in S$, but $\frac{0}{0} \neq 1$, so $(0,0) \notin R$. (Remember that division by zero is not defined.)

220 In Panel 2, R_3 is reflexive in S because _____.

$(x,x) \in R_3$ for every $x \in S$.

221 Let $S = \{1, 2, 3\}$.
Let $R = \{(x,y)\,|\,x \in S,\ y \in S,$ and x and y have the same remainder
when divided by 2$\}$.
$(1,1) \in R,\ (2,2) \in R,\ (3,3) \in R,$ so R satisfies the _____.

reflexive property

•222 Let S be the set of positive integers and let
$R = \left\{(x,y)\,|\,x \in S,\ y \in S,\ \text{and}\ \frac{x}{y} = 1\right\}$. Does R have the reflexive property? Why?

Yes, for each $a \in S$, $(a,a) \in R$.
Note: $\frac{a}{a} = 1$ since $a \neq 0$.

223 Let S be the set of nonnegative integers.
Let $R = \left\{(x,y)\,|\,x \in S,\ y \in S,\ \text{and}\ \frac{x}{y} = 1\right\}$. Does R have the reflexive
property? Why?
Note: 0 is an integer which is neither positive nor negative. Therefore the set of nonnegative integers is $S = \{0, 1, 2, \ldots\}$.

No, $0 \in S$, but $(0,0) \notin R$ since $\frac{0}{0}$ is not defined.

224 Let S be the set of integers and $a\,R\,b$ if and only if a and b are
integers and $a + b$ is an even integer. Is R reflexive?

Yes, for all integers x, it follows that $x + x = 2x$ is an even integer,
so $(x,x) \in R$.

225   Let S be the set of all humans.
      Let $R = \{(x,y) \mid x \in S, \ y \in S, \text{ and } x \text{ has the same color of hair as } y\}$.
      Is the reflexive property satisfied?

      Yes, every person has the same color hair as himself; so $x \, R \, x$
      for every $x \in S$.

226   Let S be the set of all humans.
      Let $R = \{(x,y) \mid x \in S, \ y \in S, \text{ and } x \text{ is the father of } y\}$.
      Is the reflexive property satisfied? Why?

      No, no person is the father of himself.

227   Let S be the set of integers and $R = \{(x,y) \mid x \in S, \ y \in S, \text{ and } x \cdot y > 0\}$.
      Is R reflexive? Why?

      No, $0 \in S$, but $0 \cdot 0 \not> 0$ (or $(0,0) \notin R$).

228   Let S be the set of nonzero integers and
      $R = \{(x,y) \mid x \in S, \ y \in S, \text{ and } x \cdot y > 0\}$. Is R reflexive? Why?

      Yes, for all integers $x \neq 0$, $x \cdot x > 0$, so $x \, R \, x$.

229   Let S be the set of integers and
      $R = \{(x,y) \mid x \in S, y \in S, \text{ and } x \text{ and } y \text{ have the same remainder when divided by 2}\}$.
      Is R reflexive?

      Yes, any integer has the same remainder when divided by 2 as itself
      when divided by 2, so for every $x \in S$, $(x,x) \in R$.

230   Let S be the set of integers and
      $R = \{(x,y) \mid x \in S, \ y \in S, \text{ and } x + y \text{ is an even integer}\}$.
      Is R reflexive?

      Yes, if x is any integer, $x + x = 2x$, an even integer; so $x \, R \, x$ for
      all $x \in S$.

231   Let S be the set of real numbers and
      $R = \{(x,y) \mid x \in S, \ y \in S, \text{ and } x \neq y\}$.
      Is R reflexive?

      No, if $x \in S$, it is not true that $x \neq x$; so $x \, \not\!R \, x$.

•232 In Panel 2, R_4 is reflexive since _____ .

for all $x \in S$, $x\ R_4\ x$ [or $(x,x) \in R_4$]

•233 In Panel 2, R_3 is not reflexive since _____ .

$a \in S$ but $(a,a) \notin R$, or $a \not{R} a$ (or b could be used)

234 Given a set S and a binary relation R in S which is reflexive, suppose $x \in S$; name one element which must be in R.

(x,x)

235 Let $S = \{a, b, c\}$. Copy this graph of $S \times S$.
Suppose we wish to select points representing
elements of a binary relation R in S. If we
wish R to be reflexive, certain points must
be chosen. Circle them.

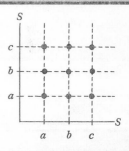

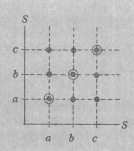

236 Let S be the set of all plane angles and
$R = \{(x,y) \mid x \in S,\ y \in S,\ \text{and } x \text{ is the complement of } y\}$.
Recall: If x and y are angles, then x is the complement of y if and
only if the sum of the measures of x and y is 90°. Is R reflexive?

No, except for an angle of 45°, $(x,x) \notin R$.

237 Let S be the set of real numbers and
$R = \{(x,y) \mid x \in S,\ y \in S,\ \text{and } x > y\}$.
Is R reflexive?

No, if x is a real number, $x \not> x$, so $(x,x) \notin R$.

238 Let S be the set of real numbers and
$R = \{(x,y) \mid x \in S,\ y \in S,\ \text{and}\ x \geq y\}$. Is R reflexive? Why?

Yes, $x \geq x$ for every $x \in S$.

239 Let S be the set of humans and
$R = \{(x,y) \mid x \in S,\ y \in S,\ \text{and}\ x\ \text{has the same parents as}\ y\}$.
Is R reflexive?

Yes, if x is a human being, x has the same parents as x, so $(x,x) \in R$.

240 Let S be the set of all lines in a plane and
$R = \{(x,y) \mid x \in S,\ y \in S,\ \text{and}\ x \perp y\}$. Is R reflexive?

No, no line is $\perp$ to itself; so if $a \in S$, $a \not{R} a$.

241 Let $S = \{1, 3, a\}$ and $R = \{(1,1), (1,3), (a,a)\}$. Is R reflexive? Why?

No, $3 \in S$, but $3 \not{R} 3$.

Self-test III   (Answers to Self-test III appear on page 311)

1 (p,q) is called a(n) _____ . p is called the _____ of (p,q), and q is called the _____ of (p,q).

2 Define symbolically the equality of two ordered pairs.

3 Let S be a set. (1) $S \times S$ is called the _____. (2) $S \times S =$ _____ (symbolically).

4 Let $S = \{1, 2\}$, and $T = \{a, b, c\}$. Write $S \times T$ in roster form.

5 Complete the following definition: R is a binary relation in a set S if and only if _____.

6 Define a reflexive binary relation R in a set S.

7 Let S be the set of integers. Consider the "$\leq$ relation" in S. Is the "$\leq$ relation" reflexive in R? Why?

8 Let $S = \{a, b, c, d\}$.
Let $R = \{(a,a), (a,b), (b,a), (c,c), (c,d), (d,d)\}$.
Is R reflexive in S? Why?

b. Symmetric

---

242 Let S be the set of all lines in a plane q, and suppose
$R = \{(x,y) \mid x \in S,\ y \in S,$ and x is perpendicular to $y\}$.
We know from plane geometry that if line l is perpendicular to
line m, then line m is perpendicular to line l. Therefore, in this
frame, if $(l,m) \in R$, we know also that (____ , ____) $\in R$.

(m,l)

---

243 Let S be the set of integers and $R = \{(x,y) \mid x \in S,\ y \in S,$ and $x < y\}$.
Suppose $p,\ q \in S$ and $p < q$. We know that $(p,q) \in R$. But, if $p < q$,
we know that $q \not< p$, so ____ $\notin R$.

(q,p)

---

244 Let S be the set of all triangles and
$R = \{(x,y) \mid x \in S,\ y \in S,$ and $x \cong y\}$.
(1) Suppose $a,\ b \in S$ and $a \cong b$. Then _____ .
(2) But if $a \cong b$, then also $b \cong a$. Therefore _____ $\in R$.

(1) $(a,b) \in R$
(2) (b,a)

---

245 Let S be the set of all *male* humans and
$R = \{(x,y) \mid x \in S,\ y \in S,$ and x is the brother of $y\}$.
(1) If $a,\ b \in S$ and a is the brother of b, then _____ $\in R$.
(2) But if a is the brother of b, then b is the brother of a; then
_____ $\in R$.
Note that we are dealing with the set of *male* humans.

(1) (a,b)
(2) (b,a)

---

246 Let S be the set of *all* humans and
$R = \{(x,y) \mid x \in S,\ y \in S,$ and x is the brother of $y\}$.
(1) Suppose $a \in S$, $b \in S$, and a is the brother of b. Then _____ .
(2) Is it necessarily true that b is the brother of a? Why?
Therefore (b,a) is not necessarily an element of R.

(1) $(a,b) \in R$
(2) No, not if b is a girl.

---

247   Let S be the set of all lines and
      $R = \{(x,y) \mid x \in S, y \in S,$ and x intersects $y\}$.
      If $p, q \in S$ and $(p,q) \in R$, then p intersects q. But then q intersects
      p. So, if $(p,q) \in R$, then also _____.

$(q,p) \in R$

248   Some of the last examples (perpendicular lines, intersecting lines,
      congruent triangles) had the following property. Whenever $(x,y) \in R$,
      _____ was also a member of R.

(y,x)
If you do not recall, review frames 242, 245, and 247.

249   A binary relation having the property mentioned above is said to be
      symmetric (or to have the symmetric property). *Definition:* A binary
      relation R is *symmetric* if and only if it satisfies the condition that
      whenever $(x,y) \in R$, it follows that _____ $\in R$.

(y,x)

250   Let R be a binary relation.
      If $(x,y) \in R$ and if $(y,x) \in R$, then R is said to be _____.

symmetric

251   Let R be a binary relation. R is said to be symmetric if and only if,
      whenever _____ , then _____.

$(x,y) \in R,$ $(y,x) \in R$

•252 A binary relation R in a set S is symmetric if and only if it satis-
      fies the following condition: _____.

whenever $(x,y) \in R$, then $(y,x) \in R$

COMMENT

If you prefer using the phrases "whenever $x \, R \, y$, then $y \, R \, x$" or
"$x \, R \, y$ implies $y \, R \, x$," these are acceptable. As long as your definition states the essential properties of symmetry, you are correct.
If you are not certain, ask your instructor.

253 If R is a binary relation in a set S, and (x,x) for every $x \in S$, then R is said to be _____.

reflexive

254 If R is a binary relation and whenever $x R y$ then $y R x$, R is said to have the _____.

symmetric property

255 Let $S = \{a, b, 1, 2\}$ and $R = \{(a,1), (1,a), (2,1), (1,2), (2,2)\}$.
  (1) Is it true that whenever $(x,y) \in R$, then $(y,x) \in R$?
  (2) R _____(is or is not) symmetric.

  (1) yes [You do not get a different element by interchanging the coordinates of $(2,2)$.]
  (2) is

256 (1) A binary relation R in a set S is symmetric if and only if whenever _____, then _____.
  (2) Let $S = \{a, b, 1\}$ and $R = \{(a,b), (b,a), (b,1), (1,b)\}$. Is R symmetric? Why?

  (1) $(x,y) \in R$, $(y,x) \in R$
  (2) Yes, whenever $(x,y) \in R$, then $(y,x) \in R$.

257 Let $S = \{1, a, x, z\}$ and $R = \{(1,a), (a,1), (1,x)\}$. Is R symmetric? Why?

No, $(1,x) \in R$, but $(x,1) \notin R$.

258 A binary relation R in S is *not* symmetric if there exists an $(x,y) \in R$ such that _____.

$(y,x) \notin R$

259 A binary relation R is _____ if there exists an $(x,y) \in R$ such that $(y,x) \notin R$.

not symmetric

260 A binary relation R *is not* symmetric if there exists a(n) _____
such that _____.

$(x,y) \in R, \qquad (y,x) \notin R$

261 Let $S = \{a, b, c, d\}$ and $R = \{(b,d), (d,b), (a,a), (a,b)\}$.
R is not symmetric since _____ (be specific).

$(a,b) \in R,$ but $(b,a) \notin R$

262 Let $S = \{17, a, d\}$ and $R = \{(17,a), (a,17), (a,a)\}$. Is R symmetric?
Why?

Yes, whenever $(x,y) \in R$, then $(y,x) \in R$.
Note: If you interchange the coordinates of (a,a), you get (a,a) which
is in R.

263 Let $S = \{1, 2, 3, 4\}$ and $R = \{(1,1), (2,2), (3,3), (4,1), (1,4)\}$.
(1) Is R reflexive? Why?
(2) Is R symmetric? Why?

(1) No, $4 \in R$, but $(4,4) \notin R$.
(2) Yes, whenever $(x,y) \in R$, then $(y,x) \in R$.

264 Let $S = \{1, 2, 3, 4\}$ and $R = \{(2,2)\}$. Is R symmetric? Why?

Yes, whenever $x \, R \, y$, then $y \, R \, x$ [or whenever $(x,y) \in R$, $(y,x) \in R$].

265 Let $S = \{1, 2, 3, 4\}$ and $R = \phi$. R is symmetric. Think about this. It
is true that whenever $(x,y) \in R$, then $(y,x) \in R$ because there is *no*
$(x,y) \in R$. R is symmetric by default; or, in mathematical terms, the
symmetric property is satisfied vacuously. Suppose $R = S \times S$. Is R
symmetric?

Yes, whenever $(x,y) \in R$, then $(y,x) \in R$ since R contains *all* of the
ordered pairs of $S \times S$.

266 Let $S = \{1, 2, 3, 4\}$ and $R = \{(2,2)\}$. Is R symmetric? Why?

Yes, whenever $(x,y) \in R$, then $(y,x) \in R$

267 Given a binary relation R in a set S:
   (1) To decide if R is reflexive, you must check that for every
      $x \in$ _____ , $(x,x) \in R$.
   (2) To decide if R is symmetric, you must check that for every
      $(x,y) \in$ _____ , $(y,x) \in R$.

   (1) S
   (2) R

268 Let $S = \{1, 2, 3, 4\}$ and $R = \{(1,1), (1,2), (2,2), (3,3), (4,4)\}$.
   (1) To decide if R is reflexive, we must check every element x of
      S to see if $(x,x) \in R$. Is R reflexive?
   (2) To decide if R is symmetric, we must check every ordered
      pair of R to see if the pair having the coordinates reversed is
      also in R. Is R symmetric?

   (1) yes
   (2) No, because $(1,2) \in R$, but $(2,1) \notin R$.

•269 (1) A binary relation R in a set S is reflexive if it satisfies the
      condition _____ .
   (2) A binary relation R in a set S is symmetric if and only if it
      satisfies the condition: _____ .

   (1) $(x,x) \in R$ for every $x \in S$
   (2) whenever $(x,y) \in R$, then $(y,x) \in R$

•270 (1) A binary relation R in a set S is *not* reflexive in S if
      _____ .
   (2) A binary relation R in a set S is *not* symmetric if
      _____ .

   (1) there is an $x \in S$ such that $(x,x) \notin R$
   (2) there is an $(x,y) \in R$ such that $(y,x) \notin R$

271 Look at Panel 2. One reason for the use of the word "symmetric"
   becomes evident if the same scale is used on both the horizontal
   and the vertical lines of the graph. The line that bisects the angle
   formed by these two lines is the axis of symmetry for all pairs of
   points that represent ordered pairs of the form (x,y) and (y,x).
   (That is, the line is the $\perp$ bisector of a line segment joining these
   points.) Draw a graph such as in Panel 2, sketch this line of symmetry, and circle the points representing (a,c) and (c,a).

▼

Note: The line is the ⊥ bisector of the line segment joining the points that represent (a,c) and (c,a).

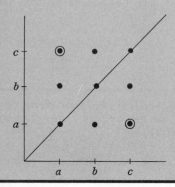

272   Let $S = \{1, a, 13\}$ and $R = \{(1,1), (a,a)\}$.
      (1) Is R reflexive? Why?
      (2) Is R symmetric? Why?

(1)   No, $13 \in S$, but $(13,13) \notin R$.
(2)   Yes, whenever $(x,y) \in R$, then $(y,x) \in R$.

273   Let $S = \{a, b, 4\}$ and $R = \{(a,a), (b,b), (4,4)\}$.
      (1) Is R reflexive? Why?
      (2) Is R symmetric? Why?

(1)   Yes, for all $x \in S$, $(x,x) \in R$.
(2)   Yes, whenever $(x,y) \in R$, then $(y,x) \in R$.

274   Let $S = \{a, b, c, d, e, 13\}$ and $R = \{(a,a)\}$.
      (1) Is R reflexive? Why?
      (2) Is R symmetric? Why?

(1)   No, $b \in S$, but $(b,b) \notin R$ (or use c, d, e, or 13).
(2)   Yes, for all $(x,y) \in R$, $(y,x) \in R$.

275   Let $S = \{a, 1, 28\}$ and
      $R = \{(a,1), (1,a), (1,1), (1,28), (28,1), (a,28), (a,a), (28,28)\}$.
      (1) Is R reflexive? Why?
      (2) Is R symmetric? Why?

(1)   Yes, for all $x \in S$, $(x,x) \in R$.
(2)   No, $(a,28) \in R$, but $(28,a) \notin R$.

276 The only way to prove that a relation R *is not* symmetric is to find
one $(x,y) \in R$ such that
(1) _____.
Let $\overline{R = \{(1,1), (3,a)\}}$.
(2) _____ , but _____ , so R *is not* symmetric.

(1) $(y,x) \notin R$
(2) $(3,a) \in R$, $(a,3) \notin R$

277 Let $S = \{p, q, r, s\}$ and
$R = \{(p,p), (p,q), (q,q), (q,r), (r,r), (r,q),$ ___ , ___ $\}$.
Fill in the blanks so that R is reflexive in S and symmetric.

$(s,s), (q,p)$

278 Let $S = \{a, b, c\}$ and $R = \phi$.
(1) Can you find an $(x,y) \in R$ such that $(y,x) \notin R$?
(2) Is R symmetric?

(1) no   (2) yes

279 Let $S = \{1, g\}$ and $R = \{(1,1), (g,g)\}$.
(1) Is R reflexive?
(2) Is R symmetric?

(1) yes   (2) yes

280 Let $S = \{1, g\}$ and $R = \{(1,1)\}$.
(1) Is R reflexive? Why?
(2) Is R symmetric? Why?

(1) No, $g \in S$, but $(g,g) \notin R$.
(2) Yes, whenever $(x,y) \in R$, then $(y,x) \in R$.

281 Let $S = \{1, g\}$ and $R = \{(1,1), (g,g), (g,1)\}$.
(1) Is R reflexive? Why?
(2) Is R symmetric? Why?

(1) Yes, $(x,x) \in R$ for every $x \in S$.
(2) No, $(g,1) \in R$, but $(1,g) \notin R$.

282 Let $S = \{1, g\}$ and $R = \{(1,1), (1,g)\}$.
(1) Is R reflexive? Why?
(2) Is R symmetric? Why?

(1) No, $(g,g) \notin R$.
(2) No, $(1,g) \in R$, but $(g,1) \notin R$.

283 Let $S = \{1, 2, 3\}$ and $R = \{(x,y) \mid x \in S, y \in S, \text{ and } x \neq y\}$.
(1) Write $S \times S$ in roster form.
(2) Write R in roster form.
(3) Is R symmetric? Why?

(1) $S \times S = \{(1,1), (1,2), (1,3), (2,1), (2,2), (2,3), (3,1), (3,2), (3,3)\}$
(2) $R = \{(1,2), (1,3), (2,1), (2,3), (3,1), (3,2)\}$
(3) Yes, whenever $(x,y) \in R$, then $(y,x) \in R$.

284 Let R be a binary relation in a set S. R is reflexive if and only if
_____.

$(x,x) \in R$ for every $x \in S$

285 Let R be a binary relation in a set S. R is symmetric if and only
if _____.

whenever $(x,y) \in R$, then $(y,x) \in R$

286 Let $S = \{a, b, 13\}$. Construct a binary relation R in S which is reflexive in S, symmetric, includes $(a,13)$, and has as few elements as
possible.

$\{(a,a), (b,b), (13,13), (a,13), (13,a)\}$

287 Look at Panel 2. Which of the relations listed are symmetric?

R_1, R_3, R_5, R_7

288 Let $S = \{x \mid x \text{ is a straight line in plane } q\}$.
Let $R = \{(w,v) \mid w \in S, v \in S, \text{ and } w \parallel v\}$.
Is R symmetric?

Yes, if line $w \parallel$ line v, then line $v \parallel$ line w.

289 $S \times S$ is illustrated graphically here. The
points circled represent elements of a binary relation R.
(1) Is R reflexive? Why?
(2) Is R symmetric? Why?

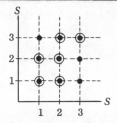

(1) Yes, for every $a \in S$, $(a,a) \in R$ (or $a\,R\,a$).
(2) No, $2\,R\,3$, but $3\,\not{R}\,2$ [or $(2,3) \in R$, but $(3,2) \notin R$].

290 Let S be the set of points in a plane and
$R = \{(x,y) \mid x \in S,\ y \in S,\ \text{the distance between } x \text{ and } y \text{ is less than } 1\}$.
(1) Is R reflexive?
(2) Is R symmetric?

(1) Yes, if $x \in S$, the distance between x and itself is 0, so
$(x,x) \in R$.
(2) Yes, if $(x,y) \in R$, then the distance between x and y is less than
1. Therefore the distance between y and x is less than 1, so
$(y,x) \in R$.

291 Let S be the set of cities in the United States and
let $R = \{(x,y) \mid x \in S,\ y \in S,\ \text{and } x \text{ is west of } y\}$.
(1) Is R reflexive?
(2) Is R symmetric?

(1) No, You could hardly say that city x is west of itself.
(2) No, if $a\,R\,b$, then a is west of b. Therefore b is not west of a,
so $(b,a) \notin R$.

292 Let $S = \{A,\ B,\ C\}$ where $A = \{1,\ 2\}$, $B = \{a\}$, and $C = \{1,\ a\}$;
and $R = \{(X,Y) \mid X \in S,\ Y \in S,\ \text{and } X \subset Y$.
Is R symmetric?

No, $B \subset C$, so $B\,R\,C$; but $C \not\subset B$, so $C\,\not{R}\,B$.

293 Let S be the set of integers, and $a\,R\,b$ if and only if a and b are
integers and $a + b$ is an even integer.
Note: This is an alternate way of writing
$R = \{(x,y) \mid x \in S,\ y \in S,\ \text{and } x + y \text{ is an even integer}\}$.
Is R symmetric?

Yes, let $(x,y) \in R$. Then $x + y$ is an even integer. Therefore $y + x$
is an even integer, so $(y,x) \in R$.

294 Let S be the set of integers; $S = \{\ldots, -2, -1, 0, 1, 2, 3, \ldots\}$.
Let $R = \{(x,y) \mid x \in S, \ y \in S, \text{ and } x \cdot y > 0\}$.
(1) Is it true that for every $x \in S$, it follows that $(x,x) \in R$?
(2) Therefore R _____ (is or is not) reflexive.
(3) Is it true that whenever $(x,y) \in R$, then it follows that $(y,x) \in R$?
(4) Therefore R _____ (is or is not) symmetric.

(1) No, $0 \in R$, but $0 \cdot 0 \not> 0$, so $(0,0) \notin R$.
(2) is not
(3) Yes, if $(x,y) \in R$, then $x \cdot y > 0$, so $y \cdot x > 0$ and $(y,x) \in R$.
(4) is

295 Let S be the set of *nonzero* integers; $S = \{\ldots, -2, -1, 1, 2, \ldots\}$.
Let $R = \{(x,y) \mid x \in S, \ y \in S, \text{ and } x \cdot y > 0\}$.
(1) Is R reflexive?
(2) Is R symmetric?

(1) Yes, if $x \in S$, $x \neq 0$, so $x \cdot x > 0$. Then $(x,x) \in R$ for every $x \in R$.
(2) Yes, if $(x,y) \in R$, then $x \cdot y > 0$. Then $y \cdot x > 0$, and $(y,x) \in R$.

296 Let S be the set of integers and
$R = \{(x,y) \mid x \in S, \ y \in S, \text{ and } x \cdot y \geq 0\}$.
(1) Is R reflexive?
(2) Is R symmetric?

(1) Yes, for all $x \in S$, $x \cdot x \geq 0$; even $0 \cdot 0 \geq 0$.
(2) yes

297 Let S be the set of *nonzero* integers and
$R = \{(x,y) \mid x \in S, \ y \in S, \text{ and } x \cdot y \geq 0\}$.
(1) Is R reflexive?
(2) Is R symmetric?

(1) yes   (2) yes

298 Let S be the set of all polygons and
$R = \{(x,y) \mid x \in S, \ y \in S, \text{ and } x \text{ has the same number of vertices as } y\}$.
(1) Is R reflexive?
(2) Is R symmetric?

(1) Yes, if x is a polygon, x has the same number of vertices as x, so $(x,x) \in R$, for every $x \in S$.
(2) Yes, if $(x,y) \in R$, then x and y are polygons and x has the same number of sides as y. Obviously $(y,x) \in R$.

299 Let S be a set, each element being a nonempty set.
Let $R = \{(X,Y) \mid X \in S, \ Y \in S, \text{ and } X \cap Y = \phi\}$.
(1) Let $A \in S$; then A is a nonempty set. Is $(A,A) \in R$? Why?
(2) Therefore R _____ (is or is not) reflexive.
(3) Let $(A,B) \in R$; that is, A and B are nonempty sets. $A \cap B = \phi$;
$\therefore B \cap A =$ _____ , so (B,A) _____ R.
(4) Therefore R _____ (is or is not) symmetric.

(1) No, if A is a nonempty set, $A \cap A \neq \phi$; $\therefore (A,A) \notin R$.
(2) is not
(3) ϕ (note that $A \cap B = B \cap A$), $\in$
(4) is

300 Let $S = \{1, 2, 3\}$.
(1) Write $S \times S$ in roster form.
(2) Consider the "$\leq$ relation" in S. Let R be the set determined by
this relation. Write R in roster form.
(3) Is R reflexive? Why?
(4) Is R symmetric? Why?

(1) $S \times S = \{(1,1), (1,2), (1,3), (2,1), (2,2), (2,3), (3,1), (3,2), (3,3)\}$
(2) $R = \{(1,1), (1,2), (1,3), (2,2), (2,3), (3,3)\}$
(3) Yes, $(x,x) \in R$ for every $x \in S$.
(4) No, $(1,2) \in R$, but $(2,1) \notin R$.
You may have used either $(1,3)$ or $(2,3)$ as an example.

c. Transitive

301 Let us consider one more property which a binary relation sometimes satisfies. Let S be the set of integers.
Let $R = \{(x,y) \mid x \in S, \ y \in S, \text{ and } x < y\}$.
Suppose p and q are integers and $p < q$; then $(p,q) \in R$. Suppose
q and r are integers and $q < r$; then $(q,r) \in R$. We have that p, q,
and r are integers, and $p < q$ and $q < r$. We know from algebra
that it must follow that _____ < _____ ; then _____ is also a member
of R.

$p < r$, (p,r)

302   Let S be set the set of positive integers.
$R = \{(x,y) \mid x \in S,\ y \in S,$ and x is a divisor of $y\}$.
(1)   Suppose $(p,q) \in R$, then p and q are _____ and p is a(n)
_____ of q.
(2)   Suppose $(q,p) \in R$, then q and r are _____ and q is a(n)
_____ of r.
(3)   From algebra, if p, q, and r are integers, and p is a divisor
of q, and q is a divisor of r, then _____ is a divisor of _____.
(4)   Therefore (_____ , _____) is also a member of R.

(1)   positive integers,   divisor
(2)   positive integers,   divisor   (3) p, r (4) (p,r)

303   Let S be a set of triangles.
Let $R = \{(x,y) \mid x \in S,\ y \in S,$ and $x \sim y\}$. ($\sim$ means "similar to.")
(1)   Suppose a and b are _____ and $a \sim b$; then $(a,b) \in R$.
(2)   Suppose b and c are _____ and ____; then $(b,c) \in R$.
(3)   You may recall from geometry that, if a, b, c are triangles and
$a \sim b$ and $b \sim c$, then _____.
(4)   Therefore _____ is also a member of R.

(1)   triangles   (2) triangles, $b \sim c$
(3) $a \sim c$ (4) (a,c)
It is also true that, if a and b are triangles and $a \sim b$, then $b \sim a$,
so $(b,a) \in R$. This is the symmetric property of the similarity relation on triangles. We will not be concerned with this at the moment.

304   Let S be the set of all cities in the United States.
Let $R = \{(x,y) \mid x \in S,\ y \in S,$ and x is west of $y\}$.
(1)   Suppose $(a,b) \in R$ and $(b,c) \in R$. Then a, b, and c are cities in
the United States and a is _____ of b and b is _____ of
c.
(2)   Make a sketch. Note that _____ is west of _____ , so that _____ is
also a member of R.

(1)   west,   west   (2) ⊢————⊦————⊦— a, c, (a,c)
                                a b c

305   Frames 301 to 304 exhibited relations having the following property:
Whenever $(x,y) \in R$ and $(y,z) \in R$, then it followed that (_____) $\in R$.

(x,z) If your answer is not correct, review frames 301 to 304.

306   A binary relation that has the property just stated is called a
transitive binary relation (or it is said to have the transitive
property).

▼

Definition: A binary relation R is said to be *transitive* if and only if it satisfies the condition: whenever $(x,y) \in R$ and $(y,z) \in R$, then ____ $\in R$.

(x,z)

---

307 If R is a binary relation such that whenever **(1)** ____ $\in R$ and **(2)** ____ $\in R$, then it follows that **(3)** ____ $\in R$, and it is said to be transitive.

(1) (x,y) **(2)** (y,z) **(3)** (x,z)

---

308 A binary relation R is said to be transitive if and only if it satisfies the property: whenever **(1)** ____ and **(2)** ____ , then **(3)** ____ .

(1) $(x,y) \in R$ **(2)** $(y,z) \in R$ **(3)** $(x,z) \in R$

•309 A binary relation is said to be transitive if and only if it satisfies the property: _____.

whenever $(x,y) \in R$ and $(y,z) \in R$, then $(x,z) \in R$

COMMENT

1. If you prefer to use "whenever $x\ R\ y$ and $y\ R\ z$, then $x\ R\ z$" or "$(x,y) \in R$ and $(y,z) \in R$ imply $(x,z) \in R$," you are equally correct.
2. Suppose (x,y) and (y,z) are members of R. Look at the positions of y.

$$(x,y), \quad (y,z)$$

If R is to be transitive, then you must be able to find (x,z) in R. Now suppose $R = \{(1,2), (3,5), (4,2), (7,3)\}$. *As they are written*, there are no ordered pairs in the pattern $(x,y), (y,z)$. Recall that the arrangement of the elements of a set is arbitrary, so we may write $R = \{(1,2), (7,3), (3,5), (4,2)\}$. Note that $(7,3), (3,5)$ is in the pattern. R *is not* transitive in this case, because $(7,5) \notin R$. In relations such as this one, written in roster form, you will have to match each ordered pair with the others, as in dominoes, to see if you can find any of the form $(x,y), (y,z)$.

In other relations $(<, \leq, \cong,$ etc.$)$ you will have algebraic techniques for determining transitivity, or you will use results with which you are familiar.

310 A binary relation R *is* transitive if and only if it satisfies the condition: whenever $(x,y) \in R$ and $(y,z) \in R$, then $(x,z) \in R$.

A binary relation R *is not* transitive if there exists $(x,y) \in R$ and $(y,z) \in R$ such that _____.

$(x,z) \notin R$

311 Let $S = \{a, b, c\}$. Let $R = \{(a,b), (b,c), (c,c)\}$. R is not transitive because $(a,b) \in R$ and $(b,c) \in R$, but _____.

$(a,c) \notin R$

312 Let $S = \{a, b, c\}$. Let $R = \{(a,b), (b,a), (a,a)\}$.
As the elements of R are arranged, you might think that R is transitive, but if $R = \{(b,a), (a,b), (a,a)\}$, _____ $\in R$ and _____ $\in R$, but _____ $\notin R$. R is not transitive.

(b,a), (a,b), (b,b)

313 Let $S = \{1, 2, 3, 4\}$. Let $R = \{(1,1), (1,2), (2,4), (1,4)\}$. Let us look for the pairs that fit the pattern.

$(1,1) \in R$ and $(1,2) \in R$. If R is to be transitive, $(1,2) \in R$. It is.
$(1,2) \in R$ and $(2,4) \in R$. If R is to be transitive, $(1,4) \in R$. It is.
$(1,1) \in R$ and $(1,4) \in R$. If R is to be transitive, $(1,4) \in R$. It is.

Whenever $(x,y) \in R$ and $(y,z) \in R$, then $(x,z) \in R$. Therefore R is _____.

transitive

314 Let $S = \{1, 2, 3, 4\}$. Let $R = \{(1,1), (1,2), (4,1)\}$. Look for the pairs that fit the pattern.

$(1,1) \in R$ and $(1,2) \in R$. If R is to be transitive, $(1,2) \in R$. It is.
$(4,1) \in R$ and $(1,2) \in R$. If R is to be transitive, $(4,2) \in R$. It is not.

Therefore, R is _____.

not transitive

315 Let $S = \{1, 2, a\}$. Let $R = \{(2,1), (a,2)\}$. Is R transitive? Why?

No, because $(a,2) \in R$ and $(2,1) \in R$, but $(a,1) \notin R$.

316 To prove that a binary relation R in a set S is *not* transitive, you
must exhibit two ordered pairs of the form (x,y) and (y,z) such that
$x\ R\ y$ and $y\ R\ z$, but $x\ \not{R}\ z$. Let $S = \{1, 2, 3\}$. Let $R = \{(1,3),\ (2,2)\}$.
Can you find two ordered pairs of R that do not satisfy the condition?

No, you cannot disprove that R is transitive. We may say that R is
transitive vacuously, because we cannot find an exception to $a\ R\ b$
and $b\ R\ c$, then $a\ R\ c$.

317 Let $S = \{1, 2, 3, 4\}$ and $R = \{(3,1),\ (2,4),\ (2,1)\}$. Is R transitive?
Why?
Note: If you say that R is not transitive, you must be prepared to
exhibit the pairs to prove it.

Yes, whenever $a\ R\ b$, and $b\ R\ c$, then $a\ R\ c$. In this frame there is
no example of a situation in which this does not hold, so R is transitive in the vacuous sense.

318 Let $S = \{a, b, c, d\}$ and $R = \{(b,c),\ (a,a),\ (c,a)\}$. Is R transitive?
Why?

No, $b\ R\ c$ and $c\ R\ a$; but $b\ \not{R}\ a$ [or $(b,c) \in R$ and $(c,a) \in R$, but
$(b,a) \notin R$].

319 Let $S = \{a, b, c, d\}$ and $R = \phi$. Is R transitive?

Yes, again there is no instance where transitivity fails to hold.

320 Let $S = \{a, b, c, d\}$ and $R = \{(b,c),\ (a,a),\ (d,d)\}$. Is R transitive?
Why?

Yes, whenever $x\ R\ y$ and $y\ R\ z$, then $x\ R\ z$ (you cannot exhibit two
ordered pairs where it does not happen).

321 Let $S = \{a, b, c, d\}$ and $R = \phi$. Is R symmetric? Why?

Yes, whenever $x\ R\ y$, then also $y\ R\ x$.

322 Let $S = \{a, b, c, d\}$ and $R = \phi$. Is R reflexive in S?

No, it must hold for all $x \in S$ that $x\ R\ x$. Here neither $a\ R\ a$ nor
$b\ R\ b$ nor $c\ R\ c$, etc.

323 Let $S = \{a, b, c, d\}$ and $R = \{(a,a), (d,b), (b,a)\}$.
Is R transitive? Why?

No, $d\ R\ b$ and $b\ R\ a$, but $d\ \not{R}\ a$.

324 Let $S = \{1, 2, 3\}$ and $R = \{(1,2), (2,3), (1,3)\}$.
Is R transitive? Why?

Yes, whenever $a\ R\ b$ and $b\ R\ c$, then $a\ R\ c$.

325 Look at Panel 2. R_1 is transitive since whenever $x\ R\ y$ and $y\ R\ z$,
then $x\ R\ z$. R_5 is not transitive since $a\ R\ b$ and $b\ R\ a$, but $a\ \not{R}\ a$.
Which of the other relations in Panel 2 are transitive?

R_1, R_2, R_3, R_6

326 In Panel 2 why is R_4 not transitive?

$(a,c) \in R$ and $(c,b) \in R$, but $(a,b) \notin R$ (or $a\ R\ c$ and $c\ R\ b$, but
$a\ \not{R}\ b$).

327 In Panel 2 why is R_7 not transitive?

$a\ R\ b$ and $b\ R\ c$, but $a\ \not{R}\ c$ (or $c\ R\ b$ and $b\ R\ a$, but $c\ \not{R}\ a$).

328 In Panel 2 why is R_5 not transitive?

$a\ R\ b$ and $b\ R\ a$, but $a\ \not{R}\ a$.

329 Let S be the set of positive integers and
$R = \{(x,y) \mid x \in S,\ y \in S,\ \text{and}\ x < y\}$.
Is R transitive? Why?

Yes, whenever $a < b$ and $b < c$, then $a < c$.

330 Let S be the set of real numbers and
$R = \{(x,y) \mid x \in S,\ y \in S,\ \text{and}\ x = y\}$.
Is R transitive? Why?

Yes, if $a = b$ and $b = c$, then $a = c$.

331   Let S be the set of all human beings and
$R = \{(x,y) \mid x \in S,\ y \in S,$ and x is the father of $y\}$.
Is R transitive? Why?

No, if a is the father of b and b is the father of c, then a is not the father of c.

•332   Does congruence of triangles define a relation which is transitive? Why?

Yes, if $a \cong b$ and $b \cong c$, then $a \cong c$.

•333   Does similarity of triangles define a relation which is transitive? Why?

Yes, if $a \sim b$ and $b \sim c$, then $a \sim c$.

•334   Does perpendicularity of lines in a plane define a relation which is transitive? Why? (A drawing may help you.)

No, if $l \perp m$ and $m \perp n$, then $l \not\perp n$.

335   Let S be the set of integers
Let $R = \{(x,y) \mid x \in S,\ y \in S,$ and $x \cdot y \geq 0\}$.
(1)   Is $(-2,-5) \in R$?
(2)   Is $(-3,0) \in R$?
(3)   Is $(0,5) \in R$?
(4)   Is $(-3,5) \in R$?
(5)   Is R transitive? Why?

(1)   yes   (2)   yes   (3)   yes   (4)   no
(5)   No, for example, $(-3,0) \in R$ and $(0,5) \in R$ but $(-3,5) \notin R$.

336   Let S be the set of integers and
$R = \{(x,y) \mid x \in S,\ y \in S,$ and $x \cdot y > 0\}$.
Is R transitive?

Yes, if $x \cdot y > 0$ and $y \cdot z > 0$, then $x \cdot z > 0$.

337   Let S be a collection of nonempty sets and
$R = \{(A,B) \mid A \in S,\ B \in S,$ and $A \subset B\}$.
Is R transitive?

Yes, if $A \subset B$ and $B \subset C$, then $A \subset C$.

338   Let S be the set of integers and $a\ R\ b$ if and only if $a + b$ is an even integer. Is R transitive?

Yes, if $(x,y) \in R$ and $(y,z) \in R$, then there are $k,\ m \in S$ such that $x + y = 2k$ and $y + z = 2m$.
$\therefore\ x - z = 2k - 2m$
$x + z = 2(k - m + z)$
Therefore $x + z$ is even. So $(x,z) \in R$.

•339   So, given a binary relation R in a set S, we have defined three properties which R may or may not have.
(1) R is reflexive in S if and only if _____ .
(2) R is symmetric if and only if _____ .
(3) R is transitive if and only if _____ .

(1)   for every $x \in S$ $(x,x) \in R$
(2)   whenever $(x,y) \in R$, then $(y,x) \in R$
(3) $(x,y) \in R$ and $(y,z) \in R$, then $(x,z) \in R$

340   These three properties are useful in describing a binary relation; and, given any binary relation R in a set S, we usually ask immediately if R satisfies any of them (reflexive, symmetric, transitive). For example, which, if any, of these properties does the $\leq$ relation on the set of real numbers have?

reflexive and transitive

341   For Panel 2 complete the following chart on a separate sheet of paper and save it. Work carefully. This material will be required for frames 342 to 348.

	Reflexive	Symmetric	Transitive
R_1		✓	✓
R_2	✓		✓
R_3			
R_4			
R_5			
R_6			
R_7			
R_8			

Which of the relations have all three properties?

R_3

342 Which of the relations of Panel 2 are reflexive in S and symmetric, but not transitive? (Look at your chart.)

R_7
If your answer is not correct, recheck until you are convinced; then change your table.

343 Which of the relations of Panel 2 are reflexive in S and transitive, but not symmetric? (Look at your chart.)

R_2

344 Which of the relations of Panel 2 have the symmetric and transitive property, but are not reflexive in S? (Look at your chart.)

R_1

345 Consider the set of all triangles.
Let P_1 be the property of having a 30° angle.
Let P_2 be the property of having a 60° angle.
Let P_3 be the property of having a 90° angle.
Suppose a triangle has any two of these properties; must it have the third property also?

yes

346 Look at the chart you completed for the binary relations of Panel 2. If a binary relation has any two of the three properties, reflexive, symmetric, and transitive, must it also have the third?

No, you have examples of each, that is, a relation having any two properties, but not the third.

347 Since a binary relation may have any two of the properties, reflexive, symmetric, or transitive, without necessarily having the third, these properties are said to be *independent*. For a triangle let P_1 be the property of being equilateral and let P_2 be the property of being equiangular. Are P_1 and P_2 independent?

No, if a triangle has one of these properties, it has the other.

348   So you see that, given a binary relation R in a set S, R may have none, any one, any two, or all three of the three properties under discussion. Check the chart you made for Panel 2. The answer for this frame will give the correct chart.

	Reflexive	Symmetric	Transitive
R_1		✓	✓
R_2	✓		✓
R_3	✓	✓	✓
R_4	✓		
R_5		✓	
R_6			✓
R_7	✓	✓	
R_8			

349   Let $S = \{a, b, c\}$. Add one more element to R so that R is symmetric and transitive but not reflexive. $R = \{(a,b), (b,a), (b,b), \underline{\quad} \}$.

(a,a)

350   Given a binary relation R in a set S, R is reflexive in S if and only if _____.

$(x,x) \in R$ for every $x \in S$

351   Look at Panel 3. Which of the relations are reflexive in S?

R_8, R_{13}, R_{14}, R_{16}

352   In Panel 3 why is R_2 not reflexive in S?

$2 \in S$, but $(2,2) \notin R_2$

353   A binary relation R in a set S is *not* symmetric if there exists a $(p,q) \in R$ such that _____.

$(q,p) \notin R$

354   Look at Panel 3. Which of the relations are symmetric?

R_1, R_2, R_5, R_8, R_9, R_{12}, R_{15}, R_{16}

355   In Panel 3 why is R_{13} not symmetric?

$(1,2) \in R_{13}$, but $(2,1) \notin R_{13}$

356   A binary relation R is *not* transitive if _____.

there exists a $(p,q) \in R$ and $(q,r) \in R$, but $(p,r) \notin R$

357   Let $S = \{1, 2, 3, 4\}$. Let $R = \{(1,1), (2,3), (3,2), (2,2)\}$. R is not transitive because _____.

$(3,2) \in R$ and $(2,3) \in R$, but $(3,3) \notin R$

358   Let $S = \{1, 2, 3, 4\}$ and $R = \{(1,1), (2,4), (3,3)\}$.
Can you find a $(p,q) \in R$ and $(q,r) \in R$ such that $(p,r) \notin R$?

No, therefore we must consider R to be transitive.

359   Look at Panel 3. Which of the relations are transitive?
To prove that any one of these relations is not transitive, you must be able to exhibit two pairs from R for which the transitive property does not hold.

R_1, R_2, R_3, R_4, R_5, R_6, R_7, R_8, R_{10}, R_{11}, R_{13}, R_{14}, R_{16}

360   Look at Panel 3. Why is R_{12} not transitive?

$2\ R\ 1$ and $1\ R\ 2$, but $2\ \cancel{R}\ 2$.

V. Equivalence Relation

361   An important type of binary relation is one which has all three properties, reflexive, symmetric, and transitive.
Let $R = \{(x,y \mid x$ and y are triangles and $x \cong y\}$.

▼

(1)   Is R reflexive?
(2)   Is R symmetric?
(3)   Is R transitive?

(1)   yes   (2)   yes   (3)   yes

362   Let $R = \{(x,y) \mid x$ and y are real numbers and $x \leq y\}$.
(1)   Is R reflexive?
(2)   Is R symmetric?
(3)   Is R transitive?

(1)   Yes, every real number is $\leq$ itself.
(2)   No, for example, $2 \leq 3$, but $3 \nleq 2$.
(3)   Yes, if $a \leq b$ and $b \leq c$, then $a \leq c$.

363   *Definition*: Any binary relation which is reflexive, symmetric, and
      transitive is called an *equivalence relation*.
      For example: let S be the set of all triangles
              let $R = \{(x,y) \mid x \in S,\ y \in S,\ \text{and } x \cong y\}$
(1)   Let a be any triangle. $a \cong a$, so for every $a \in S$, $a\,R\,a$. There-
      fore R is _____.
(2)   Suppose a and b are triangles. If $a \cong b$, then $b \cong a$. There-
      fore if $a\,R\,b$, then $b\,R\,a$. Therefore R is _____.
(3)   Let a, b, c be triangles. If $a \cong b$ and $b \cong c$, then $a \cong c$. So,
      if $a\,R\,b$ and $b\,R\,c$, then $a\,R\,c$. Therefore R is _____.
(4) R is reflexive, symmetric, and transitive, so R is a(n)

      _____ .

(1)   reflexive   (2)   symmetric   (3)   transitive
(4)   equivalence relation

364   (1)   A binary relation R is an equivalence relation if and only if R
            is _____ , _____ , and _____ . Let $S = \{a, b, c\}$. Let
            $R = \{(a,a),\ (a,c),\ (b,b),\ (c,c)\}$.
      (2) R is reflexive and transitive. Check. R is not symmetric. Why?
      (3)   Therefore R _____ (is or is not) an equivalence relation.

(1)   reflexive,   symmetric,   transitive
(2) $(a,c) \in R$, but $(c,a) \notin R$
(3)   is not

365 Let $S = \{1, 2, 3\}$ and $R = \{(1,1), (1,2), (2,1), (2,2)\}$.
Why is R *not* an equivalence relation in S?

R is not reflexive in S, $(3,3) \notin R$.
Here is an instance where we must be careful about the set within
which we work. If we take $T = \{1, 2\}$, then R is an equivalence relation in T.

•366 An equivalence relation in a set S is a binary relation which is
_____ . Let $S = \{a, b, c\}$ and $R = \{(a,a), (b,b), (c,c)\}$.
R is reflexive, symmetric, and transitive, so R is a(n) _____ .

reflexive, symmetric, and transitive
equivalence relation (in S)

•367 A binary relation in a set S which is reflexive, symmetric, and
transitive is called a(n) _____ in S.

equivalence relation

368 Let S be the set of real numbers, and $x \, R \, y$ if and only if $x < y$.
Is R an equivalence relation? Why?

No, R is not reflexive (or R is not symmetric).

369 Let S be the set of real numbers, and $x \, R \, y$ if and only if $x \le y$.
Is R an equivalence relation? Why?

No, R is not symmetric (for example, $2 \le 3$, but $3 \nleq 2$).

370 Let $S = \{a, b, c\}$ and $R = \{(a,a), (b,b), (c,c), (a,c), (c,a)\}$.
Is R reflexive in S? Why?

Yes, for each $x \in S$, $(x,x) \in R$ (or $x \, R \, x$).

371 Let $S = \{a, b, c\}$ and $R = \{(a,a), (b,b), (c,c), (a,c), (c,a)\}$.
Is R symmetric? Why?

Yes, whenever $x, y \in S$, and $x \, R \, y$, then $y \, R \, x$.

372   Let $S = \{a, b, c\}$ and $R = \{(a,a), (b,b), (c,c), (a,c), (c,a)\}$.
      Is R transitive? Why?

Yes, whenever $x, y, z \in S$ and $x R y$ and $y R z$, then $x R z$.

•373 Let $S = \{a, b, c\}$ and $R = \{(a,a), (b,b), (c,c), (a,c), (c,a)\}$. In frames
      370 to 372 you saw that R is reflexive, symmetric, and transitive;
      therefore, R is a(n) _____ .

equivalence relation

374   Look at Panel 3. Is R_2 an equivalence relation in S? Why?

No, R_2 is not reflexive. $2 \in S$, but $(2,2) \notin R_2$.

375   Look at Panel 3. Is R_{13} an equivalence relation in S? Why?

No, R_{13} is not symmetric. $(1,2) \in R_{13}$, but $(2,1) \notin R_{13}$.

376   Look at Panel 3. Is R_{14} an equivalence relation in S? Why?

No, R_{14} is not symmetric. $(2,1) \in R_{14}$, but $(1,2) \notin R_{14}$.

377   Look at Panel 3. Which of the binary relations are equivalence re-
      lations in S? Take your time.

R_8, R_{16}

378   Let S be the set of all human beings and
      $R = \{(x,y) \mid x \in S, y \in S,$ and x has the same color hair as $y\}$.
      Is R an equivalence relation?

yes

•379 Let S be the set of all triangles.
      Let $R = \{(x,y) \mid x \in S, y \in S,$ and $x \cong y\}$.
      (1) Is R reflexive? Why?
      (2) Is R symmetric? Why?

▼

(3) Is R transitive? Why?
(4) Is R an equivalence relation? Why?

(1) Yes, if x is a triangle, $x \cong x$.
(2) Yes, if x and y are triangles and $x \cong y$ and $y \cong x$.
(3) Yes, if x, y, and z are triangles and $x \cong y$ and $y \cong z$, then $x \cong z$.
(4) Yes, R is reflexive, symmetric, and transitive.

380 Let S be the set of all humans, and if $(a,b) \in S$, $(a,b) \in R$ if and only if a is exactly as tall as b.
(1) Is R reflexive?
(2) Is R symmetric?
(3) Is R transitive?
(4) Is R an equivalence relation?

(1) yes
(2) yes
(3) yes
(4) yes

381 Let S be the set of integers and if p, $q \in S$, $p \, R \, q$ if and only if $p \cdot q > 0$.
(1) Is R an equivalence relation in S?
(2) Is R reflexive? Why?

(1) No, because R is not reflexive.
(2) No, because $0 \in S$, but $(0,0) \notin R$.

382 Let S be the set of integers and if a, $b \in S$, $a \, R \, b$ if and only if $a \cdot b \geq 0$. (Note the change.)
(1) Is R reflexive? Why?
(2) Is R symmetric? Why?
(3) Is R transitive? Why?
(4) Is R an equivalence relation in S? Why?

(1) Yes, if x is an integer, $x \cdot x \geq 0$, so $(x,x) \in R$.
(2) Yes, if x, y are integers and $x \cdot y \geq 0$, then $y \cdot x \geq 0$, so $(y,x) \in R$.
(3) No, for example, $(-1,0) \in R$ and $(0,1) \in R$, but $(-1,1) \notin R$.
(4) No, because R is not transitive.

383 Let S be the set of all triangles in a plane and if a, $b \in S$, $a \, R \, b$ if and only if $a \cong b$. Is R an equivalence relation in S?

yes

384   Let S be the set of real numbers and if p, $q \in S$, $p R q$ if and only if
      $p \neq q$.
      (1)   Is R reflexive? Why?
      (2)   Is R symmetric? Why?
      (3)   Is R transitive? Why?
      (4)   Is R an equivalence relation? Why?

      (1)   No, if $x \in S$, $x = x$, so $(x,x) \notin R$.
      (2)   Yes, if $(x,y) \in R$, $x \neq y$, then $y \neq x$, so $(y,x) \in R$.
      (3)   No, for example, $(2,3) \in R$ and $(3,2) \in R$, but $(2,2) \notin R$.
      (4)   No, R is not reflexive (or because R is not transitive).

•385 Let S be the set of real numbers and
      $R = \{(x,y) \mid x \in S, \ y \in S, \text{ and } x < y\}$.
      Is R an equivalence relation? Why?

      No, R is not reflexive (or R is not symmetric).

386   Let S be the set of real numbers.
      Let $R = \{(x,y) \mid x \in S, \ y \in S, \text{ and } x \leq y\}$.
      (1)   Is R reflexive?
      (2)   Is R symmetric?
      (3)   Is R transitive?
      (4)   Is R an equivalence relation? Why?

      (1)   yes   **(2)**   no   **(3)**   yes   **(4)**   No, R is not symmetric.

387   Because of the importance of equivalence relations, a special symbol
      and wording are sometimes used. If R is an equivalence relation in
      S and $(x,y) \in R$, instead of writing $x R y$, we write $x \approx y$, and instead
      of saying "x is in the relation R to y," we say "x is equivalent
      to y." Similarly, if $(a,b) \in R$, we would write _____ and say
      "_____."

      $a \approx b$
      a is equivalent to b

388   Let $S = \{a, b, c\}$ and $R = \{(a,a), (b,b), (b,c), (c,b), (c,c)\}$.
      R is an equivalence relation in S. Check it.
      Using the new notation: $a \approx a$ which is read _____,
                          _____ which is read "b is equivalent to c."

      a is equivalent to a
      $b \approx c$

389 Let $S = \{a, b, c\}$ and $R = \{(a,a), (a,b), (b,a), (b,b), (c,c)\}$.
R is an equivalence relation. Check it. Since $(a,a) \in R$, $a \approx a$.
(1) Since $(a,b) \in R$, _____.
(2) Since $(c,c) \in R$, _____.

(1) $a \approx b$
(2) $c \approx c$

390 Let $S = \{a, b, c, d\}$. Let $R = \{(a,a), (b,b), (b,d), (c,c), (d,b), (d,d)\}$.
R is an equivalence relation in S. Check. Since $(a,a) \in R$, a is
equivalent to a. Since (b,b) and $(b,d) \in R$, b is equivalent to b and d.
(1) Since $(c,c) \in R$, c is equivalent to _____ .
(2) Since (d,b) and $(d,d) \in R$, d is equivalent to _____ and _____.

(1) c
(2) b, d

391 Let $S = \{a, b, c, d, e\}$ and
$R = \{(a,a), (b,b), (b,e), (c,c), (c,d), (d,c), (d,d), (e,b), (e,e)\}$.
R is an equivalence relation in S. Check it.
(1) List the elements a is equivalent to.
(2) List the elements b is equivalent to.
(3) List the elements c is equivalent to.

(1) a
(2) b, e
(3) c, d

392 Let $S = \{1, 2, 3, 4\}$ and $R = \{(1,1), (2,2), (3,3), (3,4), (4,3), (4,4)\}$.
Using the symbol $\approx$, read "equivalent to," $(1,1) \in R$ means $1 \approx 1$.
(1) $(2,2) \in R$ means _____.
(2) $(3,4) \in R$ means _____.

(1) $2 \approx 2$
(2) $3 \approx 4$

393 Using the notation $\approx$, the properties of an equivalence relation can
be rewritten as follows:
    Reflexive property: for every $a \in S$, $a \approx a$.
(1) Symmetric property: if a, $b \in S$ and $a \approx b$, then _____ .
(2) Transitive property: if a, b, $c \in S$, $a \approx b$, and $b \approx c$, then _____ .

(1) $b \approx a$
(2) $a \approx c$

---

394   Note that, given an equivalence relation R on a set S, if $x \in S$,
      $x \, R \, x$.
      (1)   Why?
      (2)   Therefore, for every $x \in S$, $x \approx$ _____.

---

      (1) R, being an equivalence relation, is reflexive.
      (2) x

---

395   Therefore, given an equivalence relation on a set S, every element
      x of S is equivalent to at least one element, namely, _____.

---

      x

---

396   Let $S = \{a, b, c, d, e, f\}$ and $R = \{(a,a), (a,d), (b,b), (b,c), (b,f),$
      $(c,b), (c,c), (c,f), (d,a), (d,d), (e,e), (f,b), (f,c), (f,f)\}$.
      R is an equivalence relation in S. (Check.)
           a is equivalent to a and d.
      (1) b is equivalent to _____ .
      (2) c is equivalent to _____ .
      (3) d is equivalent to _____ .
      (4) e is equivalent to _____ .
      (5) f is equivalent to _____ .

---

      (1) b, c, and f
      (2) b, c, and f
      (3) a and d
      (4) e
      (5) b, c, and f

---

397   If R is an equivalence relation in a set S and $(x,y) \notin R$, we say that
      x is not equivalent to y. Let $S = \{a, b, c\}$ and $R = \{(a,a), (b,b), (c,c)\}$.
      (1) $(a,a) \in R$, so a is equivalent to _____.
      (2) (b,c) _____ R, so b is _____ to c.

---

      (1) a **(2)** $\notin$,   not equivalent

---

398   Let $S = \{a, b, d\}$ and $R = \{(a,a), (b,b), (b,d), (d,b), (d,d)\}$.
      R is an equivalence relation in S. Check it. Let $S_1 = \{x \mid b \approx x\}$, that
      is, b is equivalent to x. Then $S_1 = \{b, d\}$. Let $S_2 = \{x \mid a \approx x\}$. Then
      $S_2 = \{$ _____ $\}$.

      $\{a\}$

399   Let $S = \{a, b, c, d, e\}$ and $R = \{(a,a), (b,b), (b,c), (c,b), (c,c), (d,d), (e,e)\}$.
      R is an equivalence relation in S. Check it.
      Let $S_1 = \{x \mid a \approx x\}$; then $S_1 = \{a\}$.
      Let $S_2 = \{x \mid b \approx x\}$; then $S_2 = \{b,c\}$.
      Let $S_3 = \{x \mid c \approx x\}$; then $S_3 = \{$ ____ $\}$.

$\{b, c\}$

400   If R is an equivalence relation in a set S, then $S_1 = \{x \mid a \approx x\}$ means
      the set of all x such that a is equivalent to x.
      Let $S = \{0, 1, 2, 3\}$ and $R = \{(0,0), (0,1), (1,0), (1,1), (2,2), (3,3)\}$.
          If $S_1 = \{x \mid 0 \approx x\}$, then $S_1 = \{0, 1\}$.
      (1) If $S_2 = \{x \mid 1 \approx x\}$, then $S_2 = $ ____.
      (2) If $S_3 = \{x \mid 3 \approx x\}$, then $S_3 = $ ____.

(1) $\{0, 1\}$ (2) $\{3\}$

401   Let $S = \{a, b, c, d, e\}$ and $R = \{(a,a), (b,b), (b,d), (b,e), (c,c), (d,b),$
                                              $(d,d), (d,e), (e,b), (e,d), (e,e)\}$.
      R is an equivalence relation in S. Check it.
          If $S_1 = \{x \mid a \approx x\}$, then $S_1 = \{a\}$.
      (1) If $S_2 = \{x \mid b \approx x\}$, then $S_2 = $ ____.
      (2) If $S_3 = \{x \mid c \approx x\}$, then $S_3 = $ ____.
      (3) If $S_4 = \{x \mid d \approx x\}$, then $S_4 = $ ____.

(1) $\{b, d, e\}$ (2) $\{c\}$ (3) $\{b, d, e\}$

402   Suppose we have an equivalence relation R in a set S and
      $S_1 = \{x \mid a \approx x\}$ and $S_2 = \{x \mid b \approx x\}$. If $y \in S_1$, then $a \approx y$. If $z \in S_2$,
      then ____.

$b \approx z$

VI. Partition of a Set and Equivalence Classes

403   Recall that if S and T are sets and $S \cap T = \phi$, then S and T are
      said to be *disjoint*. Let $S = \{a, d\}$ and $T = \{c\}$. $S \cap T = $ ____, so S
      and T are _____.

ϕ,   disjoint

404   Let $S = \{1, a, b\}$ and $T = \{2\}$. $S \cap T =$ _____, so S and T are
      _____.

ϕ,   disjoint

405   Given a number of sets, if the intersection of every pair of them is
      empty, we say that the sets are *mutually disjoint*. Let $S_1 = \{a, b, c\}$,
      $S_2 = \{d, f\}$, $S_3 = \{e\}$.
      (1) $S_1 \cap S_2 =$ _____
      (2) $S_1 \cap S_3 =$ _____
      (3) $S_2 \cap S_3 =$ _____
      (4)   Therefore S_1, S_2, and S_3 are _____.

      (1) ϕ (2) ϕ (3) ϕ (4)   mutually disjoint

406   Let $S = \{a, b, c, d, e\}$ and consider: $S_1 = \{a, d\}$, $S_2 = \{b, c\}$, $S_3 = \{e\}$.
      (1) $S_1 \cap S_2 =$ _____ (2) $S_1 \cap S_3 =$ _____ (3) $S_2 \cap S_3 =$ _____
      (4)   Therefore S_1, S_2, and S_3 are _____.
      (5)   Also note that $S_1 \cup S_2 \cup S_3 =$ _____.

      (1) ϕ (2) ϕ (3) ϕ (4)   mutually disjoint
      (5) S or $\{a, b, c, d, e\}$

407   Let $S = \{1, 2, 3, 4, 5, 6, 7\}$ and
            $S_1 = \{1\}$, $S_2 = \{2, 4, 5\}$, $S_3 = \{3, 7\}$, and $S_4 = \{6\}$.
      Note: 1. S_1, S_2, S_3, and S_4 are mutually disjoint.
            2. $S_1 \cup S_2 \cup S_3 \cup S_4 =$ _____.

S

408   Given a set S, a collection of subsets such that:
      1. the subsets are mutually disjoint and
      2. the union of the subsets $= S$
      is called a *partition of S*.
      Let $S = \{1, 2, 3, 4, 5, 6\}$ and $S_1 = \{1\}$, $S_2 = \{2, 3, 4\}$, $S_3 = \{5, 6\}$.
      S_1, S_2, and S_3 are mutually disjoint and their union $= S$; therefore
      S_1, S_2, and S_3 form a(n) _____ of S.

partition

409   Note that a collection of subsets of S, in order to partition S, must
      satisfy two conditions:
      1. they must be mutually disjoint,
      2. their union must $= S$.

▼

Let $S = \{1, 2, 3, 4, 5, 6\}$ and $S_1 = \{1, 2\}$, $S_2 = \{3, 5\}$, $S_3 = \{6\}$.
Do S_1, S_2, and S_3 partition S? Why?

No, $S_1 \cup S_2 \cup S_3 \neq S$.

410 Let S be a set. A collection of subsets of S forms a *partition* of S if and only if :
(1) the subsets are mutually _____ , and
(2) their union is _____.

(1) disjoint
(2) S

411 Let S be a set. A collection of subsets of S forms a *partition* of S if and only if:
(1) _____ , and
(2) _____ .

(1) the subsets are mutually disjoint
(2) their union is S (or $= S$)

412 Let $S = \{1, 2, 3, 4, 5, 6\}$ and $S_1 = \{1, 2, 4\}$, $S_2 = \{3, 5\}$, $S_3 = \{2, 6\}$.
Do S_1, S_2, and S_3 form a partition of S? Why?

No, $S_1 \cap S_3 \neq 0$; therefore not mutually disjoint.

413 Remember, in order to partition a set S, the subsets must be mutually disjoint and their union must equal S.
Let $S = \{a, b, c, d\}$, $S_1 = \{a\}$, $S_2 = \{b\}$, $S_3 = \{c\}$, $S_4 = \{d\}$.
Do S_1, S_2, S_3, and S_4 form a partition of S? Why?

Yes, S_1, S_2, S_3, and S_4 are mutually disjoint and $S_1 \cup S_2 \cup S_3 \cup S_4 = S$.

414 Let $S = \{1, 2, 3, 4, 5, 6\}$, $S_1 = \{1, 3, 5\}$, $S_2 = \{2, 4\}$, $S_3 = \{3, 6\}$.
Is S partitioned by S_1, S_2, and S_3? Why?

No, S_1 and S_3 are not disjoint.

415 Let $S = \{1, 2, 3, 4, 5, 6\}$, $S_1 = \{1\}$, $S_2 = \{2, 4\}$, $S_3 = \{5, 6\}$.
Is S partitioned by S_1, S_2, and S_3? Why?

No, $S_1 \cup S_2 \cup S_3 \neq S$.

416   Let S be the set of integers and
      S_1 be the set of even integers and
      S_2 be the set of odd integers.
      (1) $S_1 \cap S_2 =$ _____   (2) $S_1 \cup S_2 =$ _____
      (3) S_1 and S_2 form a(n) _____ of S.

---

(1) ϕ (2) S (3) partition

•417   Let S be the set of nonnegative integers and
      $S_1 = \{0, 3, 6, 9, \ldots, 3N, \ldots\}$
      $S_2 = \{1, 4, 7, 10, \ldots, (3N + 1), \ldots\}$
      $S_3 = \{2, 5, 8, 11, \ldots, (3N + 2), \ldots\}$
      Do S_1, S_2, and S_3 partition S? Why?

Yes, S_1, S_2, and S_3 are mutually disjoint and $S_1 \cup S_2 \cup S_3 = S$.

---

418   Let $S = \{a, b, c, d, e\}$ and $R = \{(a,a), (a,c), (b,b), (b,e), (c,a), (c,c),$
      $(d,d), (e,b), (e,e)\}$.
      R is an equivalence relation in S. Check it.
      Now let $S_1 = \{x \mid a \approx x\}$; $\therefore S_1 = \{a, c\}$
          (1) $S_2 = \{x \mid b \approx x\}$; $\therefore S_2 =$ _____
          (2) $S_3 = \{x \mid c \approx x\}$; $\therefore S_3 =$ _____
          (3) $S_4 = \{x \mid d \approx x\}$; $\therefore S_4 =$ _____
          (4) $S_5 = \{x \mid e \approx x\}$; $\therefore S_5 =$ _____

---

(1) $S_2 = \{b, e\}$ (2) $S_3 = \{a, c\}$ (3) $S_4 = \{d\}$ (4) $S_5 = \{b, e\}$

---

419   The subsets obtained in frame 418 were
      $S_1 = \{a, c\}$, $S_2 = \{b, e\}$, $S_3 = \{a, c\}$, $S_4 = \{d\}$, $S_5 = \{b, e\}$
      Note: If you choose any two of these subsets, they are either equal
      or disjoint. If we list the distinct subsets, we have $S_1 = \{a, c\}$,
      $S_2 = \{b, e\}$, $S_4 = \{d\}$ where we have disregarded S_3 and S_5 because
      they were merely repetitious. Recall that $S = \{a, b, c, d, e\}$. Do S_1,
      S_2, and S_4 partition S?

Yes, S_1, S_2, and S_4 are mutually disjoint and $S_1 \cup S_2 \cup S_4 = S$.

---

420   Let S be the set of integers and
      $R = \{(x,y) \mid x \in S, y \in S,$ and $x + y$ is an even integer$\}$.
      We have already seen that R is an equivalence relation in S.
      Now let $S_1 = \{z \mid z \approx 0\}$ and $S_2 = \{z \mid z \approx 1\}$.
      Then $S_1 = \{\ldots, -4, -2, 0, 2, 4, \ldots, 2N, \ldots\}$
          $S_2 = \{\ldots, -3, -1, 1, 3, 5, \ldots, (2N + 1), \ldots\}$

▼

Note: 1. If $a, b \in S_1$ $a \approx b$.
      2. If $a, b \in S_2$ $a \approx b$.
      3. If $a, \in S_1$, $b \in S_2$, $a \not\approx b$.
      4. S_1 and S_2 form a(n) _____ of S.

partition

421   Now let $S = \{a, b, c, d\}$ and $R = \{(a,a), (a,c), (b,b), (c,a), (c,c), (d,d)\}$.
R is an equivalence relation in S. Check it. If we form subsets of S,
putting in each subset those elements which are equivalent to each
other and putting in different subsets elements which are not equivalent to each other, and if we do not list any equal subsets more than
once, we get
$S_1 = \{a, c\}$, $S_2 = \{b\}$, $S_3 = \{d\}$
S_1, S_2, and S_3 are mutually disjoint and $S_1 \cup S_2 \cup S_3 = S$, so S_1, S_2,
and S_3 form a(n) _____ of S.

partition

422   Let $S = \{a, b, c, d, e, f\}$ and $R = \{(a,a), (a,b), (b,a), (b,b), (b,e), (e,b),$
$(a,e), (e,a), (c,c), (d,d), (e,e), (f,f)\}$
R is an equivalence relation in S. Check it. Form subsets of S,
putting in the same subset those elements which are equivalent to
each other and in different subsets elements which are not equivalent
to each other, and do not list any subset more than once.

$S_1 = \{a, b, e\}$, $S_2 = \{c\}$, $S_3 = \{d\}$, $S_4 = \{f\}$

423   Do the subsets listed in the answer of frame 422 form a partition
of S? Remember that $S = \{a, b, c, d, e, f\}$.

yes

424   Given an equivalence relation R in a set S, there is a natural way
of partitioning S with respect to R; that is, form subsets by including in the same subset elements which are in the relation R to each
other, and put into different subsets elements which are not in the
relation R to each other. Let $S = \{a, b, c\}$ and
$R = \{(a,a), (b,b), (b,c), (c,b), (c,c)\}$. Form the subsets just described.

$S_1 = \{a\}$, $S_2 = \{b,c\}$

425   This obvious partitioning of S is one of the most important properties of an equivalence relation R. The subsets formed in this manner are called *equivalence classes* of S with respect to R.

▼

Let $S = \{1, 2, 3, 4, 5\}$ and $R = \{(1,1), (2,2), (2,4), (3,3), (3,5), (4,2),$
$(4,4), (5,3), (5,5)\}$.
R is an equivalence relation in S. Check it.
List the equivalence classes of S with respect to R.

$S_1 = \{1\}$, $S_2 = \{2, 4\}$, $S_3 = \{3, 5\}$

---

426   Let $S = \{a, b, c, d, e\}$ and $R = \{(a,a), (a,c), (b,b), (c,a), (c,c), (d,d),$
$(d,e), (e,d), (e,c)\}$.
R is an equivalence relation in S.
If $S_1 = \{x \mid x \in S$ and $a\ R\ x\}$, then $S_1 = \{a, c\}$.
$S_2 = \{x \mid x \in S$ and $b\ R\ x\}$, then $S_2 = \{b\}$.
$S_3 = \{x \mid x \in S$ and $d\ R\ x\}$, then $S_3 = \{d, e\}$.
S_1, S_2, and S_3 are called _____ of S with respect to R.

equivalence classes

---

427   Look at Panel 2. R_3 is an equivalence relation in S. List the equivalence classes of S with respect to R_3.

$S_1 = \{a, b\}$, $S_2 = \{c\}$

•428   Look at Panel 4. R_6 is an equivalence relation in S. List the equivalence classes into which S is partitioned by R_6.

$S_1 = \{a\}$, $S_2 = \{b, e\}$, $S_3 = \{c, d\}$

---

429   Look at Panel 4. R_2 is an equivalence relation in S. List the equivalence classes into which S is partitioned by R_2.

S (or $\{a,b,c,d,e\}$)

---

430   Let $S = \{a, b, c, d, e\}$ and $R = \{(a,a), (b,b), (b,d), (b,e), (c,c), (d,b),$
$(d,d), (d,e), (e,b), (e,d), (e,e)\}$.
The equivalence classes formed are:
$S_1 = \{a\}$, $S_2 = \{b, d, e\}$, $S_3 = \{c\}$
Note: 1. S_1, S_2, S_3 partition S.
       2. If x and y are two elements chosen from the same equiva-
          lence class, $x \approx y$.
       3. If x and y are elements from different equivalence classes,
          then ____.

$x \not\approx y$ (or x is not equivalent to y)

431 *This partitioning of a set S into equivalence classes is one of the
     most important properties of an equivalence relation.* Write the fol-
     lowing information on a separate sheet of paper and save it for
     frames 432 to 435.
     Let $S = \{a, b, c, d, e, f\}$ and $R = \{(a,a), (a,c), (b,b), (b,d), (b,e), (c,a),$
     $(c,c), (d,b), (d,e), (d,d), (e,b), (e,d),$
     $(e,e), (f,f)\}$.
     R is an equivalence relation having equivalence classes:
     $S_1 = \{a, c\}$, $S_2 = \{b, d, e\}$, $S_3 = \{f\}$

No answer is required.

432 Is every $x \in S$ a member of some equivalence class?

yes

433 Is any $x \in S$ a member of more than one equivalence class?

no

434 If x, y are members of the same equivalence class, then $x \approx y$. If
     x, y are members of different equivalence classes, then ____.

$x \not\approx y$ (or x is not equivalent to y)

435 If $x \approx y$, then x and y are members of the same equivalence class.
     If x is not equivalent to y, then x and y are members of
     _____.

different equivalence classes

436 Remember if x, y are members of the same equivalence class, then
     $x \approx y$ (and $y \approx x$). Suppose $S_1 = \{a, b\}$ is an equivalence class of a
     set S. Then $a \approx a$, $a \approx b$, $b \approx a$, $b \approx b$. Therefore, ____, ____,
     ____, ____, must be elements of the equivalence relation.

(a,a), (a,b), (b,a), (b,b)

•437 Suppose $S_1 = \{1, 2, 4\}$ is an equivalence class with respect to an
      equivalence relation in a set S. List the elements which must belong
      to the equivalence relation in order that S_1 be a subset of S.

(1,1), (1,2), (1,4), (2,1), (2,2), (2,4), (4,1), (4,2), (4,4)

438   Let S be the set of positive rational numbers. Notice that your definition of equality of rational numbers is an equivalence relation and note that, for example,

$$S_1 = \left\{ 1, \frac{2}{2}, \frac{3}{3}, \frac{4}{4}, \cdots \right\}$$

$$S_2 = \left\{ \frac{1}{2}, \frac{2}{4}, \frac{3}{6}, \frac{4}{8}, \cdots \right\}$$

$$S_3 = \left\{ \frac{5}{8}, \frac{10}{16}, \frac{15}{24}, \cdots \right\}$$

are _____ of S with respect to the equivalence relation.

---

equivalence classes

---

439   So, if R is an equivalence relation in a set S, S is partitioned into equivalence classes with respect to R. Conversely, if S is partitioned, then there exists an equivalence relation R such that the subsets forming the partition are exactly the equivalence classes of R. For example, let $S = \{a, b, c, d, e\}$ be partitioned by
$S_1 = \{a\}$, $S_2 = \{b, d\}$, $S_3 = \{c\}$, $S_4 = \{e\}$.
The equivalence relation R such that S_1, S_2, S_3, and S_4 are the equivalence classes is $R = \{(a,a), (b,b), (b,d),$ _____ $\}$.

(d,b), (d,d), (c,c), (e,e)

---

440   Let $S = \{a, b, c\}$ be partitioned by $S_1 = \{a\}$, $S_2 = \{b, c\}$. List the equivalence relation R in S such that S_1 and S_2 are the equivalence classes.

$R = \{(a,a), (b,b), (b,c), (c,b), (c,c)\}$

---

441   Let $S = \{0, 1, 2, 3, 4\}$ be partitioned by $S_1 = \{0\}$, $S_2 = \{2, 4\}$, $S_3 = \{1, 3\}$. List the equivalence relation R such that S_1, S_2, and S_3 are the equivalence classes.

$R = \{(0,0), (2,2), (2,4), (4,2), (4,4), (1,1), (1,3), (3,1), (3,3)\}$

•442   The subsets formed from a set S by an equivalence relation R on S are called *equivalence classes*.
Let $S = \{1, 2, 3, 4, 5, 6, 7\}$ and $R = \{(1,1), (2,2), (3,3), (4,4), (5,5),$
                                    $(6,6), (7,7), (2,4), (4,2), (5,6),$
                                      $(6,5)\}$

R is an equivalence relation. Check it. The equivalence classes defined by R are:

▼

(1) $S_1 =$ ____
(2) $S_2 =$ ____
(3) $S_3 =$ ____
(4) $S_4 =$ ____
(5) $S_5 =$ ____

(1) $\{1\}$ (2) $\{2, 4\}$ (3) $\{3\}$ (4) $\{5, 6\}$ (5) $\{7\}$

443 Let $S = \{a, b, c\}$ and $R = \{(a,a), (a,b), (b,a), (b,b)\}$.
Is R an equivalence relation? If so, list the equivalence classes.

No, R is not reflexive.

444 Let $S = \{a, b, c\}$ and $R = \{(a,a), (b,b), (c,c)\}$.
Is R an equivalence relation? If so, list the equivalence classes.

Yes, $S_1 = \{a\}$, $S_2 = \{b\}$, $S_3 = \{c\}$

445 Let S be a set having an equivalence relation $\approx$ and suppose
$S_1 = \{a, b, c\}$ and $S_2 = \{f, 10\}$ are two of the equivalence classes of
S with respect to $\approx$. Insert the proper symbol, $\approx$ or $\not\approx$.
a ____ c, c ____ b, f ____ c

$\approx$, $\approx$, $\not\approx$

446 Let S be the set of nonzero integers and
$R = \{(x,y) \mid x \in S, y \in S, \text{and } x \cdot y > 0\}$.
We have seen that R is an equivalence relation in S.
Let $S_1 = \{a \mid a \approx -1\}$ [all a such that $a \cdot (-1) > 0$]
$\quad\;\; S_2 = \{a \mid a \approx 1\}$ [all a such that $a \cdot (1) > 0$]
(1) List some of the elements of S_1.
(2) List some of the elements of S_2.

(1) You should have negative integers listed.
(2) You should have positive integers listed.

447 Thus, if S is the set of nonzero integers, the equivalence relation
$R = \{(x,y) \mid x \in S, y \in S, \text{and } x \cdot y > 0\}$ has two equivalence classes,
namely, $S_1 =$ _____ and $S_2 =$ _____.

the positive integers,
the negative integers

VII. Review Test for Part One   (Answers on page 312)

Problems 1 to 40 will constitute a review of the work to this point. If
you miss any one of them, review that section of the program concerning the material of that problem.

1   Look at Panel 4. The set $S = \{a, b, c, d, e\}$.
   The twenty-five points arranged in a square array in Panel 4 can be
   used to represent the twenty-five elements of _____.

2   In Panel 4 what element of $S \times S$ is circled?

3   Each element of $S \times S$ is a(n) _____.

4   In Panel 4, with $S = \{a, b, c, d, e\}$, does the ordered pair
   $(a,c) = (c,a)$?

5   In the ordered pair (a,b), a is called the _____ and b is called
   the _____.

6   R is a binary relation in S if and only if _____.

7   In Panel 4, for example, if the elements of $S \times S$ represented by
   those points having special marks about them (square, circle, triangle, check) are chosen, we have a subset of $S \times S$, say
   $R_3 = \{(b,c), (c,b), (d,a), (d,d)\}$.
   R_3 is a(n) _____.

8   (1)   Write $T \times T$ symbolically.
   (2) $T \times T$ is called _____.

9   Given a set S and a binary relation R in S, R is reflexive in S if
   and only if it satisfies the condition: _____.

10   Which of the relations in Panel 4 are reflexive?

11   A binary relation R is symmetric if and only if it satisfies the condition: _____.

12   A binary relation R is transitive if and only if it satisfies the condition: _____.

13   In Panel 4 which of the relations are transitive?

14   Define an equivalence relation.

15   In Panel 4 which of the relations is an equivalence relation?

16   Given an equivalence relation in a set S, there is a natural way of
   constructing subsets of S. We do this by putting those elements which

are equivalent to each other into the same subset. Those elements which are not equivalent to each other are included in different subsets. In this way we form a(n) _____ of S, and each subset of S so formed is called a(n) _____ .

17 R_6 is an equivalence relation in S. (Check.) Write the equivalence classes in roster form.

18 In Panel 4 R_2 is an equivalence relation in S. What are the equivalence classes?

19 Let S be the set of nonzero integers and if a, $b \in S$, $a\,R\,b$ if and only if $a \cdot b > 0$.
    (1) Is R an equivalence relation in S?
    (2) If so, describe the equivalence classes.

20 Let S be the set of integers and if a, $b \in S$, $a\,R\,b$ if and only if $a + b$ is an even integer.
    (1) Is R an equivalence relation in S?
    (2) If so, describe the equivalence classes into which S is partitioned.

21 Let $S = \{0, 1, 2, 3, 4, 5, 6, 7, 8, 9, 10\}$, and
    let $R = \{(x,y) \mid x \in S,\ y \in S,$ and x and y have the same remainder when divided by $4\}$.
    Obviously, R is an equivalence relation. List the equivalence classes defined by R.

22 The decomposition of a set into equivalence classes by an equivalence relation is an important property of an equivalence relation.
    Let $S = \{a, b, c, d, e, f\}$ and $R = \{(a,a), (b,b), (c,c), (d,d), (e,e), (f,f),$
    $(a,d), (d,a), (a,e), (e,a), (d,e), (e,d),$
    $(b,f), (f,b)\}$.
    R is an equivalence relation. Check this. The equivalence classes determined by R are $S_1 = \{a, d, e\}$, $S_2 = \{b, f\}$, $S_3 = \{c\}$.
    Note: 1. S_1, S_2, S_3 are nonintersecting.
              2. $S_1 \cup S_2 \cup S_3 = (1)$ _____ .
              3. If x and y are elements of the same equivalence class,
                 (2) x _____ y.
    If x and y are elements of two different classes, then
    (3) x _____ y.

23 Conversely, if a set S is decomposed into nonintersecting subsets S_1, S_2, ..., we can define an equivalence relation in S by: $x\,R\,y$ if and only if the subsets containing x and y respectively are identical. For example, let $S = \{a, b, c, d, e\}$ and consider the decomposition: $S_1 = \{a, d\}$, $S_2 = \{b, c\}$, $S_3 = \{e\}$. For any x, $y \in S$ we define $x\,R\,y$ if and only if the subsets which contain x and y respectively are identical. For example:

$$b \in S_2, \ b \in S_2; \ \therefore \ b \ R \ b$$
$$c \in S_2, \ b \in S_2; \ \therefore \ c \ R \ b$$
$$a \in S_1, \ b \in S_2; \ \therefore \ a \ \not R \ b$$

List the elements of R. Note that R is an equivalence relation.

24 Let $S = \{0, 1, 2, 3\}$ and $S_1 = \{0, 2\}$, $S_2 = \{1\}$, $S_3 = \{3\}$. List the elements of the equivalence relation R whose equivalence classes are exactly S_1, S_2, S_3.

25 Given two elements a and b, (a,b) is called a(n) _____ .

26 In the ordered pair (a,b) a is called the _____ and b is called the _____ .

27 $(a,b) = (c,d)$ if and only if _____ .

28 Given a set S:
    (1) $S \times S =$ _____ (symbolically)
    (2) $S \times S$ is called _____ .

29 Let $S = \{a, b, c\}$. $S \times S = \{(x,y) \mid x \in S, \ y \in S\}$. Write $S \times S$ in roster form.

30 So, given a set S, $S \times S$ is a new set consisting of ordered pairs of elements from S. Choose any subset of $S \times S$. This subset is called a(n) _____ in S.

31 In fact, given any set R of ordered pairs, we can find a set S such that R is a subset of $S \times S$; so any set of ordered pairs can be thought of as a binary relation. For example, let $R = \{(a,2), (1,b), (5,a)\}$. R is a subset of $S \times S$ where $S = \{$ ____, ____, ____, ____, ____ $\}$; so R is a(n) _____ .

32 Given a set S and a binary relation R in S, R is reflexive in S if and only if _____ .

33 Given a set S and a binary relation R in S, R is symmetric if and only if it satisfies the condition: _____ .

34 Given a set S and a binary relation R in S, R is transitive if and only if it satisfies the condition: _____ .

35 Let $S = \{1, 2, 3, 4\}$ and $R = \{(2,4), (2,2), (1,2), (3,3)\}$.
    Is R transitive? Why?

36 Define an equivalence relation.

37 Let $S = \{0, 1, 2, 3\}$ and $R = \{(0,0), (1,1), (1,3), (3,1), (2,2), (3,3)\}$.
    (1) Is R reflexive?
    (2) Is R symmetric?

(3) Is R transitive?

(4) Is R an equivalence relation?

38 Let $S = \{0, 1, 2, 3\}$.

$R = \{(0,0), (0,1), (1,0), (1,1), (1,3), (3,1), (2,2), (3,3)\}$.

(1) Is R reflexive? If not, why not?

(2) Is R symmetric? If not, why not?

(3) Is R transitive? If not, why not?

(4) Is R an equivalence relation?

39 An equivalence relation R on a set S divides S into nonintersecting subsets called equivalence classes whose union is S and such that:

1. if x and y are members of the same equivalence class, then $x\,R\,y$,

2. if x and y are members of different equivalence classes, then $x\,\not\!R\,y$.

Let $S = \{a, b, c\}$ and $R = \{(a,a), (a,c), (b,b), (c,a), (c,c)\}$. Find the equivalence classes defined on S by R.

40 Conversely, given any partition of a set S, a binary relation is determined whose equivalence classes are exactly those subsets into which S is partitioned. For example, let $S = \{1, 2, 3, 4\}$. $S_1 = \{1, 3\}$, $S_2 = \{2\}$, $S_3 = \{4\}$ partition S. List the binary relation R having S_1, S_2, S_3 as equivalence classes.

Part Two   BINARY OPERATIONS ON A SET

In Part One, you studied the concept of a binary relation in a set S and, in particular, a special type of binary relation, *viz.*, an equivalence relation. You found that some of the relations with which you were familiar, such as the "equals relation" in the set of real numbers and the "congruence relation" in the set of triangles, are equivalence relations. Moreover, one of the important properties of an equivalence relation in a set S, the correspondence between an equivalence relation in S and a partition of S, was investigated. You discovered, but did not prove, that each equivalence relation in S corresponds to a unique partition of S (in which the subsets of S are called equivalence classes) and, conversely, that every partition of S corresponds to a unique equivalence relation in S.

At this point, it would be possible to define and study another type of binary relation, perhaps one with properties corresponding to those of the "$\leq$ relation" in the set of real numbers. If you are interested in this type of binary relation, it is suggested that you read *Sets, Logic, and Axiomatic Theories.*[1]

We will continue on the path leading to the study of groups and fields. From this point on, given any set S you may assume that there also is given an equivalence relation in S which will be denoted by "=." In its simplest form, the equivalence relation will be one of identity; i.e., every element is identical to itself ($x = x$) and any statement such as "$x = y$" can be interpreted to mean that the symbol x and the symbol y have been used for some reason to represent the *same* element of S. On purely logical grounds, then, this identity relation satisfies the reflexive, symmetric, and transitive properties.

If the equivalence relation is other than that of identity or than those, such as "equals," in the set of real numbers, it will be discussed in more detail.

In any event, the = symbol will have the following properties:

1. $x = x$ for all $x \in S$.
2. For all $x, y \in S$, if $x = y$, then $y = x$.
3. For all $x, y, z, \in S$, if $x = y$ and $y = z$, then $x = z$.

[1]Robert R. Stoll, *Sets, Logic, and Axiomatic Theories*, W. H. Freeman and Company, San Francisco, 1961.

In your earliest experiences in arithmetic, probably the first concept
you had was the binary relations of "less than" or "greater than"
in the set of positive integers. The only equivalence relation was
that of identity; i.e., the only number equal to 7, for example, was
7. Soon you were expected to know something about a process called
"addition," a process which was such that to every pair of nonnegative integers, e.g., 3 and 4, in a given order, there was associated a
unique, positive integer denoted by 3 + 4. You became familiar with
other examples, such as multiplication and subtraction, in larger
sets of a similar nature.

In Part Two, a *binary operation in a set S*, of which addition in the
set of integers is a particular example, will be defined and studied
in detail. A binary operation in *S* will be defined as a certain type
of function. For this reason, in the first section of Part Two the
concept of function will be reviewed.

I. Functions and Mapping

---

448 Let $S = \{1, 2, 3, 4\}$ and $T = \{a, b, c\}$. Let a binary relation R in
$S \times T$ be given by:
$R = \{(1,a), (1,b), (3,b), (4,a)\}$
(1) Write in roster form the set of first coordinates of the ordered
pairs of R.
(2) Write in roster form the set of second coordinates of the ordered pairs of R.

(1) $\{1, 3, 4\}$
(2) $\{a, b\}$

•449 Let $S = \{1, 2, 3, 4\}$ and $T = \{a, b, c, d\}$.
Let $R = \{(1,b), (1,d, (2,a), (2,b)\}$ be a binary relation in $S \times T$.
(1) Write in roster form the set of first coordinates of the ordered
pairs of R.
(2) Write in roster form the set of second coordinates of the ordered pairs of R.

(1) $\{1, 2\}$
(2) $\{a, b, d\}$

---

450 Let S and T be arbitrary sets. Let R be a binary relation in $S \times T$.
(1) An element p is a member of the set of _____ coordinates
of the ordered pairs in R if and only if there is a q such that
$(p,q) \in R$.

▼

(2) An element y will be a member of the set of second coordinates of the ordered pairs in R if and only if there is an x such that _____ .

---

(1) first   (2) $(x,y) \in R$

---

451 Let $S = \{1, 2, 3, 4\}$ and $T = \{a, b, c\}$. Suppose that R is a binary relation in $S \times T$.
(1) R is a(n) _____ of $S \times T$ and each element of R is a(n) _____ .
(2) Consider $2 \in S$. 2 will be a member of the set of first coordinates of ordered pairs in R if and only if there is a y such that $(2,y) \in R$. In general, the set of first coordinates of ordered pairs in R is given by:
$\{x \mid$ there is a y for which _____ $\}$.

---

(1) subset,   ordered pair
(2) $(x,y) \in R$

---

452 Similarly, if R is a binary relation in $S \times T$, then y will be a member of the set of *second* coordinates of the ordered pairs of R if and only if there is an x such that _____ .

$(x,y) \in R$

---

453 (1) Thus the set of first coordinates of the ordered pairs of a binary relation R is denoted by:
$\{x \mid$ there is a y such that _____ $\}$
(2) The set of second coordinates is denoted by:
$\{y \mid$ there is an x such that _____ $\}$

---

(1) $(x,y) \in R$ (2) $(x,y) \in R$

---

454 The set of first coordinates of the ordered pairs of a binary relation R in $S \times T$ is called the domain of R (written dom R).
Definition: dom $R = \{x \mid$ _____ $\}$.

---

there is a y such that $(x,y) \in R$

---

455 The set of second coordinates of the ordered pairs of a binary relation R in $S \times T$ is called the range of R (written ran R).
Definition: ran $R = \{y \mid$ _____ $\}$.

---

there is an x such that $(x,y) \in R$

•456 Let R be a binary relation in $S \times T$.
  (1) The set of first coordinates of R is called the domain of R and is defined by: _____.
  (2) The set of second coordinates of R is called the range of R and is defined by: _____.

  (1) dom $R = \{x \mid$ there is a y such that $(x,y) \in R\}$
  (2) ran $R = \{y \mid$ there is an x such that $(x,y) \in R\}$

•457 Of course, symbols other than x and y may be used in the definition. Let R be a binary relation in $S \times T$.
  (1) _____ $= \{p \mid$ there is a q such that $(p,q) \in R\}$.
  (2) _____ $= \{t \mid$ there is an S such that $(s,t) \in R\}$.

  (1) dom R (2) ran R

458 Let $S = \{a, b, c\}$, $T = \{p, q, r, s\}$, and $R = \{(a,p), (a,q), (c,q)\}$.
  (1) Write dom R in roster form.
  (2) Write ran R in roster form.

  (1) dom $R = \{a, c\}$ (2) ran $R = \{p, q\}$

459 Let R be a binary relation in $S \times T$.
  (1) dom R is a subset of ____, i.e., dom $R \subset$ ____.
  (2) ran R is a subset of ____, i.e., ran $R \subset$ ____.

  (1) S, S (2) T, T

•460 (1) dom $R =$ _____ (symbolically)
  (2) ran $R =$ _____ (symbolically)

  (1) $\{x \mid$ there is a y such that $(x,y) \in R\}$
  (2) $\{y \mid$ there is an x such that $(x,y) \in R\}$
  You may have used symbols other than x and y. You may also have used $x \, R \, y$ instead of $(x,y) \in R$.

461 Let $S = \{1, 2, 3\}$ and $T = \{a, b, c, d\}$. Suppose $R = \{(1,a), (1,b), (2,a), (3,a)\}$. Show the graphical representation of $S \times T$ and circle the elements of R. Circle the points along line S

▼

which represent the domain of R and circle the points along line T
which represent the elements of the range of R.

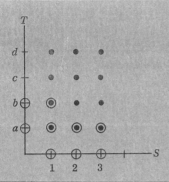

462 Let $R = \{(a,1),\ (b,2),\ (b,3)\}$.
 (1) The set $\{a,\ b\}$ is called the _____.
 (2) The set $\{1,\ 2,\ 3\}$ is called the _____.

 (1) domain of R (or dom R)
 (2) range of R (or ran R)

463 Let $S = \{a,\ b,\ c\}$ and $T = \{1,\ 2\}$. Let $R = \phi$. Then dom $R =$ ____
  and ran $R =$ ____.

 $\phi,\qquad \phi$

464 Let $S = \{a,\ b,\ c\}$ and $T = \{1,\ 2\}$. Let $R = S \times T$.
 (1) Write dom R in roster form.
 (2) Write ran R in roster form.

 (1) dom $R = \{a,\ b,\ c\}$ (or S)   **(2)** ran $R = \{1,\ 2\}$ (or T)

465 **(1)** If R is a binary relation in $S \times T$, dom $R \subset$ ____ and
   ran $R \subset$ ____.
 (2) If T is a nonempty set, then for any subset S_1 of S, a binary
   relation R having a dom $R = S_1$ can be found. For example,
   let $a \in T$ and $R = \{(x,a) \mid x \in S_1\}$. dom $R =$ ____
   ran $R =$ ____
 Note: If T is empty, your choice of R is restricted.
 (3) Those binary relations in $S \times T$ that have the domain $= S$ are
   of particular interest.
 In Panel 1, which of the binary relations have the domain $= S$?

 (1) $S,\qquad T$ **(2)** $S_1,\qquad \{a\}$ **(3)** R_5, R_7, R_8, R_9

466   *Definition*: A binary relation R with dom $R = S$ in $S \times T$ is called a *binary relation from S into T*. Look at Panel 1. Which of the binary relations tabulated there are binary relations from S into T ?

R_5, R_7, R_8, R_9

---

467   (1)   A binary relation R in $S \times T$ with dom $R = S$ is called a binary relation from _____ .
      (2)   As a special case, if $T = S$, that is, if R is a binary relation in $S \times S$, and dom $R = S$, R is called a binary relation from

            _____ .

      (3)   Which of the binary relations from Panel 2 are binary relations from S into S?

---

      (1) S into T
      (2) S into S
      (3) R_2, R_3, R_4, R_7, R_8

---

468   (1)   A binary relation R in $S \times T$ is called a binary relation from
            _____ if and only if dom $R = S$.
      (2)   Look at Panel 3. Which are the binary relations from S into S?

---

      (1) S into T
      (2) R_7, R_8, R_9, R_{10}, R_{12}, R_{13}, R_{14}, R_{15}, R_{16}

•469   Complete the following definition. A binary relation R in $S \times T$ is called a binary relation from S into T if and only if _____ .

---

dom $R = S$

---

470   Look at Panel 1. R_4 is *not* a binary relation from S into T because dom $R_4 = \{a, c\}$, and $\{a, c\} \neq S$. (Check.) We can say that R_4 *is* a binary relation from S_1 into T if we define $S_1 = \{a, c\}$.
      (1) R_3 is not a binary relation from S into T because _____ .
      (2)   We can say that R_3 *is* a binary relation from S_2 into T if we define $S_2 = $ _____ .

---

      (1)   dom $R_3 = \{a, b\}$ ($\{a, b\} \neq S$)   (2) $\{a, b\}$

---

471   Let $R = \{(1,b), (2,b), (2,c), (5,d)\}$.
      R *is* a binary relation from S into T where $S = $ _____ and T is any set that has _____ as a subset.

$S = \{1, 2, 5\}$, $\{b, c, d\}$

COMMENT

From frames 470 and 471 you should see that, if a binary relation R in $S \times T$ is not a binary relation from S into T, R *is* a binary relation from S_1 into T where $S_1 = $ dom R and S_1 is a proper subset of S (i.e., a subset of S but not = to S). In our discussions, however, we will ordinarily have some particular sets S and T given, and in considering a binary relation R in $S \times T$, we will be concerned whether R is a binary relation from S into T. The situation is analogous to that which sometimes occurred in our study of equivalence relations. Consider $S = \{a, b, c\}$ and $R = \{(a,a), (a,b), (b,a), (b,b)\}$. R is *not* an equivalence relation *in* S because it is not reflexive *in* S. However, R *is* an equivalence relation in S_1 where $S_1 = \{a, b\}$. But in most of our problems, the set S was fixed, and we were considering whether R was an equivalence relation in S, not in some other set.

---

472   Look at Panel 3. Which of those tabulated are binary relations from S into S?

$R_7, R_8, R_9, R_{10}, R_{12}, R_{13}, R_{14}, R_{15}, R_{16}$

•473   **(1)**   Let R be a subset of $S \times T$. R is called a(n) _____ in $S \times T$.

(2)   dom $R =$ _____ (symbolically).

(3)   ran $R =$ _____ (symbolically).

(4) R is a binary relation from S into T if and only if _____.

---

(1)   binary relation

(2) $\{x \mid$ there is a y such that $(x,y) \in R\}$

(3) $\{y \mid$ there is an x such that $(x,y) \in R\}$

(4)   dom $R = S$

COMMENT

If R is a subset of $S \times T$ and dom $R = S$, we say that R is a binary relation from S into T. The only restriction placed on ran R is ran $R \subset T$. For example, let $S = \{1, 2, 3\}$, $T = \{a, b, c, d\}$, and $R = \{(1,b), (1,c), (2,c), (2,d), (3,b), (3,c)\}$, dom $R = S$, so R is a binary relation from S into T. ran $R = \{b, c, d\}$, a proper subset of T. If we let T^* be any set containing $\{b, c, d\}$ as a subset, R is a binary relation from S into T^*. As before, T will ordinarily be given. When it is not, you may take T as any superset of ran R.

474   Look at Panel 1. R_5, R_7, R_8, and R_9 are binary relations from S into T. Which of these have a range $= T$?

R_7, R_8, R_9 (ran $R_5 = \{1\} \neq T$)

II. Permutations of Degree N

475   (1)   Let R be a binary relation from S into T. Then dom R = ____ and ran $R \subset$ ____.

      (2)   The binary relations from S into T with ran $R = T$ are of particular interest.

Definition: If R is a binary relation from S into T and ran $R = T$, then R is called a *binary relation from S onto T*. (Note *onto*.) In Panel 1, R_5, R_7, R_8, R_9 are binary relations from S *into* T. Which of these are binary relations from S *onto* T?

(1) S, T

(2) R_7, R_8, R_9

476   Let R be a subset of $S \times T$.

      (1)   If dom $R = S$, R is a binary relation from S _____ T.

      (2)   If, in addition to this, ran $R = T$, then R is a binary relation from S _____ T.

(1)   into   **(2)**   onto

477   (1)   If R is a binary relation in $S \times T$ and _____, then R is called a binary relation from S into T.

      (2)   If, in addition to this, _____, then R is called a binary relation from S onto T.

(1)   dom $R = S$ **(2)**   ran $R = T$

478   Beware! Before a relation can be *onto* it must be *into*.

      (1)   That is, R is a binary relation from S *onto* T if and only if R is a binary relation from S *into* T (i.e., dom R = ___) and, in addition, ran R = ___.

      (2)   Every _____ relation is an _____ relation, but the converse does not hold.

(1) S, T **(2)**   onto,   into

479   Look at Panel 1. Which of the binary relations tabulated there are binary relations from *S* *onto* *T*?

R_7, R_8, R_9 (If you have included R_3 and R_4 review frame 478).

•480   Look at Panel 2.
(1)   List the binary relations from *S* *into* *S*.
(2)   List the binary relations from *S* *onto* *S*.

(1) R_2, R_3, R_4, R_7, R_8 (2) R_2, R_3, R_4, R_7

•481   Define a binary relation *R* from *S* *onto* *T*.

A binary relation *R* in $S \times T$ is a binary relation from *S* onto *T* if and only if *R* is a binary relation from *S* into *T* and ran *R* = *T*.

•482   An alternative definition would be:
A binary relation in $S \times T$ is a binary relation from *S* onto *T* if and only if dom *R* = ____ and ran *R* = ____.

S,   *T*

•483   In our alternative definition first *R* is specified as an arbitrary binary relation in (1) _____. Then, the condition (2) _____ = *S* requires that *R* must be a binary relation from (3) *S* _____ *T*. Finally, the condition (4) _____ = *T* changes the "into" to "onto."

(1) $S \times T$ (2)   dom *R*   (3)   into   (4)   ran *R*

•484   Look at Panel 3. Which of the binary relations tabulated are binary relations from *S* *onto* *S* ?

R_8, R_9, R_{12}, R_{13}, R_{14}, R_{15}, R_{16}

•485   Let $S = \{a, b, c\}$. Let $R = \{(a,a), (a,b), (b,b), (c,a)\}$.
(1)   dom *R* = _____ , ran *R* = _____.
(2)   *R* is a binary relation from *S* into *S* because _____.
(3)   *R* is *not* a binary relation from *S* onto *S* because _____.
(4)   *R* is a binary relation from *S* onto S_1 if we define
        S_1 = _____.

(1) $\{a, b, c\}$ (or S), $\{a, b\}$ (2)   dom *R* = *S*
(3)   ran *R* ≠ *S*   (4) $\{a, b\}$ (or ran *R*)

•486   Let R be a subset of $S \times T$.

(1)   If _____, then R is a binary relation from S *into* T.

(2)   If _____ and _____, then R is a binary relation from S *onto* T.

(1)   dom $R = S$

(2)   dom $R = S$ (or R is a binary relation from S *into* T), ran $R = T$

COMMENT

In this course, as in most mathematics courses, you will find it extremely profitable to construct your *own* examples illustrating the various topics under discussion. You might, as is done most frequently in this program, use very simple finite sets. You might also draw from your past experience in algebra, geometry, or trigonometry. Indeed, the use of the present terminology applied to your previous work may very well help you to understand both.

For example, let us go back to elementary algebra. Let X be the set of real numbers and Y be the set of real numbers. Then the cross product $X \times Y = \{(x,y) \mid x \in X \text{ and } y \in Y\}$ is the set of ordered pairs of real numbers.

We represent $X \times Y$ graphically in the familiar manner; and using the usual technique of associating with each point p in the plane its rectangular coordinates (x,y) where x represents the distance from the point to the Y axis and y represents the distance from the point to the X axis, we have:

1. To each $(x,y) \in X \times Y$ there corresponds exactly one point p in the plane of the graph [namely, the point with rectangular coordinates (x,y)].

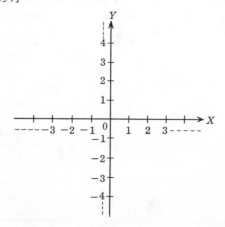

2. To each point p in the plane there corresponds exactly one ordered pair $(x,y) \in X \times Y$ [namely, the ordered pair (x,y) having coordinates equal to the rectangular coordinates of p].

Now consider the expression: $4x^2 + 9y^2 = 36$. If we let $R = \{(x,y) \mid x \in X, y \in Y, \text{ and } 4x^2 + 9y^2 = 36\}$, then R is a binary relation in $X \times Y$. R consists of those ordered pairs (x,y) of $X \times Y$ which satisfy the expression $4x^2 + 9y^2 = 36$. You can verify that

$$(-3,0) \in R, \left(-2,\frac{2\sqrt{5}}{3}\right) \in R, \left(-1,\frac{4\sqrt{2}}{3}\right) \in R, (0,2) \in R, \left(\frac{3\sqrt{3}}{2},1\right) \in R,$$

etc.

Now R is a subset of $X \times Y$, and if, on the graphical representation of $X \times Y$, we mark those points corresponding to ordered pairs of R, we obtain the curve (an ellipse) shown below, which is called "the graph of R."

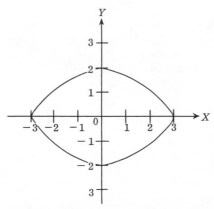

So each point of the ellipse corresponds to an element of R and, conversely, each ordered pair of R corresponds to a point of the ellipse. From the graph of R we see quite easily that:

1. R is not a binary relation from X *into* Y because dom $R \neq X$ (for example, $10 \notin R$).
2. dom $R = [-3,3]$ ($[-3,3]$ means $\{x \mid x \in X \text{ and } -3 \leq X \leq 3\}$), so R is a binary relation from $[-3,3]$ *into* Y.
3. R is not a binary relation from $[-3,3]$ *onto* Y because ran $R \neq Y$ (for example, $2.5 \notin$ ran Y).
4. ran $R = [-2,2]$ ($[-2,2]$ means $\{y \mid y \in Y \text{ and } -2 \leq y \leq 2\}$), so R is a binary relation from $[-3,3]$ *onto* $[-2,2]$.

---

487   Let R be a subset of $S \times T$.

(1) R is a(n) _____ in $S \times T$.

(2) R is a binary relation from S into T if and only if _____ .

---

(1)   binary relation

(2)   dom $R = S$

488   Consider R_7 from Panel 1. The dom $R_7 = S$, so R_7 is a binary relation from S into T. (It is also "onto," but at times we need not
consider this.) For each $x \in S$ there is *at least one* $y \in T$ such that
$(x,y) \in R_7$. In this example, $c \in S$ and two elements, namely, ____
and ____ $\in T$ such that (_____) $\in R_7$ and (_____) $\in R_7$.

1,   2, $(c,1)$, $(c,2)$

•489   Let R be a binary relation from S into T.
(1)   Then dom $R = S$. For each $x \in S$ there is at least one $y \in T$
such that _____.
Of particular interest are those binary relations R from S into T
such that *for each* $x \in S$ there is *exactly one* $y \in T$ for which
$(x,y) \in R$.
(2)   Let $S = \{p, q, r\}$ and $T = \{1, 2, 3, 4\}$.
Let $R_1 = \{(p,1), (p,2), (q,2), (r,3)$
$R_2 = \{(p,2), (q,3), (r,3)\}$, and
$R_3 = \{(q,2), (r,3)\}$.
Which of these binary relations in $S \times T$, if any, have the
quality mentioned?

---

(1) $(x,y) \in R$ (2) R_2

---

490   $R_1 = \{(p,1), (p,2), (q,2), (r,3)\}$. R_1 is not a binary relation from S
onto T because_____.

---

ran $R_1 \neq T$

---

491   $R_3 = \{(q,2), (r,3)\}$
R_3 is not a binary relation from S _____ T because dom $R_3 \neq S$.

---

into

---

492   We are interested in a binary relation R in $S \times T$ such that:
(1) R is a binary relation from S _____ T (i.e., dom $R =$ ____).
(2)   For each $x \in$ dom R, there is _____ $y \in T$ such that
$(x,y) \in R$.

---

(1)   into, S
(2)   exactly one (or one)

493 Look at Panel 2.
  (1) Which of the binary relations have a domain = S (i.e., which
       are binary relations from S into S)?
  (2) Of these, which also satisfy the condition that for each $x \in S$
       there is *exactly one* $y \in T$, such that $(x,y) \in R$?

---

  (1) R_2, R_3, R_4, R_7, R_8 (2) R_8

---

494 *Definition*: A binary relation R in $S \times T$ is a function from
     _____ if and only if:
  1. dom $R = S$, and
  2. for each $x \in$ dom R, there is *exactly one* $y \in T$, such that
      $(x,y) \in R$.

  S into T

---

495 Look at Panel 3. Which of the binary relations are functions from
     S into S?

  R_7, R_8, R_9, R_{10}

---

496 Let $S = \{a, b, c\}$ and $T = \{1, 2, 3, 4\}$. Let $R = \{(a,3), (b,2), (c,3)\}$.
  (1) _____, so R is a binary relation from S into T, and
  (2) for each $x \in S$ there is *exactly one* $y \in T$ such that _____;
       therefore R is a(n) _____ from S into T.

---

  (1) dom $R = S$ (2) $(x,y) \in R$,   function

COMMENT

Look at Panel 1. Consider R_3. R_3 is *not* a function from S into T
because dom $R_3 \neq S$. You may notice that R_3 *is* a function from S_1
into T where $S_1 = \{a, b\}$. But as before, we remark that in most of
your work, some set A will be specified and we will be interested
in whether R is a function from A into T. For our purposes, the
word "function" applied to a binary relation R in $S \times T$ having the
property that for each $x \in$ dom R there is exactly one $y \in T$ such
that $(x,y) \in R$ is not restrictive enough. We will be just as concerned about the dom R as we are about this above-mentioned property. For this reason, we will never use the word function without
adding "from A into B" (where A and B are properly chosen).
Finally, a binary relation which is a function from S into T is
usually denoted by a small letter such as f, g, or h or by Greek
letters α, β, γ, rather than by R.

497 A binary relation f in $S \times T$ is a function from S into T if and only if dom $f =$ _____, and for each _____ there is exactly one _____ such that _____ ϵf.

$S,$ $x \epsilon S$ (or $x \epsilon$ dom f), $y \epsilon T,$ (x,y)

---

498 A binary relation α in $S \times T$ is a function from S into T if and only if **(1)** _____ and **(2)** _____.

---

(1) dom $\alpha = S$ (or α is a binary relation from S into T)
(2) for each $x \epsilon S$ there is exactly one $y \epsilon T$ such that $(x,y) \epsilon \alpha$

---

499 Look at Panel 3. Which of the binary relations are functions from S into S?

R_7, R_8, R_9, R_{10}

---

500 Graphically, a function f from S into T must be such that there is a point on the graph for every $x \epsilon$ _____. In addition, it must be such that any vertical line drawn through a point representing an element of f _____ (will or will not) go through any other point representing an element of f.

$S,$ will not

---

501 Let $S = \{a, b, c\}$ and $T = \{1, 2, 3, 4\}$. Let $R = \{(a,1), (b,2), (c,4)\}$.
(1) Represent $S \times T$ graphically.
(2) Circle each point corresponding to an element of R.
(3) Draw a vertical line through each of the elements of R on the graph.
(4) Each vertical line intersects _____ point of the graph R.

---

(1), **(2)**, **(3)**

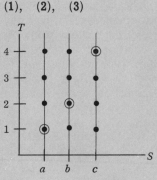

(4) exactly one (or no other)

502   Let X be the set of real numbers and
         Y be the set of real numbers.
      Let $R = \{(x,y) \mid x \in X, y \in Y, \text{ and } 4x^2 + 9y^2 = 36\}$.
      The graph of R is shown:

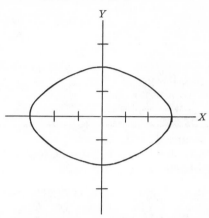

      R is a binary relation from $[-3,3]$ into $[-2,2]$. Except for the points
      with the coordinates of $(-3,0)$ and $(3,0)$, a vertical line through any
      point representing an element of R has on it ____ (how many) points
      of the graph R. From this we can see that R _____ (is or is not)
      a function from $[-3,3]$ into $[-2,2]$.

      two,   is not

503   A binary relation f in $S \times T$ is a function from S _____ T if and
      only if f is a function from S _____ T and ran $f = T$.

      onto,   into

504   Let $S = \{a, b, c\}$ and $T = \{1, 2, 3\}$. Let $\alpha = \{(a,1), (b,1), (c,2)\}$.
      (1) α is a function from S into T because _____ .
      (2) α is not a function from S onto T because _____ .

      (1)   dom $\alpha = S$ (or α is a binary relation from S into T) and for
              each $x \in S$ there is exactly one $y \in T$ such that $(x,y) \in \alpha$
      (2)   ran $\alpha \neq T$ (or ran $\alpha = \{1, 2\}$)

505   Look at Panel 3.
      (1)   Which of the binary relations are functions from S *into* S?
      (2)   Which of the binary relations are functions from S *onto* S?

      (1) R_7, R_8, R_9, R_{10} (2) R_8, R_9

• 506   Let R be a subset of $S \times T$.
1. If dom $R = S$, then R is called a(n) (1) _____.
2. If, in addition to condition 1, for every $x \in$ dom R there is exactly one $y \in T$ such that $(x, y) \in R$, then R is called a(n) (2) _____.
3. If, in addition to conditions 1 and 2, ran $R = T$, then R is called a(n) (3) _____.

(1) binary relation from S into T
(2) function from S into T
(3) function from S onto T

• 507   Let $S = \{a, b\}$ and $T = \{1, 2\}$.
(1) Write in roster form all possible functions from S *into* T.
(2) Write in roster form all possible functions from S *onto* T.

(1) $f_1 = \{(a,1), (b,1)\}$
$f_2 = \{(a,1), (b,2)\}$
$f_3 = \{(a,2), (b,1)\}$
$f_4 = \{(a,2), (b,2)\}$
The functions can be in any order.
(2) $f_2 = \{(a,1), (b,2)\}$
$f_3 = \{(a,2), (b,1)\}$

• 508   Define a function from S onto T.

The simplest definition would be: f is a function from S onto T if and only if f is a function from S into T and ran $f = T$. (Any equivalent definition, of course, is correct.)

509   The word "mapping" is often used in place of the word "function." We may write "f is a _____ from S into T," instead of "f is a function from S into T." We may also write "f is a mapping of S onto T," instead of "f is a _____ from S onto T."

mapping,   function

510   Let $S = \{p, q, r\}$ and $T = \{1, 2, 3, 4\}$. Let $f = \{(p,1), (q,1), (r,3)\}$ be a mapping from S into T. (Check.) We sometimes say that "x is mapped into y by the mapping f."

In the above example:
(1) p is mapped into ____ by the mapping f.

▼

(2) q is _____ into ____ by the _____ f.
(3) r is _____.

---

(1) 1
(2) mapped,   1,   mapping
(3) mapped into 3 by the mapping f

---

511 Let $S = \{p, q, r\}$ and $T = \{1, 2, 3, 4\}$.
Let $f = \{(p,2), (q,2), (r,4)\}$ be a function from S into T. (Check.)
In mapping, we see the sets S and T as shown below, and we see
the mapping as a rule which associates with each $x \in S$ a unique
$y \in T$. Note the arrows.

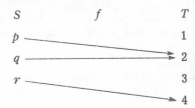

(1) p is mapped into ____ by the mapping f.
(2) q is mapped by f into ____.
(3) r is mapped by ____ into ____.

---

(1) 2   **(2)** 2   **(3)** f,   4

---

512 Let $S = \{1, 2, 3, 4\}$ and $T = \{5, 10, 15\}$.
Let $\alpha = \{(1,10), (2,15), (3,5), (4,15)\}$ be a mapping of S onto T. Illustrate α as was done in frame 511, with arrows to indicate the
mapping.

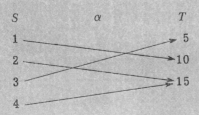

---

513 Look at Panel 2. R_8 is a mapping of S into S. Illustrate R_8 as in
frames 511 and 512.

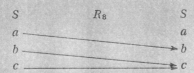

514   Let S and T be nonempty sets. Let f be a function (mapping) of S onto T.

(1)   For each $x \in S$, there is a unique $y \in T$ such that _____ .
This unique $y \in T$ is called the *image of x under the mapping*
f. If $S = \{a, b, c\}$, $T = \{1, 2\}$, and $f = \{(a,2), (b,1), (c,1)\}$,

(2)   the image of a under the mapping f is ____ .

(3)   ____ is the _____ of b under the mapping f.

(4)   ____ is the _____ of c under the _____ .

(1) $(x, y) \in f$

(2)   2

(3)   1,   image

(4)   1,   image,   mapping f

515   Let a mapping α from S onto T be illustrated as below.

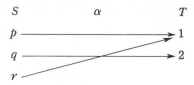

(1)   The image of p under the mapping α is ____ .

(2)   The image of q under the mapping α is ____ .

(3)   The _____ of r under the mapping α is ____ .

(4) $\alpha = $ _____ in roster form.

(1)   1

(2)   2

(3)   image,   1

(4) $\{(p,1), (q,2), (r,1)\}$

516   *Definition*: Let f be a function from S into T, and $x \in S$. The _____ of x under f is the unique $y \in T$ such that _____ .

image, $(x, y) \in f$

517   Let $S = \{1, 2, 3, 4\}$ and $T = \{p, q, r\}$.
Let $f = \{(1,q), (2,q), (3,q), (4,q)\}$

(1) f is a function (or mapping) from S into T because _____ .

(2)   The image of 1 under f is ____ .
The image of 2 under f is ____ .

▼

The image of 3 under f is ____.
The image of 4 under f is ____.

---

(1) dom $R = S$ (or f is a binary relation from S into T) and for each $x \in S$ there is *exactly one* $y \in T$ such that $(x,y) \in f$
(2) q, q, q, q

518   Let $S = \{1, 2, 3, 4\}$. Let $\alpha = \{(1,2), (2,2), (3,4), (4,4)\}$.
(1) α is a _____ from S _____ T.
(2) The _____ of 3 under α is ____.

---

(1) function (or mapping),   into
(2) image,   4

---

519   Let f be a function from S into T. Let $x \in S$. The unique image of x under the function f is denoted by $f(x)$ [sometimes $(x)f$]. For example, let $S = \{1, 2, 3, 4\}$, $T = \{p, q, r, s\}$, and $f = \{(1,q), (2,r), (3,s), (4,s)\}$.
(1) $f(1)$ is the image of 1 under the function f, so $f(1)$ is ____.
(2) ____ is the image of 2 under the function f, so ____ is ____.

---

(1) q (2) $f(2)$, $f(2)$, r

• 520   (1) Let f be a mapping of S into T. Let $x \in S$. There is a unique $y \in T$ such that _____.
(2) y is called the _____ of x under f and is denoted by _____.

---

(1) $(x,y) \in f$
(2) image, $f(x)$ [or $(x)f$]

---

521   Let f be a mapping of S into T as illustrated below.

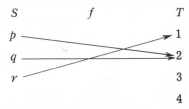

(1) The image of p under the mapping f is ____, and is denoted by _____.
(2) The image of q under the mapping f is ____, and is denoted by _____.

▼

(3) The image of r under the mapping f is ____, and is denoted by
_____.

---

(1) 2, $f(p)$ or $(p)f$
(2) 2, $f(q)$ or $(q)f$
(3) 1, $f(r)$ or $(r)f$

---

522 Let $S = \{1, 2, 3, 4\}$. Let $\alpha = \{(1,2), (2,3), (3,4), (4,2)\}$ be a function from S into T.
(1) $f(2)$ denotes the _____ of ____ under f and $f(2) =$ ____.
(2) $f(3)$ denotes the _____ of ____ under f and $f(3) =$ ____.

---

(1) image,   2,   3   (2) image,   3,   4

---

523 Let f be a function from S into T.
(1) For each _____ there is a unique ____ such that _____.
(2) y is called the _____ of ____ under f and is denoted by
_____.

---

(1) $x \in S$ (or $x \in$ dom f), $y \in T$, $(x,y) \in f$
(2) image, x, $f(x)$ [or $(x)f$]

---

524 Let $S = \{1, 2, 3, 4\}$ and $T = \{p, q, r\}$.
Let $\alpha = \{(1,q), (2,q), (3,r), (4,r)\}$, α is a function from S into T.
(1) $\alpha(1)$ denotes the image of ____ under the mapping α, so
$\alpha(1) =$ ____.
(2) $\alpha(2)$ denotes the image of ____ under the mapping α, so _____.
(3) $\alpha(3) =$ ____.
(4) $\alpha(4) =$ ____.

---

(1) 1, q (2) 2, $\alpha(2) = q$ (3) r (4) r

COMMENT

Let f be a function from S into T. Let $x \in S$. In this section, we have denoted the image of x under the mapping f by $f(x)$, and not by $(x)f$. Note that if f were simply a binary relation in $S \times T$, and not a function from S into T, the symbolism $f(x)$ where $x \in S$ would be either meaningless or else ambiguous. For example, let $S = \{a, b, c\}$ and $T = \{1, 2, 3\}$. Let $R = \{(a,1), (a,2), (b,2)\}$ be a binary relation in $S \times T$. R is not a function from S into T. If we attempted to use the symbolism for the image of an element under a function, $R(c)$ would not exist and $R(a)$ would not be uniquely determined.

But if f is a *function* from S into T, we are guaranteed that:

1. dom $f = S$. Therefore for each $x \in S$ there *is* a $y \in T$ such that $(x, y) \in f$.
2. each such $y \in T$ is *unique*; that is, it cannot happen that $(x, y_1) \in f$ and $(x, y_2) \in f$ where $y_1 \neq y_2$.

So the symbolism $f(x)$ where f is a function from S into T has meaning.

In this case, it sometimes helps to imagine S, T, and f as follows:

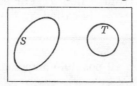

Imagine the elements of S to be represented by the points inside the figure marked S and the elements of T to be represented by the points inside the figure marked T. Let f be a mapping from S into T. Then each $x \in S$ is mapped by f into a unique $y \in T$, indicated by $f(x)$. So, choose any point x in the figure marked S. The function f maps x into a unique point of T as shown by the arrow.

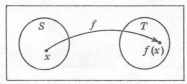

The unique point of T associated with x by the mapping f is called the image of x under f and is denoted by $f(x)$. We have shown the mapping of just one element of S. If f is a function from S into T, *every* element of S must be mapped into a unique element of T. Note, however:

1. Every $x \in S$ is mapped into exactly one element of T.
2. Different elements of x can be mapped into the same element of T.
3. Not every element of T need be an image of some element of S unless f is a mapping of S *onto* T.

Self-test IV   (Answers to Self-test IV appear on page 314)

1 Let R be a subset of $S \times T$. R is a binary relation in $S \times T$.
  (1)   dom $R =$ _____ (symbolically).
  (2)   ran $R =$ _____ (symbolically).

2 Let R be a subset of $S \times T$. R is a binary relation in $S \times T$. If _____, then R is called a binary relation from S into T.

3 Let R be a subset of $S \times T$. R is a binary relation from S *onto* T if and only if _____ and _____ .

4 Let R be a subset of $S \times T$. R is a function (or mapping) from S into T if and only if _____ .

5 Let α be a function from S into T. Then α is a function from S onto T if and only if _____ .

6 Let f be a function from S into T. For each $x \in S$ there is a unique $y \in T$ such that _____ . y is called _____ and is denoted by _____ .

---

525 Let $S = \{a, b\}$.
Write in roster form all possible mappings of S *onto* S.

$\{(a,a), (b,b)\}, \{(a,b), (b,a)\}$

---

526 Let $S = \{a, b, c\}$.
Write in roster form all possible mappings of S onto S.

$\{(a,a), (b,b), (c,c)\}, \{(a,a), (b,c), (c,b)\},$
$\{(a,b), (b,a), (c,c)\}, \{(a,b), (b,c), (c,a)\},$
$\{(a,c), (b,a), (c,b)\}, \{(a,c), (b,b), (c,a)\}$

---

527 *Definition*: Let S be a finite set having N members. Any function from S *onto* S is called a *permutation of degree N*.
Let $S = \{a, b, c, d\}$ and $f = \{(a,b), (b,d), (c,c), (d,a)\}$. f is a function from S into S. Moreover, ran f = ___ , so that f is a function from S onto S. Therefore f is called a(n) _____ of degree ___ .

S,   permutation,   4

•528 A permutation of degree N is a(n) _____ from S _____ S, where S is a set having ___ elements.

function (or mapping),   onto, N

COMMENT

In all of the examples of permutations of degree N, we will use the set of positive integers and indicate a set of N elements by $\{1, 2, 3, ..., N\}$. We will have no loss of generality from using this notation.

529 Let $S = \{1, 2, 3, 4\}$ and $R = \{(1,1), (2,3), (3,4), (4,2)\}$. R is a mapping of S onto itself, so R is a _____ of degree ___.

---

permutation,   4

---

530 Let $S = \{1, 2, 3\}$. Let $R = \{(1,3), (2,2), (3,1)\}$.
(1) R is a mapping of _____, so R is called a(n) _____. It is customary to write R as follows:

$$R = \begin{pmatrix} 1 & 2 & 3 \\ 3 & 2 & 1 \end{pmatrix}$$

The ordered pairs are written with the first coordinates on the top row and the second coordinates underneath.
(2) If $f = \{(1,2), (2,3), (3,1)\}$, write S in permutation notation.

---

(1) S onto S,   permutation of degree 3
(2) $\begin{pmatrix} 1 & 2 & 3 \\ 2 & 3 & 1 \end{pmatrix}$

---

531 In the permutation notation, then, the first n natural numbers appear in the top line; and directly underneath each natural number is the number into which it is mapped by the function. Thus, if $R = \{(1,4), (2,3), (3,1), (4,2)\}$, then $R = \begin{pmatrix} 1 & 2 & 3 & 4 \\ 4 & 3 & 1 & 2 \end{pmatrix}$. Under the mapping, 1 is mapped into 4, 2 is mapped into 3, 3 is mapped into ___, 4 is mapped into ___.

1,   2

---

532 Let $R = \{(1,4), (2,2), (3,3), (4,1)\}$. Write R in permutation notation.

$\begin{pmatrix} 1 & 2 & 3 & 4 \\ 4 & 2 & 3 & 1 \end{pmatrix}$

---

533 Suppose $R = \begin{pmatrix} 1 & 2 & 3 \\ 3 & 1 & 2 \end{pmatrix}$. Write R as a set of ordered pairs.

$\{(1,3), (2,1), (3,2)\}$

---

534 Let $R = \begin{pmatrix} 1 & 2 & 3 & 4 & 5 \\ 1 & 3 & 4 & 2 & 5 \end{pmatrix}$. R is a _____.

---

permutation of degree 5 (or mapping of $\{1, 2, 3, 4, 5\}$ onto $\{1, 2, 3, 4, 5\}$)

535   Under the permutation $\begin{pmatrix} 1 & 2 & 3 & 4 \\ 2 & 1 & 3 & 4 \end{pmatrix}$

(1)   1 is mapped into ____.
(2)   2 is mapped into ____.
(3)   3 is mapped into ____.
(4)   4 is mapped into ____.

(1)   2   (2)   1   (3)   3   (4)   4

536   Consider the permutations:

$R_1 = \begin{pmatrix} 1 & 2 & 3 & 4 \\ 2 & 1 & 4 & 3 \end{pmatrix}$ $R_2 = \begin{pmatrix} 1 & 3 & 2 & 4 \\ 2 & 4 & 1 & 3 \end{pmatrix}$

(1)   Write R_1 and R_2 in roster form.
(2)   Does $R_1 = R_2$?

(1) $R_1 = \{(1,2), (2,1), (3,4), (4,3)\}$
        $R_2 = \{(1,2), (3,4), (2,1), (4,3)\}$
(2)   Yes, their elements are the same, only the order is different.

537   It is customary to write the numbers in the top line of a permutation in their natural order. Rewrite $\begin{pmatrix} 2 & 3 & 1 & 4 \\ 1 & 2 & 4 & 3 \end{pmatrix}$ in this manner.

$\begin{pmatrix} 1 & 2 & 3 & 4 \\ 4 & 1 & 2 & 3 \end{pmatrix}$

538   Let $S = \{1, 2, 3, 4\}$. There are twenty-four distinct permutations of order 4. On a separate sheet of paper write them in permutation form.

Answer is on Panel 6. Your order may, of course, be different.

539   Let $R = \begin{pmatrix} 1 & 2 & 3 & 4 \\ 4 & 2 & 3 & 1 \end{pmatrix}$.

The permutation may be represented as a mapping such as shown below.

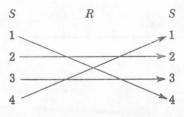

▼

(1)   1 is mapped by R into ____.
(2)   2 is mapped by R into ____.
(3)   3 is mapped by R into ____.
(4)   4 is mapped by R into ____.

---

(1)   4   (2)   2   (3)   3   (4)   1

540

Let $R = \begin{pmatrix} 1 & 2 & 3 & 4 \\ 4 & 1 & 2 & 3 \end{pmatrix}$.

Show this permutation as a mapping as was done in frame 539.

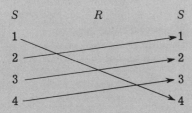

III. Permutation Multiplication

541

Let $R_1 = \begin{pmatrix} 1 & 2 & 3 \\ 3 & 1 & 2 \end{pmatrix}$ and $R_2 = \begin{pmatrix} 1 & 2 & 3 \\ 3 & 1 & 2 \end{pmatrix}$ be two permutations of degree 3. Consider the mapping R_1 *followed by* the mapping R_2, as illustrated below:

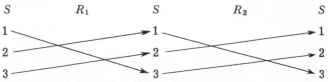

(1)   Follow the element 1 as it is mapped first by R_1 and then as its image under R_1 is mapped by R_2: 1 is mapped by R_1 into ____, which in turn is mapped by R_2 into ____. The *total effect* of R_1 followed by R_2 on the element 1 is that 1 is mapped into 2.
(2)   Follow the element 2 as it is mapped first by R_1 and then by R_2: 2 is mapped by R_1 into ____ which in turn is mapped by R_2 into ____. The total effect of R_1 followed by R_2 on the element 2 is that 2 is mapped into ____.
(3)   Similarly, 3 is mapped by ____ into ____ which in turn is mapped by ____ into ____. The total effect of R_1 followed by R_2 on the element 3 is that 3 is mapped into ____.

---

(1)   3,   2   (2)   1,   3,   3   (3) R_1,   2, R_2,   1,   1

542   Let $R_1 = \begin{pmatrix} 1 & 2 & 3 \\ 2 & 1 & 3 \end{pmatrix}$ and $R_2 = \begin{pmatrix} 1 & 2 & 3 \\ 2 & 3 & 1 \end{pmatrix}$ be two permutations of degree 3. Again, let us find the total effect of the mapping R_1 followed by the mapping R_2. This time we will follow the mappings in permutation form as follows:

$$R_1 = \begin{pmatrix} 1 & 2 & 3 \\ 2 & 1 & 3 \end{pmatrix} \qquad R_2 = \begin{pmatrix} 1 & 2 & 3 \\ 2 & 3 & 1 \end{pmatrix}$$

As you read, follow the arrows:
(1) 1 is mapped by R_1 into ____, which in turn is mapped by R_2 into ____. The total effect of the mapping R_1 followed by R_2 on the element 1 is that 1 is mapped into ____.
(2) 2 is mapped by R_1 into ____, which in turn is mapped by R_2 into ____. The total effect of the mapping R_1 followed by R_2 on the element 2 is that 2 is mapped into ____.
(3) Following the same reasoning, the mapping ____ followed by the mapping ____ causes 3 to be mapped into ____.

(1) 2,   3,   3
(2) 1,   2,   2
(3) R_1, R_2,   1

•543   Let $R_1 = \begin{pmatrix} 1 & 2 & 3 \\ 1 & 3 & 2 \end{pmatrix}$ and $R_2 = \begin{pmatrix} 1 & 2 & 3 \\ 2 & 3 & 1 \end{pmatrix}$. As before, find the total effect of R_1 followed by R_2.
(1) 1 is mapped by R_1 followed by R_2 into ____.
(2) 2 is mapped by R_1 followed by R_2 into ____.
(3) 3 is mapped by R_1 followed by R_2 into ____.

(1) 2
(2) 1
(3) 3
If your answer is not correct, review frames 541 and 542.

544   Look at R_5 and R_7 from Panel 6. Consider the total effect of the mapping R_5 followed by the mapping R_7.
(1) Under R_5 followed by R_7, 1 is mapped into ____.
(2) Under R_5 followed by R_7, 2 is mapped into ____.
(3) Under R_5 followed by R_7, 3 is mapped into ____.
(4) Under R_5 followed by R_7, 4 is mapped into ____.

(1) 2
(2) 4
(3) 1
(4) 3

545   From frame 544 we see that under the mapping R_5 followed by the
      mapping R_7 the total effect is that:

      1 is mapped into 2
      2 is mapped into 4
      3 is mapped into 1
      4 is mapped into 3

      There is a single permutation listed in Panel 6 which achieves this
      mapping in only one step. Which one is it?

      R_{11}

546   Look at Panel 6. Consider the effect of R_{11} followed by R_{14}.
      (1)   1 is mapped by R_{11} followed by R_{14} into ____.
            2 is mapped by R_{11} followed by R_{14} into ____.
            3 is mapped by R_{11} followed by R_{14} into ____.
            4 is mapped by R_{11} followed by R_{14} into ____.
      (2)   But again there is a single permutation listed on Panel 6 which
            achieves the same result in one step. Which one is it?

      (1)   1,   2,   3,   4   (2) R_1

547   Look at Panel 6. Consider the effect of R_{16} followed by R_{15}.
      (1)   1 is mapped by R_{16} followed by R_{15} into ____.
            2 is mapped by R_{16} followed by R_{15} into ____.
            3 is mapped by R_{16} followed by R_{15} into ____.
            4 is mapped by R_{16} followed by R_{15} into ____.
      (2)   But again there is a single permutation listed on Panel 6 which
            achieves the same result in one step. Which one is it?

      (1)   1,   2,   4,   3   (2) R_2

548   If R_1 and R_2 are two _____ of degree N, then there exists a
      single permutation of degree N which has the same result as R_1
      _____ R_2. This will be proved later.

      permutations,   followed by

549   In frame 547, we found that R_{16} followed by R_{15} has the same effect
      as the single permutation R_2. In order to simplify our notation, we
      will indicate the two given permutations as an ordered pair, written
      in the order in which they are performed. So instead of writing R_{16}
      followed by R_{15}, we may write (_____).

      (R_{16}, R_{15})

550 *Note*: We will use Panel 6 for frames 550 to 564.

Complete the permutation $R_{23} = \begin{pmatrix} 1 & 2 & 3 & 4 \\ \_ & \_ & \_ & \_ \end{pmatrix}$.

$$\begin{pmatrix} 1 & 2 & 3 & 4 \\ 4 & 3 & 1 & 2 \end{pmatrix}$$

---

551 Write the permutation $R_{10} = \Big(\qquad\qquad\Big)$.

$$\begin{pmatrix} 1 & 2 & 3 & 4 \\ 2 & 3 & 4 & 1 \end{pmatrix}$$

---

552 We now have R_{23} and R_{10}. Let us find the permutation that corresponds to the total effect of R_{23} followed by R_{10}.

$$R_{23} = \begin{pmatrix} 1 & 2 & 3 & 4 \\ 4 & 3 & 1 & 2 \end{pmatrix} \quad R_{10} = \begin{pmatrix} 1 & 2 & 3 & 4 \\ 2 & 3 & 4 & 1 \end{pmatrix}$$

(1) Under the relationship "followed by," (R_{23}, R_{10}) corresponds to
$\begin{pmatrix} 1 & 2 & 3 & 4 \\ 1 & 4 & & \end{pmatrix}$.

(2) (R_{23}, R_{10}) corresponds to the single permutation ____.

---

(1) $\begin{pmatrix} 1 & 2 & 3 & 4 \\ 1 & 4 & 2 & 3 \end{pmatrix}$ (2) R_5

---

553 Under "followed by," as we shall call this relationship, (R_{16}, R_{15}) corresponds to ____.

R_2

•554 If R_1 and R_2 are two permutations of degree N, then there exists a(n) _____ of degree N which has the same result as R_1 followed by R_2.

---

single permutation

•555 Another way to indicate R_1 followed by R_2 is to write the ordered pair (_____). The order in which the permutations are written ____ (is or is not) important, because it ____ (does or does not) indicate the order in which they are performed.

(R_1, R_2),   is,   does

•556 Under "followed by," (R_{19},R_{20}) corresponds to ____.

R_{11}

557 Under "_____," (R_{10},R_{15}) corresponds to R_8. (Check.)

followed by

558 We have seen that under "followed by" (R_{10},R_{15}) corresponds to the single permutation R_8. Let us see if a single permutation followed by *itself* will correspond to a single permutation. We would indicate R_{18} followed by itself by the ordered pair (_____).

(R_{18},R_{18})

559 Using the same method as before, under "followed by," (R_{18},R_{18}) corresponds to ____.

R_8

560 Under "followed by," (R_1,R_1) corresponds to ____.

R_1

561 Under "followed by," (R_1,R_5) corresponds to ____.

R_5

562 **(1)** Under "followed by," (R_5,R_7) corresponds to ____.
     (2) Under "followed by," (R_7,R_5) corresponds to ____.

(1) R_{11} **(2)** R_{19}

•563 Since (R_5,R_7) and (R_7,R_5) _____ (do, do not) correspond to the *same* single permutation, we have demonstrated that the _____ in which the permutations are written is indeed important.

do not,   order

564 We have been investigating several of the ordered pairs of permutations from Panel 6. Let us see how many we would have to investigate in order to cover *all* ordered pairs of permutations.
$S = \{1, 2, 3, 4\}$
(1) The set has _____ elements.
(2) These elements produce _____ permutations of degree ____.
(3) There are 24^2 (or _____) ordered pairs of permutations to investigate.

(1) four   **(2)** twenty-four   **(3)** 576

565 Let $S = \{1, 2, 3\}$.
(1) The set has _____ elements.
(2) These elements produce _____ permutations of degree ____.
(3) There would be 6^2 (or _____) ordered pairs of permutations to investigate.

(1) three   **(2)** six,   three   **(3)** thirty-six

566 Let $S = \{1, 2, 3\}$. We will indicate the set of permutations by $P = \{a, b, c, d, e, f\}$. Complete the permutations:

$$a = \begin{pmatrix} 1 & 2 & 3 \\ 1 & 2 & 3 \end{pmatrix} \qquad b = \begin{pmatrix} 1 & 2 & 3 \\ 2 & 3 & 1 \end{pmatrix} \qquad c = \begin{pmatrix} 1 & 2 & 3 \\ 3 & 1 & 2 \end{pmatrix}$$

$$d = \begin{pmatrix} & & \\ 1 & 3 & 2 \end{pmatrix} \qquad e = \begin{pmatrix} 1 & 2 & 3 \\ 3 & & \end{pmatrix} \qquad f = \begin{pmatrix} 1 & 2 & 3 \\ & & 3 \end{pmatrix}$$

Make a *correct* copy of this frame and save it.

$$d = \begin{pmatrix} 1 & 2 & 3 \\ 1 & 3 & 2 \end{pmatrix} \qquad e = \begin{pmatrix} 1 & 2 & 3 \\ 3 & 2 & 1 \end{pmatrix} \qquad f = \begin{pmatrix} 1 & 2 & 3 \\ 2 & 1 & 3 \end{pmatrix}$$

567 We indicate the _____ (number) elements of $P \times P$ (the ordered pairs of permutations) in this manner:

$$P \times P = \{(a,a), (a,b), (a,c), (a,d), (a,e), (a,f), (b,a), (b,b), (b,c), ...\}$$

thirty-six

568 Consider some element of $P \times P$, say (d,c).
(1) Complete the following permutations.

$$d = \begin{pmatrix} 1 & 2 & 3 \\ 1 & 3 & 2 \end{pmatrix} \quad \text{and} \quad c = \begin{pmatrix} 1 & 2 & 3 \\ \_ & \_ & \_ \end{pmatrix}$$

(d,c) corresponds to $\left(\dfrac{\quad}{} \ \dfrac{\quad}{} \ \dfrac{\quad}{}\right)$

(2) Under "followed by," (d,c) corresponds to ____.

(1) $c = \begin{pmatrix} 1 & 2 & 3 \\ 3 & 1 & 2 \end{pmatrix}$ $(d,c) = \begin{pmatrix} 1 & 2 & 3 \\ 3 & 2 & 1 \end{pmatrix}$

(2) e

In frames 569 to 574, we are going to find the single permutation corresponding to every element of $P \times P$ under the process we have called "followed by." Since there are thirty-six elements of $P \times P$, there will be thirty-six such problems. We will do six in each frame. This is tedious work, but you need the results and you can use the practice. Save the results of frames 569 to 574. (*Correct any errors.*)

569 Under "followed by,"
(1) (a,a) corresponds to ____
(2) (a,b) corresponds to ____
(3) (a,c) corresponds to ____
(4) (a,d) corresponds to ____
(5) (a,e) corresponds to ____
(6) (a,f) corresponds to ____

(1) a (2) b (3) c (4) d (5) e (6) f

570 Under "followed by,"
(7) (b,a) corresponds to ____
(8) (b,b) corresponds to ____
(9) (b,c) corresponds to ____
(10) (b,d) corresponds to ____
(11) (b,e) corresponds to ____
(12) (b,f) corresponds to ____

(7) b (8) c (9) a (10) e (11) f (12) d

571 Under "followed by,"
    (13) (c,a) corresponds to ____
    (14) (c,b) corresponds to ____
    (15) (c,c) corresponds to ____
    (16) (c,d) corresponds to ____
    (17) (c,e) corresponds to ____
    (18) (c,f) corresponds to ____

(13) c **(14)** a **(15)** b **(16)** f **(17)** d **(18)** e

572 Under "followed by,"
    (19) (d,a) corresponds to ____
    (20) (d,b) corresponds to ____
    (21) (d,c) corresponds to ____
    (22) (d,d) corresponds to ____
    (23) (d,e) corresponds to ____
    (24) (d,f) corresponds to ____

(19) d **(20)** f **(21)** e **(22)** a **(23)** c **(24)** b

573 Under "followed by,"
    (25) (e,a) corresponds to ____
    (26) (e,b) corresponds to ____
    (27) (e,c) corresponds to ____
    (28) (e,d) corresponds to ____
    (29) (e,e) corresponds to ____
    (30) (e,f) corresponds to ____

(25) e **(26)** d **(27)** f **(28)** b **(29)** a **(30)** c

574 Under "followed by,"
    (31) (f,a) corresponds to ____
    (32) (f,b) corresponds to ____
    (33) (f,c) corresponds to ____
    (34) (f,d) corresponds to ____
    (35) (f,e) corresponds to ____
    (36) (f,f) corresponds to ____

(31) f **(32)** e **(33)** d **(34)** c **(35)** b **(36)** a

575 We have found that under "followed by," *every* element of $P \times P$ corresponds to exactly _____ (how many) element(s) of P.

one

576 Every element of $P \times P$ is a(n) _____ of permutations and corresponds to exactly *one* element of ____.

---

ordered pair, P

---

577 Let us represent the results of frames 569 to 574 pictorially. Let "followed by" be represented by α. Show the "followed by" relationship by drawing lines for (a,e), (a,f), (b,a), (b,b), and (b,c).

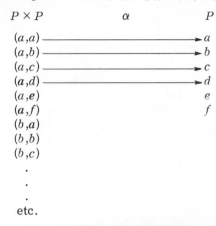

$$
\begin{array}{ccc}
P \times P & \alpha & P \\
(a,a) & \longrightarrow & a \\
(a,b) & \longrightarrow & b \\
(a,c) & \longrightarrow & c \\
(a,d) & \longrightarrow & d \\
(a,e) & & e \\
(a,f) & & f \\
(b,a) & & \\
(b,b) & & \\
(b,c) & & \\
\end{array}
$$

etc.

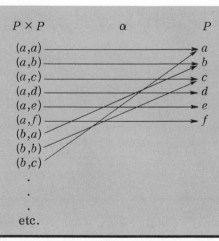

$$
\begin{array}{ccc}
P \times P & \alpha & P \\
(a,a) & & a \\
(a,b) & & b \\
(a,c) & & c \\
(a,d) & & d \\
(a,e) & & e \\
(a,f) & & f \\
(b,a) & & \\
(b,b) & & \\
(b,c) & & \\
\end{array}
$$

etc.

---

578 (From frame 577 we can see that α represents a function from _____ into ____ (actually onto).

$P \times P$, P

579 If we define $\alpha = \big\{((x,y),z) \mid (x,y) \in P \times P, \; z \in P,$ and under
                      "followed by," (x,y) corresponds to $z\big\}$, then α is
a binary relation in $(P \times P) \times P$ with
(1) dom $f =$ _____.
(2) for each $(x,y) \in$ dom α, there is _____ $z \in P$ such that
     $((x,y),z) \in \alpha$.

(1) $P \times P$ (2) exactly one

IV. Binary Operations on a Set

580 *Definition*: (1) Let S be a nonempty set. A function from _____
into ____ is called a *binary operation in* S.
(2) We have determined that α (the function defined by "followed
by") is a function from $P \times P$ into P. Therefore α is a(n)
_____.

(1) $S \times S, \qquad S$
(2) binary operation in P

581 Refer again to the results of frames 569 to 574. Recall our earlier
notation concerning images of an element under a function from S
into T.
(1) The image of (d,e) under α is c, so we write $\alpha(d,e) =$ ____.
(2) The _____ of (b,f) under α is d, so we write _____ $=$ ____.

(1) c (2) image, $\alpha(b,f) = d$

582 The image of (e,f), under α is ____, so we write _____.

$c, \qquad \alpha(e,f) = c$

•583 We read $\alpha(e,b) = d$ as: The _____ under α is d.

image of (e,b)

584 Let S be a nonempty set. A binary operation in S is a(n)
_____ from $S \times S$ into S.

mapping (or function)

585 Let S be a nonempty set. A(n) _____ from _____ into ____ is called a binary operation in S.

mapping (or function), $S \times S$, S

586 If f is a binary operation in S, then for every $(x,y) \in S \times S$ there is a unique $z \in S$ called the _____ of (x,y) under f and it is denoted by _____.

image, $f(x,y)$

587 If α is a(n) _____ in P which is determined by "followed by," the image of (a,b) under α is b, and it is denoted by ____ = b.

binary operation, $\alpha(a,b)$

588 It is customary to represent a binary operation in a nonempty set S by a special symbol ($*$, $\cdot$, $+$, $\circ$, etc.). Let $*$ be a binary operation in S, and the image of (x,y) under $*$ be z. Instead of writing $*(x,y) = z$, it is customary to write $x * y = $ ____. Let $\cdot$ represent the binary operation P which was determined by "followed by." Instead of writing $\cdot (b,c) = a$, we write _____.

z, $b \cdot c = a$

589 Consider the set S of integers and the process of addition. Under this process, for each $(x,y) \in S \times S$ there is associated a unique $z \in S$. In other words, this process defines a function, $+$, mapping _____ into ____.

$S \times S$, S

590 The image of $(3,2)$ under the mapping $+$ is 5. Instead of writing $+(3,2) = 5$, we write _____.

$3 + 2 = 5$

591 Let S be a nonempty set. A binary operation in S is a(n) _____ from _____.

mapping (or function), $S \times S$ into S

592   Thus, if * is a binary operation in a set S, for *every* ordered pair
      $(x, y) \in S \times S$ there exists a unique $z \in S$ such that _____ .

Any one of the following answers is correct:
z is the image of (x, y) under *, or $*(x, y) = z$, or $x * y = z$

593   If * is a binary operation in a set S, there is a(n) _____ $z \in S$
      such that $x * y = z$, for _____ ordered pair $(x, y) \in S \times S$.

unique,   every (or each)

594   Let $S = \{1, 2, 3, 4, 5\}$. Let us see if $(5, 1) \in S \times S$ can be mapped
      into S by ordinary addition.
      (1) $+(5, 1) =$ ____ (or $5 + 1 =$ ____).
      (2)   6 ____ ($\in$ or $\notin$) S.
      (3)   Therefore $(5, 1)$ _____ (can or cannot) be mapped into S.

(1)   6,   6   (2) $\notin$ (3)   cannot

595   Let $S = \{1, 2, 3, 4, 5\}$.
      (1)   Can $(4, 3)$ be mapped into S by ordinary addition?
      (2)   Show why or why not.

(1)   no
(2) $4 + 3 = 7$, $7 \notin S$. Therefore $(4, 3)$ cannot be mapped into S.

596   Let $S = \{1, 2, 3, 4, 5\}$.
      (1)   In order for + to be a binary operation in S, for every ordered
            pair $(x, y) \in$ ____ there must exist a unique $z \in$ ____ such that
            $x * y = z$.
      (2)   Is + a binary operation in S?

(1) $S \times S$, S (2)   no

•597   Let S be a nonempty set. A binary operation in S is a(n) _____ .

function (or mapping) of $S \times S$ into S

•598   Let S be a nonempty set. Let * be a binary operation in S.
      (1)   * is a mapping of ____ into ____.
      (2)   For _____ $(x, y) \in S \times S$ there exists a(n) _____ $z \in S$
            such that _____ .

▼

(3) dom $*$ = _____, ran $*$ _____

(4) If $*$ maps (x,y) into z, that is, if z is the image of (x,y) under $*$, we write _____.

---

(1) $S \times S$, S

(2) each (or every),   unique,
the image of (x,y) under $*$ is z (or $x * y = z$)

(3) $S \times S$, $\subset S$

(4) $x * y = z$

COMMENT

For finite sets, it is often instructive to construct a table showing the results of a binary operation. A table is a compact and clear way in which to show a great deal of information. Let us construct one for the binary operation $\cdot$ in P, the set of permutations of order 3. (Use your copy of this information from frames 569 to 574.)

Since $P = \{a, b, c, d, e, f\}$ has six elements, we begin by making the following drawing. Copy this drawing and save it.

$\cdot$	a	b	c	d	e	f
a						
b						
c						
d						
e						
f						

---

599 The $\cdot$ in the upper left-hand corner serves to identify the binary operation. (In this case the binary operation is defined by "followed by.") The six letters a through f correspond to the six elements of _____. The thirty-six spaces correspond to the thirty-six elements of _____.

P, $P \times P$

600   In this book, the row headings represent the first coordinate of the ordered pair. The column headings represent the (1) _____ of the ordered pair. (2)   Label the rows and the columns.

·	a	b	c	d	e	f
a						
b						
c						
d						
e						
f						

(1)   second coordinate
(2)

columns

rows→

·	a	b	c	d	e	f
a						
b						
c						
d						
e						
f						

601   (1)   The space at the intersection of row b and column d corresponds to the ordered pair ____.
      (2)   Using the results of frames 569 to 574, the image of that ordered pair is ____. Put the image into the space where row b and column d intersect.

(1) (b,d)
(2) e

·	a	b	c	d	e	f
a						
b				e		
c						
d						
e						
f						

602 Put the following images into the table.

$(a,b) = b$ $(e,e) = a$
$(b,f) = d$ $(f,c) = d$

·	a	b	c	d	e	f
a		b				
b						d
c						
d						
e					a	
f			d			

603 Using the results of frames 569 to 574, complete the table.

The answer is on Panel 7.

604 A binary operation in a nonempty set S is _____.

a function (or mapping) of $S \times S$ into S

605 * fails to be a binary operation in S if there exists even _____
$(x,y) \in S \times S$ which has no image under *. In this case * does not
map ____ into ____.

one, $S \times S$, S

606 If * does not map $S \times S$ into S, * _____ (can or cannot) be a
binary operation in some subset of S.

can
An example follows.

607 Let S be the set of real numbers.
Consider ordinary division ($\div$). Find an example of an element of
$S \times S$ having no image under $\div$, so that $\div$ is not a binary operation
in the set of real numbers.

$(1,0)$, $(0,0)$, $(\sqrt{3},0)$, etc. (any ordered pair from $S \times S$ having zero
as the second coordinate, since division by zero is not defined)

608   * fails to be a(n) _____ in S if there is even one
$(x,y) \in S \times S$ whose _____ under * is not an element of S. In
this case, * does not map $S \times S$ into S.

binary operation,   image

609   Let S be the set of real numbers. $\div$ does not map $S \times S$ into S.
Therefore $\div$ is not a binary operation in S.

Define S_1 (a subset of S) such that $\div$ will be a binary operation
in S_1.

Let S_1 be the set of real numbers excluding zero.

610   Let S be the set of *nonnegative* integers. Consider the operation of
ordinary subtraction $(-)$.
(1) $(5,7) \in S \times S$. Does $-(5,7)$ have an image in S under subtraction?
(2) $(9,2) \in S \times S$. Does $-(9,2)$ have an image in S under subtraction?
(3) $(10,11) \in S \times S$. Does $(10,11)$ have an image in S under subtraction?

(1)   no, $5 - 7 = -2$, $-2 \notin S$
(2)   yes, $9 - 2 = 7$, $7 \in S$
(3)   no, $10 - 11 = -1$, $-1 \notin S$

611   Let S be the set of *nonnegative* integers.
(1)   Under ordinary subtraction, any ordered pair $(a,b) \in S \times S$
with b _____ a will give a negative number.
(2)   Negative numbers are not included in the set ____.

(1) $>$ or "greater than"   (2) S

612   Is ordinary subtraction a binary operation in the set of nonnegative
integers?

no

613   * fails to be a binary operation in S if there is even _____
$(x,y) \in S \times S$ whose image under * is not an element of ____.

one, S

614 * fails to be a binary operation in S if, under *, there is even
_____ $(x,y) \in S \times S$ which is associated with *more than one* element of S. That is, the image must be *unique*.

one

615 For example, let S be the set of real numbers. Suppose we were to
try to define a binary operation * as follows:

* $(a,b) = c$ where c is a real number such that $c^2 = a^2 + b^2$.

(1) Consider (3,4). $(3)^2 + (4)^2 = (\pm 5)^2$. $c =$ ____ or $c =$ ____ .
(2) Since c is not unique, we do not have a(n) _____ .

(1) +5,   −5   (2) binary operation

•616 When deciding if * is a binary operation in S, we must ask these
questions:
(1) Does each _____ $(a,b) \in$ _____ have an image
under *?
(2) Is that image a(n) _____ of ____ ?
(3) Is that _____ unique?
(4) If the answer to any of these questions is no, * is not a(n)
_____ .

(1) ordered pair, $S \times S$
(2) element, S
(3) image
(4) binary operation in S

COMMENT

Many of the subsequent items concern well-known binary operations
in the set of real numbers. It is assumed that you are familiar with
properties of such binary operations, and you may use any such information whenever you wish. Thus, if you are asked whether ordinary multiplication in the set of real numbers R is a binary operation in R, the question is merely one of information. You are not
asked to prove it. On the other hand, if the answer to such a question is "No," you should exhibit a specific example showing why.

For example: Consider the set S of odd integers and ordinary addition (+). Is it a binary operation in S? The answer is "No."
Consider $(1,3) \in S \times S$, under +, (1,3) has no image in S.

In some of the other frames, new binary operations will be defined
in terms of familiar binary operations. For example, we might let
S be the set of integers and define: for each $(a,b) \in S \times S$, $a * b = 2ab$.

The expression on the right indicates ordinary multiplication. To show that $*$ is a binary operation in S you may appeal to all of the well-known facts about multiplication in the set of integers, *viz.*, that it is a binary operation in the set of integers and that $2ab$ is a unique element of S for every ordered pair of integers (a,b).

In the binary operation of multiplication, the symbol $\cdot$ is often omitted. Similarly, we will often omit the $\cdot$ signifying "followed by" in the set of permutations of degree N.

---

617   For a finite set with few elements, a table illustrating $*$ is helpful. If _____ space of the table can be filled, *in exactly one way*, with with an element of ____ , then you have demonstrated that $*$ is a(n) _____ in S, for you have essentially exhibited the mapping from $S \times S$ into S.

---

every (or each), S,   binary operation

---

618   For example: Show that ordinary multiplication is a binary operation in the set $\{1, -1\}$. Complete the table.

$\cdot$	1	-1
1	1	
-1	-1	

$\cdot$	1	-1
1	1	-1
-1	-1	1

---

619   (1)   Suppose _____ (how many) of the spaces of the table had not been filled by using $\cdot$ on $S \times S$.
         (2)   Suppose the spaces could have been filled by more than one element of ____ .
         (3)   Suppose any one of the entries had not been an element of ____ .
         (4)   If any of these conditions had existed, then $\cdot$ would not have been a(n) _____ in S.

---

         (1)   one
         (2) S
         (3) S
         (4)   binary operation

620 Let $S = \{A, B, C, D\}$ where $A = \phi$, $B = \{a\}$, $C = \{a, b\}$, $D = \{a, b, c\}$. Show that $\cup$ (union) *is* a binary operation in S by completing the following table.

$\cup$	A	B	C	D
A	A	B	C	D
B	B	B	C	D
C				
D				

$\cup$	A	B	C	D
A	A	B	C	D
B	B	B	C	D
C	C	C	C	D
D	D	D	D	D

621 Let $S = \{A, B, C, D\}$ where $A = \phi$, $B = \{a, b\}$, $C = \{b, c\}$, $D = \{c, d\}$. Show that $\cap$ (intersection) is not a binary operation in S. (Exhibit one $X \cap Y = \{x\}$ such that $\{x\} \notin S$.)

$B \cap C = \{b\}$, $C \cap D = \{c\}$
Neither $\{b\}$ nor $\{c\}$ is an element of S

622 Let $S = \{1, -1, i, -i\}$ under ordinary multiplication. Complete the table illustrating that ordinary multiplication is a binary operation in S. (Note $i = \sqrt{-1}$ and $i^2 = -1$)

$\cdot$	1	-1	i	$-i$
1	1	-1	i	$-i$
-1				
i				
$-i$				

$\cdot$	1	-1	i	$-i$
1	1	-1	i	$-i$
-1	-1	1	$-i$	i
i	i	$-i$	-1	1
$-i$	$-i$	i	1	-1

V. Properties of a Binary Operation

a. Commutative

---

623   Look at Panel 7.
    (1) $d \cdot c = e$. In other words, under the binary operation $\cdot$ (determined by "followed by"), the ordered pair _____ is mapped into ____.
    (2) $c \cdot d =$ ____ indicates that, under the binary operation $\cdot$, the ordered pair _____ is mapped into ____.

    (1) (d,c), e
    (2) f, (c,d), f

---

624   Let S be the set of integers. Consider the binary operation of ordinary subtraction $(-)$ in S.
    (1) The image of $(5,2)$ under $(-)$ is ____.
    (2) The image of $(2,5)$ under $(-)$ is ____.

    (1) 3   **(2)** -3

---

625   From frames 623 and 624 we see that, if $*$ is a binary operation on a set S, it need *not* be true that: $*(a,b) =$ _____ for every a and $b \in S$.

    $*(b,a)$

---

626   However, let S be the set of integers with respect to the binary operation of ordinary multiplication $(\cdot)$.
    (1) The image of $(5,3)$ under $\cdot$ is ____.
    (2) The image of $(3,5)$ under $\cdot$ is ____.
    (3) In this case: $a \cdot b =$ ____ for every a and $b \in S$.

    (1) 15
    (2) 15
    (3) $b \cdot a$

---

627 Let S be the set of integers with respect to the binary operation of ordinary addition.
(1) Is it true that $a + b = b + a$ for every a and $b \in S$?
(2) Cite an example.

(1) yes
(2) $9 + 5 = 14$ $(-3) + 10 = 7$
     $5 + 9 = 14$ $10 + (-3) = 7$
Any example that demonstrates the point will be considered correct.

628 Let $*$ be a binary operation on a set S. If $*$ indicates $(+)$, then $+(a,b) = +(b,a)$ for every $a, b \in S$. If $*$ indicates $(\cdot)$, then $\cdot(a,b)$ ____ for every $a, b \in S$.

$= \cdot(b,a)$

629 *Definition*: Let $*$ be a binary operation in a nonempty set S. Then $*$ is a *commutative binary operation in S* if and only if $a * b = b * a$ for every _____.

$a, b \in S$

630 Let $*$ be a binary operation in a nonempty set S. Then $*$ is a mapping of ____ into ____. To say that $*$ is *commutative* implies that the image of (x,y) under $*$ is the same element as the image of ____ under $*$ for every $x, Y \in S$. That is $*(x,y) = *(y,x)$ for every $x, y \in S$.

$S \times S$, S, (y,x)

631 From now on, instead of using the notation $*(x,y) = *(y,x)$ for every $x, y \in S$, we will use the more conventional notation, $x * y = $ _____.

$x * y = y * x$ for every $x, y \in S$

•632 Complete the following. A binary operation $*$ in a nonempty set S is called *commutative* if and only if ____ $=$ ____ for every _____.

$x * y = y * x$, $x, y \in S$

•633 Complete the following. A binary operation ∗ in a nonempty set
_____ (is or is not) commutative if there is at least one pair of
elements $x, y \in S$ such that _____ .

---

is not, $x ∗ y \neq y ∗ x$

---

634 Let S be the set of integers. Let · represent ordinary multiplication. From past experience, you know that $a \cdot b =$ ____ for every
$a, b \in S$. Therefore, ordinary multiplication is a(n) _____ binary
operation in the set of integers.

$b \cdot a$,   commutative

---

635 Let $S = \{a, b, c\}$. Look at the table.
(1) Is ∗ a binary operation in S?
(2) Is ∗ commutative? (Check all possibilities.) Why?

∗	a	b	c
a	b	a	c
b	a	b	b
c	c	a	b

---

(1) yes   **(2)** no, since $b ∗ c \neq c ∗ b$.

---

636 Consider S the set of *negative* integers under ordinary multiplication. Is this a binary operation in S? Why?

No; for example, $(-1, -2)$ has no image in S under ordinary multiplication.

---

637 Let S be the set of negative integers. Is ordinary addition a binary
operation in S? Why?

Yes, for every $a, b \in S$, $a + b$ is a unique element in S. Notice how
you are allowed to use past experience for a question of this type.

---

638 A variety of symbols is used to indicate arbitrary operations on
sets: +, ·, ×, ∗, ∘, etc. If the additive notation is used and we read
$a + b$ as "a plus b" and if a table is set up, we call the table an addition table. Let $S = \{0, 1, 2, 3\}$ have the table for + as follows:

▼

+	0	1	2	3
0	0	1	2	3
1	1	2	3	0
2	2	3	0	1
3	3	0	1	2

(1) Is + a binary operation in S? Why?

(2) Is + commutative? Why?

(1)   Yes, for each $a, b \in S$, $a + b$ is a unique element of S.

(2)   Yes, for each $a, b \in S$, $a + b = b + a$.

639 If the symbol $\cdot$ or $\times$ is used for a binary operation in a set S, $a \times b$, $a \cdot b$ is read "a times b"; and if a table is set up, the table is called a multiplication table. Consider the multiplication table for $S = \{0, 1, 2, 3\}$ as shown.

$\cdot$	0	1	2	3
0	0	0	0	0
1	0	1	2	3
2	0	2	0	2
3	0	3	2	1

(1) Is $\cdot$ a binary operation in S?

(2) Is $\cdot$ commutative?

(1) yes   **(2)** yes

640 If the symbols $*, \circ$, etc., are used for a binary operation in a set S, $a * b$, $a \circ b$, etc., is read "a operation b" or "a operating on b." Let $S = \{0, 1, 2, 3\}$ have a table for $*$ as given here.

$*$	0	1	2	3
0	0	1	2	3
1	1	2	3	4
2	2	3	4	5
3	3	4	5	6

Is $*$ a binary operation in S? Why?

No, it is not true that for all $a, b \in S$, $a * b$ is a unique element of S. For example, $3 * 2 = 5$; but $5 \notin S$.

641   Given a set S and a binary operation ∘ in S, if for all $a, b \in S$, $a \circ b = b \circ a$, the binary operation is _____.

---

commutative

---

642   The word "commute" means to move or to travel from one place to another. In $a * b$ and $b * a$ the elements have changed position or commuted. If $a * b = b * a$ for _____ pair $a, b \in S$, then the binary operation $*$ is _____.

---

every,   commutative

---

643   If a table showing a binary operation $*$ in a set S is constructed, commutativity of the operation will be exhibited by *symmetry about the diagonal* as shown here.

$*$	a	b	c
a	a		
b		a	
c			b

Notice that for all $x, y \in S$, $x * y$ and $y * x$ occupy symmetrically placed positions about the dotted diagonal line. Suppose the lower three spaces of the table are filled in as follows:

c
a b

If $*$ is to be commutative, how must the upper three spaces look?

---

c a
    b

---

644   Given a table for a binary operation $*$ in a set S, then, if the entries in the table are symmetric about the diagonal from upper left to lower right, the binary operation is _____ and conversely. If the table is not symmetric about that diagonal, the binary operation is _____ and conversely.

---

commutative,   not commutative

645   Is the binary operation in S shown below commutative?

*	0	1	2
0	1	0	1
1	0	1	2
2	1	2	0

yes

646   Let us construct some new binary operations in the set S of integers. For example, suppose we define for all $x, y \in S$,
$x * y = (2 \cdot x) + y$ where $\cdot$ and $+$ represent ordinary multiplication
and addition respectively.
Thus: $3 * 5 = (2 \cdot 3) + 5$
      $3 * 5 = 11$
In this manner every ordered pair of integers $(x, y) \in$ _____ will be
mapped by $*$ into a(n) _____ element of ___. Note that we have
relied on past experience to assure ourselves that $(2 \cdot x) + y$ is a
unique element of S for each $a, b \in S$.

$S \times S$,   unique, S

647   From frame 646: S is the set of integers and a binary operation $*$
was defined by: for all $x, y \in S$, $x * y = (2 \cdot x) + y$.
Thus, $4 * 3 = (2 \cdot 4) + 3$
      So $4 * 3 = 11$
Similarly, $3 * 4 =$ _____
      So $3 * 4 =$ _____

$(2 \cdot 3) + 4$,   10

648   In frame 647 we found that $3 * 4 \neq 4 * 3$. Therefore $*$ is not a(n)
_____ binary operation in S.

commutative

649   Let S be the set of integers and $x * y = (x \cdot y) + 3$, where $\cdot$ and $+$
are ordinary multiplication and addition, respectively. For example:
(1) $2 * 4 =$ _____
(2) $2 * 4 =$ _____
Similarly,
(3) $4 * 2 =$ _____
(4) $4 * 2 =$ _____

▼

We know that $\cdot$ and $+$ are binary operations in S, so for every $x, y \in S$, $(x \cdot y) + 3$ is a unique element of S.

(1) $(2 \cdot 4) + 3$ (2) 11
(3) $(4 \cdot 2) + 3$ (4) 11

650   From frame 649: S is the set of integers, and for all $x, y \in S$, a binary operation $*$ was defined by $x * y = (x \cdot y) + 3$.
Note: $x * y = (x \cdot y) + 3$
   $y * x = (y \cdot x) + 3$
From previous experience, we know that ordinary multiplication is a commutative binary operation in S, so $(x \cdot y) + 3 = (y \cdot x) + 3$. Hence $x * y = y * x$ for all _____. Thus $*$ is a(n) _____ binary operation in S.

$x, y \in S$,   commutative

651   Let S be the set of integers. Define $*$ as follows: For all $x, y \in S$, $x * y = x^2 + y^2$, where $+$ represents ordinary addition. Thus, $3 * (-2) =$ _____ .

$3^2 + (-2)^2 = 9 + 4 = 13$

652   From frame 651: $x * y = x^2 + y^2$ for all $x, y \in S$, where S is the set of integers, then
   $x * y = x^2 + y^2$
and $y * x = (1)$ _____.
In the set of integers, ordinary addition is a commutative binary operation, so $x^2 + y^2 = y^2 + x^2$. $\therefore x * y = y * x$ for all $x, y \in S$.
(2) Thus, $*$ is a(n) _____ in S.

(1) $y^2 + x^2$
(2) commutative binary operation

•653   Let S be the set of integers. Define $*$ as follows: $x * y = x + (2 \cdot y)$ for every $x, y \in S$, where $+$ and $\cdot$ indicate ordinary addition and multiplication in S.

Since $+$ and $\cdot$ *are* binary operations in S, $x + (2 \cdot y)$ is a unique element of S for every $x, y \in S$. Thus, $*$ is a binary operation in S.

▼

Prove that * is not commutative. (You need only exhibit a single counterexample to the definition of commutativity.)

One example would be:
5 * 3 = 5 + (2 · 3) = 11
3 * 5 = 3 + (2 · 5) = 13
∴ 5 * 3 ≠ 3 * 5

•654 Let S be the set of integers, and define $x * y = 2 \cdot x \cdot y$, for all $x, y \in S$, where · indicates ordinary multiplication.

Since we know that · is a binary operation in S and $2 \cdot x \cdot y$ is a unique element of S for every $x, y \in S$, * is a binary operation in S.

Show that * is commutative.

Let $x, y \in S$ $x * y = 2 \cdot x \cdot y$
            $y * x = 2 \cdot y \cdot x$
· is a commutative binary operation in S, so $2xy = 2yx$.
∴ $x * y = y * x$ for all $x, y \in S$
So * is commutative.

•655 Given a binary operation * in a nonempty set S, * is commutative if and only if _____.

$a * b = b * a$ for all $a, b \in S$

b. Associative

656 Let * be a binary operation in a nonempty set S. An expression such as $x * y * z$ has no meaning since *, as a mapping of $S \times S$ into S, applies to _____, not to triples. The expression $(x * y) * z$ does have meaning when the grouping symbols are interpreted in the usual manner, that is, that the $x * y$ represents the image of (x, y) under *. Thus, the expression in parentheses is a(n) _____ element of S, say a, and thus $(x * y) * z = a * z$.

ordered pairs,   unique

657 Similarly, in $x * (y * z)$, the expression in parentheses is the image of (y, z) under *, say b, so $x * (y * z) = $ ____.

$x * b$

658   There is no guarantee, from our information to this point, that
        $x * (y * z) = ($ ____ $)$ ____ .

$(x * y) * z$

---

659   Let $S = \{a, b, c, d\}$ have a binary operation $*$ shown below.

*	a	b	c	d
a	a	b	c	d
b	b	a	c	d
c	c	d	a	b
d	d	c	b	a

Note: From the table $(c * b) * d = d * d = a$, and
        $c * (b * d) = $ _____ .

$c * d = b$
In this example $(c * b) * d \neq c * (b * d)$

---

660   *Definition*: Given a nonempty set S and a binary operation $*$ in S,
        if $x * (y * z) = (x * y) * z$ for all $x, y, z \in S$, then the binary opera-
        tion $*$ is *associative*. In frame 659, we found that for c, b, and d,
        $c * (b * d) \neq (c * b) * d$, so the binary operation of that example
        _____ (is or is not) *associative*.

---

is not

---

661   The word "associate" is descriptive. In $(x * y) * z$ the elements x
        and y are associated first, and the resulting element operates on z.
        In $x * (y * z)$, y and z are associated and the resulting element is
        operated on by ____. If a binary operation $\cdot$ is associative, it makes
        no difference which of the two associations is made, $(x \cdot y) \cdot z$ or
        $x \cdot (y \cdot z)$.

---

x

---

662   Let S be the set of integers and the binary operation in S be sub-
        traction. Consider, for example, $5, 3, 1 \in S$.
        (1) $5 - (3 - 1) = $ ____
        (2) $(5 - 3) - 1 = $ ____
        (3) Therefore subtraction in S is _____ .

---

(1) 3   (2) 1   (3) not associative

663 Let S be the set of integers and the binary operation be multiplication. From previous experience, you know that $(x \cdot y) \cdot z = x \cdot (y \cdot z)$, for all $x, y, z \in S$; therefore multiplication of integers is _____.

associative

COMMENT

We mentioned previously that the expression $x * y * z$ has no meaning in a set having a binary operation $*$. However, if $*$ is *associative*, we adopt the convention that $x * y * z = (x * y) * z$ or $x * (y * z)$. Since $*$ is associative, no ambiguity results; that is, either interpretation of $x * y * z$ gives the same result.

If $*$ is not associative in S, we can still give meaning to the expression $x * y * z$ by agreeing that it always means $(x * y) * z$. This is often done in the operation of subtraction in the set of real numbers. It is understood that $8 - 3 - 5 = (8 - 3) - 5$ and *not* $8 - (3 - 5)$.

664 Complete the following: A binary operation $*$ in a set S is *associative* if and only if _____ for all _____.

$(x * y) * z = x * (y * z)$
$x, y, z \in S$

•665 Let $S = \{a, b\}$ with a binary operation $+$ given below:

+	a	b
a	a	b
b	b	a

Is $+$ a commutative binary operation?

yes

•666 Let S be a set with a binary operation $+$. If for all $a, b \in S$, $a + b = b + a$, then the binary operation is _____.

commutative

•667   Let S be a set with a binary operation +. If for all a, b $c \in S$, $a + (b + c) = (a + b) + c$, then the binary operation is _____.

associative

668   Let S be the set of integers and define $x * y = (2x) + y$ for all $x, y \in S$. $*$ is a binary operation in S. Consider $(3 * 2) * 5$. The parentheses indicate that the image of $(3,2)$ under $*$ is to operate on 5 by $*$. First we find $3 * 2$ as follows:

$x = 3$ $y = 2$

Substitute in definition of $*$:
   $x * y = (2x) + y$
   $3 * 2 = (2 \cdot 3) + 2$
so $3 * 2 =$ _____
Then $(3 * 2) * 5 = 8 * 5$
      $(3 * 2) * 5 = (2 \cdot 8) + 5$
      $(3 * 2) * 5 =$ _____

8,   21

669   Let S be the set of integers and define $x * y = 2x + y$ for all $x, y \in S$. Consider $(1 * 3) * 4$. First find the image of $(1 * 3)$:
$1 * 3 = (2x) + y$
(1) $1 * 3 =$ _____
Then $(1 * 3) * 4 = 5 * 4$
      $(1 * 3) * 4 = (2x + y)$
(2) $(1 * 3) * 4 =$ _____

(1) $1 * 3 = (2 \cdot 1) + 3 = 5$ (2) $(1 * 3) * 4 = (2 \cdot 5) + 4 = 14$
      $1 * 3 = 5$ $(1 * 3) * 4 = 14$

670   Again let S be the set of integers and for all $x, y \in S$, $x * y = (2x) + y$. $3 * (2 * 5)$ means to let 3 operate on the image of $2 * 5$.
First we find $2 * 5 = (2 \cdot 2) + 5$
              $2 * 5 = 9$
Then $3 * (2 * 5) = 3 * 9$
         $3 * (2 * 5) = (2 \cdot 3) + 9$
         $3 * (2 * 5) = 15$
Find $1 * (3 * 4)$.

         $3 * 4 = (2 \cdot 3) + 4$
         $3 * 4 = 10$
Then $1 * (3 * 4) = 1 * 10$
     $1 * (3 * 4) = (2 \cdot 1) + 10$
     $1 * (3 * 4) = 12$

671 Using the binary operation ∗ of frames 669 and 670, we found that
     $(1 ∗ 3) ∗ 4 = 14$ and $1 ∗ (3 ∗ 4) = 12$. ∴$(1 ∗ 3) ∗ 4 ≠ 1 ∗ (3 ∗ 4)$. So ∗
     is not a(n) _____ binary operation in S.

---

associative

•672 So far we have two properties descriptive of a binary operation ∗ in
     a set S.
     (1) ∗ is commutative if and only if _____.
     (2) ∗ is associative if and only if _____.

---

(1) $a ∗ b = b ∗ a$ for all $a, b ∈ S$
(2) $(a ∗ b) ∗ c = a ∗ (b ∗ c)$ for all $a, b, c ∈ S$

---

673 The binary operation + in the set S of real numbers is commutative
     since _____.

---

for all $a, b ∈ S, a + b = b + a$

---

674 The binary operation + in the set S of real numbers is associative
     since _____.

---

for all $a, b, c ∈ S, a + (b + c) = (a + b) + c$

---

675 Let S be the set of rational numbers. Let $x ∗ y = 2 · x · y$ for all
     $x, y ∈ S$, where · represents ordinary multiplication. Copy this in-
     formation and save it for frames 676 to 680.

You should have a correct copy of the information from frame 675.

---

676 Ordinary multiplication is a binary operation in the set of rational
     numbers, so for each $x, y ∈ S$, $2xy$ is a(n) _____ element of S.
     Thus, for each $x, y ∈ S$, $x ∗ y$ is a unique element of S, so ∗ is
     a(n) _____ in S.

---

unique,   binary operation

---

677 Find $3 ∗ \frac{2}{3}$, using the binary operation of frames 675 and 676.

Substituting $x = 3$ and $y = \frac{2}{3}$ in the definition of ∗, we find
$3 ∗ \frac{2}{3} = 2 · 3 · \frac{2}{3} = 6 · \frac{2}{3} = 4$.

678   Find $\frac{2}{3} * (\frac{-5}{7})$, using the $*$ of frame 675.

$$\frac{2}{3} * (\frac{-5}{7}) = 2 \cdot \frac{2}{3} \cdot (-\frac{5}{7}) = -\frac{20}{21}$$

679   Prove that $*$ is commutative. Let $x, y \in S$. $x * y = 2xy$.

$x * y = 2 \cdot x \cdot y$
$y * x = 2 \cdot y \cdot x$
$\cdot$ is a commutative binary operation in the set of rational numbers, and $2 \cdot x \cdot y = 2 \cdot y \cdot x$. Therefore $x * y = y * x$ for all $x, y \in S$. Therefore $*$ is commutative.

680   Prove that $*$ is associative. Let $x, y, z \in S$.
     $(x * y) * z = (2xy) * z = 2 \cdot (2xy) \cdot z = 4xyz$
(1) $x * (y * z) = x * (2yz) = $ _____
(2) $(x * y) * z = $ _____, so $*$ is associative.

(1) $2 \cdot x(2yz) = 4xyz$
(2) $x * (y * z)$ for all $x, y, z \in S$

681   Let S be the set of rational numbers and define $x \oplus y = x + (2 \cdot y)$ for all $x, y \in S$. The $+$ and $\cdot$ indicate ordinary additional and multiplication.) Copy this information and save it for frames 682 to 684. Find $\frac{3}{5} \oplus 7$.

Using $x = \frac{3}{5}$ and $y = 7$ in the definition,
$\frac{3}{5} \oplus 7 = \frac{3}{5} + (2 \cdot 7) = \frac{3}{5} + \frac{70}{5} = \frac{73}{5}$

682   Since $+$ and $\cdot$ are binary operations in S, then for each $x, y \in S$, $x + (2 \cdot y)$ is a(n) _____ element in S. Thus for each $x, y \in S$, $x \oplus y$ is a unique element in S, so $\oplus$ is a(n) _____ in ____.

unique,   binary operation, S

683   Prove that $\oplus$ is not commutative. You need to produce one counter-example.

One example would be:
$3 \oplus 4 = 3 + (2 \cdot 4) = 11$
$4 \oplus 3 = 4 + (2 \cdot 3) = 14$
$\therefore 3 \oplus 2 \neq 2 \oplus 3$, so $\oplus$ is not commutative

684   Prove that $\oplus$ is not associative. You need to produce one counter-example.

$3 \oplus (4 \oplus 5) = 3 \oplus [4 + (2 \cdot 5)]$
$\qquad\qquad\quad = 3 \oplus 14 = 3 + (2 \cdot 14) = 31$
$(3 \oplus 4) \oplus 5 = [3 + (2 \cdot 4)] \oplus 5$
$\qquad\qquad\quad = 11 \oplus 5 = 11 + (2 \cdot 5) = 21$
$\therefore 3 \oplus (4 \oplus 5) \neq (3 \oplus 4) \oplus 5$, so $\oplus$ is not associative

c. Identity Element

685   Sometimes, given a binary operation $*$ in a set S, there is a peculiar element in S which "has no effect" when operating on or operated on by any element in S. For example, in the binary operation $+$ in the set of real numbers for any real number x, $x + \underline{\quad} = x$ and $\underline{\quad} + x = x$.

0,   0

686   Given a set S with a binary operation $\circ$, if there exists an element of S, say e, such that for every $x \in S$, $x \circ e = x$ and $e \circ x = x$, then e is called a *unit* or *identity element* with respect to that operation in S. For example, let S be the set of integers with respect to addition. Consider the element $0 \in S$. For every integer, p, $p + 0 = p$ and $0 + p = p$. Therefore 0 is a(n) _____ element with respect to addition in the set of integers.

unit or identity

687   We will prove shortly that there can be, at most, one identity element with respect to a binary operation in a set S. Thus, if there is an identity element, we will call it *the* identity element with respect to that operation. Let S be the set of integers with respect to multiplication. For every $x \in S$, $x \cdot 1 = x$ and $1 \cdot x = x$. Therefore 1 is the _____ with respect to multiplication of integers.

identity element

688   The unit or identity element with respect to a binary operation, say $*$, in a set S is sometimes called the neutral element. When it operates on (or is operated on by) any element a of S, you get a as a result; roughly speaking, it does nothing to a. For example, consider

▼

the set S of rational numbers with respect to multiplication. The identity element is 1 since if a is any rational number, $a \cdot 1 = 1 \cdot a =$ ____.

a

•689 Let S be a set having a binary operation *. An element $e \in S$ is called an identity element with respect to * if and only if _____ and _____ for _____ $x \in S$.

$e * x = x,$ $x * e = x,$ each (or every)

690 Let $S = \{a, b, c, d\}$ have a binary operation *. Suppose S has an identity element with respect to *, and suppose it is b. Fill in the row labeled b and the column labeled b of the table.

*	a	b	c	d
a				
b				
c				
d				

*	a	b	c	d
a		a		
b	a	b	c	d
c		c		
d		d		

For a finite set in which a table is given, this pattern indicates the simplest way to find an identity element, if it exists.

691 Let $S = \{a, b, c\}$ have a binary operation * defined in the table below:

*	a	b	c
a	c	a	b
b	a	b	c
c	b	c	c

Note from the table: $b * a = a$ and $a * b = a$
$b * b = b$ and $b * b = b$
$b * c = c$ and $c * b = c$
Therefore ____ is the *identity* for the binary operation * in S.

b

692 Let $S = \{0, 1\}$ have a binary operation + as shown below.

+	0	1
0	0	0
1	0	1

Note that $0 + 0 = 0$ and $0 + 1 = 0$
$1 + 0 = 0$ and $1 + 1 = 1$
Therefore for every $x \in S$, $1 + x = x + 1 = x$. Therefore ____ is the
identity element in this frame.

1

693 Look at Panel 7. Does S have an identity element with respect to
permutation multiplication? If so, which element is it?

Yes, a, since for all $x \in S$, $a \cdot x = x \cdot a = x$.

694 Let S be the set of even integers and consider the binary operation
addition. Does S have an identity element with respect to addition?
If so, what is it?

Yes, 0
Note: 0 is an even integer.

695 Let set $S = \{A, B, C\}$, where $A = \phi$, $B = \{1, 2\}$,
$C = \{1, 2, 3\}$. Complete the table showing the operation $\cup$ (union) in S. Save the completed table.

	A	B	C
A	A	B	C
B	B		
C			

$\cup$	A	B	C
A	A	B	C
B	B	B	C
C	C	C	C

696 From the table you have constructed, is $\cup$ a binary operation in S?

Yes, for all $X, Y \in S$, $X \cup Y$ is a unique element of S.

697   From the table you have constructed, is $\cup$ a commutative binary operation in S?

Yes, $X \cup Y = Y \cup X$ for all $x, y \in S$.

698   From the table, does S have an identity element with respect to $\cup$? If so, what is it?

Yes, A (or ϕ), since $\phi \cup X = X$ and $X \cup \phi = X$ for all $X \in S$.

699   Let $S = \{A, B, C, D\}$ where $A = \phi$, $B = \{a, b\}$, $C = \{a, b, c\}$, $D = \{c\}$.
Note: $A \cap B = A$
        $D \cap C = D$
        $B \cap C = B$
        etc.
Set up a table showing the operation $\cap$ in S and save it.

$\cap$	A	B	C	D
A	A	A	A	A
B	A	B	B	A
C	A	B	C	D
D	A	A	D	D

700   From the table, is $\cap$ a binary operation in S?

yes

701   From the table, is $\cap$ commutative in S?

yes
Note the symmetry around the diagonal.

702   From the table, is there an identity element for $\cap$ in S? If so, what is it?

yes, since C, $X \cap C = X$ and $C \cap X = X$ for all $x \in S$.

703   A set S can have at most one identity element with respect to a binary operation.
Proof: Suppose S contains two identity elements, say e_1 and e_2, with respect to a binary operation $*$. Then $e_1 * x = x * e_1 = x$ and $e_2 * x = x * e_2 = x$ for all $x \in S$.
Now consider $e_1 * e_2$. If e_1 is thought of as an identity element, $e_1 * e_2 = e_2$. If e_2 is thought of as an identity element, $e_1 * e_2 = $ ____.
Therefore we would have $e_2 = $ ____.

$e_1, \quad e_1$

704   Since a set can have at most one identity element with respect to a binary operation $*$, we refer to it (if it exists) as *the* identity element with respect to that binary operation. What is the identity element with respect to addition in the set of even integers?

0

705   The proof of the existence of at most one identity element with respect to a binary operation in a set S might be simpler to understand if we consider the following example. Let $S = \{a, b, c, d\}$ and suppose we try to define a binary operation $*$ in S by setting up a table showing $*$. Moreover, suppose we wish b to be an identity element with respect to $*$. Then part of the table is determined. Now suppose we wish also that d be an identity element. Where would you run into difficulty in filling in the table?

$*$	a	b	c	d
a		a		
b	a	b	c	d
c		c		
d		d		

We would need $d * b = b$ and $b * d = b$, but these spaces are already filled by d.

706   Thus, if a set has an identity element with respect to a certain binary operation, it is unique. Does this set have an identity element with respect to this operation? If so, what is it?

$\cdot$	0	1
0	0	1
1	1	0

yes, 0

•707   Let S be a set with a binary operation ($\cdot$).
(1)   If for all $x, y \in S$, $x \cdot y = y \cdot x$, then the binary operation is

_____.

▼

(2)   If for all $x, y, z \in S$, $x \cdot (y \cdot z) = (x \cdot y) \cdot z$, then the binary operation is _____.

(3)   If there exists an element, say $e \in S$, such that for every $x \in S$, $x \cdot e = e \cdot x = x$, then e is called the _____ with respect to that binary operation.

(1)   commutative   (2)   associative
(3)   identity, unit, or neutral element

708   Let $S = \{a, b, c\}$ have a binary operation $*$ as given in the table.
(1)   Is $*$ commutative?
(2)   Is $*$ associative?
(3)   Does $*$ have an identity element? If so, what is it?

$*$	a	b	c
a	b	c	a
b	a	b	c
c	c	a	b

(1)   no, for example, $a * b \neq b * a$
(2)   no, for example, $a * (b * c) \neq (a * b) * c$
(3)   no

709   Let S be the set of rational numbers and define $x * y = 2xy$. We proved earlier that $*$ is a *commutative* and *associative* binary operation in S. Prove that $\frac{1}{2}$ is the identity element with respect to the binary operation $*$.

Let $x \in S$. $\frac{1}{2} * x = 2 \cdot \frac{1}{2} \cdot x = x$
$\qquad\qquad x * \frac{1}{2} = 2 \cdot x \cdot \frac{1}{2} = x$
Thus $\frac{1}{2} * x = x$ and $x * \frac{1}{2} = x$ for all $x \in S$, so $\frac{1}{2}$ is the identity element with respect to $*$.

Self-test V (Answers to Self-test V appear on page 314)

1   Complete the definition: Let S be a nonempty set. A binary operation in S is a(n) _____.

2   Complete the definition: A binary operation $*$ is commutative if and only if _____.

3   Let $*$ be a binary operation in S. Then $*$ is associative if and only if _____.

4   Let $*$ be a binary operation in S. If there exists an element $e \in S$ such that _____, then e is called the identity element with respect to $*$.

5 (1) Addition (+) _____ (is or is not) a binary operation in the
       set of integers.
  (2) Moreover + _____ (is or is not) commutative, and
  (3) + _____ (is or is not) associative in the set of integers.
  (4) Does there exist an identity element with respect to + in the
       set of integers? If so, what is it?

6 Consider the set of integers under ordinary multiplication ($\cdot$).
  (1) Is $\cdot$ a binary operation in the set of integers?
  (2) Is $\cdot$ commutative?
  (3) Is $\cdot$ associative?
  (4) Does there exist an identity element with respect to $\cdot$? If so,
       what is it?

7 Consider ordinary division ($\div$) in the set of integers. Is $\div$ a binary
  operation in the set of integers?

8 Let S be the set of rational numbers. Is ordinary division a binary
  operation in this set?

9 Let S be the set of *negative integers*. (1) Is ordinary addition a
  binary operation in S? (2) If so, does there exist an identity element in S under +?

10 Let S be the collection of all subsets of $\{a, b, c\}$. (You may want to
   set up at least a partial table for $\cup$ to help you.)
   (1) Is $\cup$ (union) a binary operation in S?
   (2) Is $\cup$ commutative?
   (3) Is $\cup$ associative?
   (4) Does there exist an identity element with respect to $\cup$ in S?
        If so, what is it?

d. Inverse

710 Look at Panel 7. The identity element with respect to $\cdot$ is a. Look
     closely and you will discover that, for *each* $x \in S$, there is a unique
     $y \in S$ such that $x \cdot y = a$ and $y \cdot x = a$. For example, consider c.
     You find that b is such an element since $c \cdot b = a$ and $b \cdot c = a$.
     Similarly, for f, $f \cdot$ ____ $= a$ and ____ $\cdot f = a$.

$f,$ f

711   Similarly, let S be the set of integers under the binary operation addition. The identity element with respect to addition is zero, and for every integer x, there is a $y \in S$ such that $x + y = 0$ and $y + x = 0$. For example, consider $-3 \in S$. $-3 + $ ____ $= 0$ and ____ $+ (-3) = 0$.

     3,   3

712   Similarly, let S be the set of *nonzero* rational numbers. 1 is the identity element with respect to multiplication, and for every $x \in S$ there is a $y \in S$ such that $x \cdot y = 1$ and $y \cdot x = 1$. For example, $(-\frac{3}{8}) \cdot$ ____ $= 1$ and ____ $\cdot (-\frac{3}{8}) = 1$.

     $-\frac{8}{3}$, $-\frac{8}{3}$

713   *Definition*: Given a set S having a binary operation $*$ with an identity element e, if $x \in S$ and there exists an element $y \in S$ such that $x * y = y * x = e$, then y *is an inverse of x* under $*$. For example, let S be the set of integers with respect to addition. The identity element is (1) ____. An inverse of 5 is -5 since $5 + (-5) = (-5) + 5 = 0$. An inverse of -3 is (2) ____ since (3) _____.

     (1)   0   **(2)**   3   **(3)** $(-3) + 3 = 3 + (-3) = 0$

714   Similarly, consider the set of rational numbers with respect to multiplication. The identity element is 1. An inverse of -3 with respect to multiplication is ____ since $-3 \cdot$ ____ $= 1$ and ____ $\cdot (-3) = 1$.

     $-\frac{1}{3}$, $-\frac{1}{3}$, $-\frac{1}{3}$

715   Note, then, that an inverse of x with respect to some binary operation having an identity element is an element which, when operating on x or operated on by x, will "give back" the identity element of that operation. Thus, in the set of rational numbers, an inverse of $\frac{1}{3}$ with respect to multiplication is 3 because $3 \cdot \frac{1}{3} = 1$ and $\frac{1}{3} \cdot 3 = 1$. An inverse of $\frac{1}{3}$ with respect to addition is ____ since _____.

     $-\frac{1}{3}$, $\frac{1}{3} + (-\frac{1}{3}) = 0$ and $(-\frac{1}{3}) + \frac{1}{3} = 0$

716 Let S be the set of *integers*.
  (1) Find in S, if it exists, an inverse of 7 with respect to addition.
  (2) Find in S, if it exists, an inverse of 7 with respect to multiplication.

(1) -7 (2) There is none in S.
Note: $\frac{1}{7}$ is not an element of S.

717 Let S be the set of rational numbers. An inverse of 7 with respect to multiplication is ____ since _____.

$\frac{1}{7}$, $7 \cdot \frac{1}{7} = 1$ and $\frac{1}{7} \cdot 7 = 1$

718 *Note*: If you wish to find an inverse of some $x \in S$ with respect to a binary operation $*$, you must first find, if it exists, the identity element with respect to $*$. Suppose the identity element with respect to $*$ is j. Now, an inverse of x under $*$, if it exists, is some $y \in S$ such that _____.

$x * y = j$ and $y * x = j$

719 For example, consider the multiplication table shown here. The question "find an inverse of b" makes sense if there is an identity element with respect to binary operation.

$*$	a	b	c
a	a	b	c
b	b	c	a
c	c	a	b

  (1) Look at the table and you see that for all $x \in S$, $x *$ ____ $= x$ and ____ $* x = x$, so ____ is the identity element with respect to binary operation.
  (2) Find, from the table, an inverse of b with respect to $*$

(1) a, a, a
(2) c, since $b * c = c * b = a$

720 Let S be the set of real numbers. The identity element with respect to multiplication is 1. 0 has no inverse with respect to multiplication since there is no $x \in S$ such that _____.

$0 \cdot x = 1$ and $x \cdot 0 = 1$

721   Let S be the set of real numbers. For all $x \neq 0$, an inverse of x with respect to multiplication is $\dfrac{1}{x}$ since _____ .

$x \cdot \dfrac{1}{x} = 1, \dfrac{1}{x} \cdot x = 1$
Note: $x \neq 0$.

---

722   If multiplicative symbolism is used, an inverse of an element x is usually denoted by x^{-1}. Thus, if x is an element of a set S having a binary operation $\cdot$ and an identity element e, an inverse of x is an element $x^{-1} \in S$ such that

·	a	b	c
a	a	b	c
b	b	c	a
c	c	a	b

$x \cdot x^{-1} = x^{-1} \cdot x = e$. In the operation shown in the table, the identity element is a. An inverse of c is b since $c \cdot b = b \cdot c = a$, so we write $c^{-1} = b$. An inverse of b is ____ since $b \cdot$ ____ $=$ ____ $\cdot b = a$, so we write _____ .

$c, \quad c, \quad c,$
$b^{-1} = c$

---

723   Look at Panel 6. The identity element is R_1. Consider R_{10}.

$R_{10} \cdot R_{19} = R_{19} \cdot R_{10} = R_1$

Therefore $(R_{10})^{-1} = $ ____ .

R_{19}

---

724   Let $S = \{1, -1, i, -i\}$ under ordinary multiplication. The identity element is 1, since $1 \cdot 1 = 1 \cdot 1 = 1$, $1^{-1} = 1$; since $(-1)(-1) = (-1)(-1) = 1$, $(-1)^{-1} = -1$; since i ____ $=$ ____ $i = $ ____ , $i^{-1} = $ ____ .

·	1	−1	i	−i
1	1	−1	i	−i
−1	−1	1	−i	i
i	i	−i	−1	1
−i	−i	i	1	−1

$-i, \quad -i, \quad 1, \quad -i$

725 Let S be the set of rational numbers with respect to multiplication. The identity element is 1. An inverse of 7, written 7^{-1}, is $\frac{1}{7}$ since $7 \cdot \frac{1}{7} = \frac{1}{7} \cdot 7 = 1$.
(1) Find 13^{-1}.
(2) Find $(-5)^{-1}$.
(3) Find 0^{-1}.

(1) $\frac{1}{13}$ (2) $\frac{-1}{5}$ (3) There is none.

726 Recall that the identity element with respect to a binary operation $*$ on a set is a unique element. There is only one identity element with respect to the binary operation $*$ in S. For example, the identity element with respect to addition of rational numbers is ____.

0

727 There is only one identity element with respect to a binary operation $*$ in a set S. In the examples thus far, note that each element has its own inverse with respect to $*$. There is not just one inverse for the set. For example, let S be the set of rational numbers with respect to multiplication. The identity element is 1 since for all $x \in S$, $x \cdot 1 = 1 \cdot x = x$. However, there is no single inverse which works for all elements.

$(\frac{3}{8})^{-1} = \frac{8}{3}$ since $\frac{3}{8} \cdot \frac{8}{3} = \frac{8}{3} \cdot \frac{3}{8} = 1$ $(5)^{-1} = \frac{1}{5}$ since $5 \cdot \frac{1}{5} = \frac{1}{5} \cdot 5 = 1$

An inverse of $(-\frac{2}{3})$ is ____ since _____ = _____ = ___.

$(-\frac{3}{2})$, $(-\frac{2}{3}) \cdot (-\frac{3}{2})$, $(-\frac{3}{2}) \cdot (-\frac{2}{3})$,   1

728 In frame 729, we will prove that, in a set S having an *associative* binary operation $*$, if an element has an inverse with respect to $*$, then that inverse is unique. In other words, we will show that:
(1) If $*$ is a(n) _____ binary operation in S and
(2) y and z are the inverses of x with respect to $*$, then y = ____.

(1) associative   (2) z

729 Given a set S having an associative binary operation $*$ and an identity element e with respect to $*$, an inverse of $x \in S$ is unique. Proof: suppose both $y, z \in S$ are inverses of x with respect to $*$, i.e., $x * y = y * x = e$ and $x * z = z * x = e$. We wish to prove that $y = z$.

▼

Since $x * y = e$ and $x * z = e$, then $x * y = x * z$. Operating by y, we get $y * (x * y) = y * (x * z)$. Because $*$ is associative, $(y * x) * y = (y * x) * z$. But y is an inverse of x, so $e * y = e * z$.

Since e is the identity element with respect to $*$, then ____.

$y = z$

---

730   Suppose a set S has a binary operation $*$. Let $x \in S$. Suppose that $*$ is associative. "Does x have an inverse with respect to $*$, and if so, what is it?" This question has *no* meaning *unless there is a(n)* _____ e *with respect to* $*$. This is true because an inverse of x with respect to $*$ is defined in terms of the identity element.

---

identity element

---

731   For example: Let S be the set of even integers with respect to multiplication ($\cdot$).
(1)   Multiplication is a(n) _____ in this set, since for any two even integers x, y the product $x \cdot y$ is a(n) _____ element of S.
(2)   Moreover, $\cdot$ is _____ and associative in S.
(3)   The question "Find an inverse of 8 with respect to $\cdot$" has no meaning, since there is no _____ in S with respect to $\cdot$. (Note that $1 \notin S$.)

---

(1)   binary operation,   unique
(2)   commutative
(3)   identity element

---

732   In the definition of an inverse of an element under a binary operation $*$, you should begin by saying:
(1)   "Let S be a set having a(n) _____ $*$ *and* a(n) _____ e with respect to $*$."
(2)   Then $y \in S$ is an inverse of $x \in S$ if and only if $x * y = e$ and _____ .

---

(1)   binary operation,   identity element
(2) $y * x = e$

733 Let S be the set of *positive integers*. Consider ordinary addition (+).
  (1) Is + a binary operation in S?
  (2) Does S have an identity element with respect to +? (Assume the previous answer is yes.)

  (1) yes (The sum of two positive integers is again an element of S.)
  (2) no $(0 \notin S)$

734 Let S be the set of *nonnegative* integers with respect to addition (+).
  (1) The identity element is ___ since for all $x \in S$, _____.
  (2) Does 15 have an inverse in S with respect to +? If so, what is it?

  (1) 0, $x + 0 = x$ and $0 + x = x$
  (2) no, note that $-15 \notin S$.

735 Now let S be the set of *integers* with respect to addition (+). The identity element is 0. The inverse of 8 is ___ since _____.

  -8,
  $8 + (-8) = 0$ and $(-8) + 8 = 0$ [or $8 + (-8) = (-8) + 8 = 0$]

736 Let S be the set of integers with respect to multiplication ($\cdot$).
  (1) The identity element with respect to $\cdot$ is ___ since for all $x \in S$, _____.
  (2) Does 5 have an inverse with respect to $\cdot$? If so, what is it?

  (1) 1, $x \cdot 1 = x$ and $1 \cdot x = x$ (or $1 \cdot x = x \cdot 1 = x$)
  (2) No, note that $\frac{1}{5} \notin S$.

737 Let S be the set of rational numbers. Does 5 have an inverse with respect to multiplication? If so, what is it?

  Yes, $\frac{1}{5}$, since $5 \cdot \frac{1}{5} = \frac{1}{5} \cdot 5 = 1$, the identity with respect to $\cdot$.

738 **(1)** Given a nonempty set S, a binary operation $*$ in S is a mapping from ___ into ___.
  (2) If $*$ maps (x, y) into z, we write _____.
  (3) $*$ is commutative if and only if _____.

  (1) $S \times S$, S
  (2) $x * y = z$
  (3) $x * y = y * x$ for all $x, y \in S$

•739 A binary operation * in S is associative if and only if _____.

$(x * y) * z = x * (y * z)$ for all $x, y, z \in S$

•740 Given a set S having a binary operation *, if there exists a $j \in S$ such that _____, then j is called the identity element with respect to *.

$j * x = x$ and $x * j = x$ for all $x \in S$

•741 Let e be the identity element with respect to a binary operation * in S. Suppose $x \in S$. If there exists a $y \in S$ such that _____, then y is an inverse of x with respect to *.

$x * y = e$ and $y * x = e$

•742 Define an identity element with respect to a binary operation *.

Let S be a set having a binary operation *. If there exists $e \in S$ such that for every $x \in S$, $e * x = x$ and $x * e = x$, then e is called the identity element with respect to *.

•743 Define an inverse of x with respect to *.

Let S be a set having a binary operation * and an identity element e with respect to *. Let $x \in S$. An inverse of x with respect to * is an element $y \in S$ such that $x * y = e$ and $y * x = e$.

VI. Review Test for Part Two   (Answers on page 315)

1 Let $S = \{a, b\}$. Let X be the set of all mappings of S into S.
   There are four such functions. Let us indicate these functions as
   we did permutations of degree N. Thus $x = \{M, N, P, Q\}$ where

$$M = \begin{pmatrix} a & b \\ a & b \end{pmatrix} \qquad N = \begin{pmatrix} a & b \\ b & a \end{pmatrix} \qquad P = \begin{pmatrix} a & b \\ a & a \end{pmatrix} \qquad Q = \begin{pmatrix} a & b \\ b & b \end{pmatrix}$$

   Let us define a binary operation $*$ in X in the same way we did
   multiplication of permutations of degree N. Make a copy of these
   functions and save them for problems 2, 3, and 5. Find $N * P$.

2 (1) Prove that $*$ is a binary operation in X; that is, show that the
        result of $*$ on any two elements of X is $\epsilon \, X$.
   (2) Prove that $*$ is not commutative in X.

3 (1) Does X have an identity element with respect to $*$? If so,
        what is it?
   (2) Which elements of X have an inverse with respect to $*$?
        (Assume "inverse" has meaning in X.)

4 Assuming I, the set of integers, has the binary operation of addition, answer these questions:
   (1) Is the binary operation commutative? If not, prove it.
   (2) Is the binary operation associative? If not, prove it.
   (3) Is there an element of the set which is the identity element
        with respect to addition? If so, what is it?
   (4) Does every element of the set have an inverse with respect to
        the binary operation? If not, exhibit one element of the set
        having no inverse with respect to the operation.

5 Let S be the set of permutations of degree 3. These are the six
   permutations:

$$A = \begin{pmatrix} 1 & 2 & 3 \\ 1 & 2 & 3 \end{pmatrix} \qquad B = \begin{pmatrix} 1 & 2 & 3 \\ 1 & 3 & 2 \end{pmatrix} \qquad C = \begin{pmatrix} 1 & 2 & 3 \\ 2 & 1 & 3 \end{pmatrix}$$

$$D = \begin{pmatrix} 1 & 2 & 3 \\ 2 & 3 & 1 \end{pmatrix} \qquad E = \begin{pmatrix} 1 & 2 & 3 \\ 3 & 1 & 2 \end{pmatrix} \qquad F = \begin{pmatrix} 1 & 2 & 3 \\ 3 & 2 & 1 \end{pmatrix}$$

   Make a copy of these sets and save them for problem 6. Let the
   set S have the binary operation multiplication of permutations. Is
   multiplication commutative? If not, prove it.

6 (1) Is the binary operation associative? If not, prove it.
   (2) Is there an element of the set which is the identity element?
        If so, what is it?
   (3) Does every element of the set have an inverse with respect to
        the binary operation? If not, exhibit one element of the set
        having no inverse with respect to multiplication.

7 Let P be the set of all subsets of a nonempty set A and the binary operation be union ($\cup$) of sets.
   (1) Is the binary operation commutative? If not, prove it.
   (2) Is the binary operation associative? If not, prove it.

8 Using the set named in problem 7, answer these questions:
   (1) Is there an element of the set which is the identity element with respect to the binary operation? If so, what is it?
   (2) Does every element of the set have an inverse with respect to the binary operation? If not, exhibit an element of the set having no inverse with respect to the operation.

9 If S is a set having the binary operation $*$ and an identity element e with respect to $*$, then e is unique (that is, e is the only identity element with respect to $*$ in S). To prove there is only one identity element here, suppose $e_1 \in S$ is also an identity element. Prove $e_1 = e$.

10 Let R be the set of rational numbers. Define a binary operation $*$ in R as follows:

$$a * b = 5 \cdot a \cdot b$$

where $\cdot$ represents ordinary multiplication.
   (1) Prove that $*$ is commutative.
   (2) Prove that $*$ is associative.
   (3) Show that $\frac{1}{5}$ is the identity element with respect to $*$.
   (4) Show that $\frac{1}{15}$ is the inverse of $\frac{3}{5}$ under $*$.

Part Three   GROUPS

In its simplest form, an algebraic structure consists of a set of elements having at least one binary relation and one binary operation and which satisfies a given set of axioms. In Part Three we will study, in some detail, a very important algebraic structure called a *group*. A *group* consists of a set of elements having one binary relation (an equivalence relation denoted by "=") and one binary operation which satisfies a certain set of axioms to be discussed later. You will find that you are already familiar with a large number of examples of sets that satisfy the group properties. It is for this reason, and also because the group properties are relatively simple, that we have chosen to study the group concept rather than some other structure. There are simpler algebraic structures, such as semigroups, loops, etc., about which you might want to read later. There are more complicated algebraic structures, such as rings, integral domains, and fields, in which two binary operations are defined. In the subsequent Part Four, we will discuss the field concept.

For the study of groups, we will begin by introducing a set and a binary operation which are probably new to you, but which illustrate some of the ideas from Parts One and Two for review, and, at the same time, will give us another example to which we may refer.

I. Symmetries of an Equilateral Triangle

744 Cut out an *equilateral* triangle *ABC* and label it.

Label both sides of the paper at each vertex with the same letter so that if you turned the triangle over, it would look like this (complete the drawing):

745 If the triangle were revolved counterclockwise about its center (in its own plane) through 120°, it would look like this:

Suppose the triangle is revolved counterclockwise about its center in its own plane through 240°. Show how it would look.

746   Suppose the triangle is revolved counterclockwise

about its center in its own plane through 0°. Show how it would look.

747   Suppose the triangle is revolved counterclockwise

about its center in its own plane through 360°. Show how it would look.

748   If the triangle were flipped over about the altitude

through the upper vertex, the resulting triangle would look like this:

(*Note*: Pick the triangle out of the plane and turn it over.)

▼

Suppose the triangle is flipped over about the altitude

through the lower left vertex. Show how the resulting triangle would look.

749   Suppose the triangle 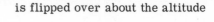 is flipped over about the altitude

through the lower right vertex. Show how the resulting triangle would look.

750   First rotate the triangle 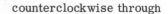 counterclockwise through

120° in its own plane, getting:

Now flip the *resulting* triangle over about the altitude from the upper vertex. Show how the resulting triangle will look.

751 Take the triangle 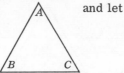 and let

R_0 = a counterclockwise rotation through $0°$
R_1 = a counterclockwise rotation through $120°$
R_2 = a counterclockwise rotation through $240°$
F_1 = a flip about altitude through the upper vertex
F_2 = a flip about altitude through the lower left vertex
F_3 = a flip about altitude through the lower right vertex

On a separate sheet of paper draw the result of each of these manipulations on the given triangle.

Answer on Panel 8

752 Take the triangle 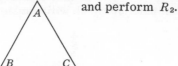 and perform R_2.

Then on the *resulting* triangle perform F_1.

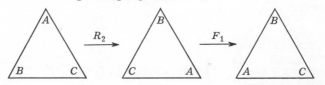

There is a single manipulation which will have the same result, that is, will carry  into directly. What is it?

(Check Panel 8.)

F_3

753 In frame 752 first one manipulation on the triangle was made (R_2) and then a second manipulation followed (F_1). We will indicate such a process by $R_2 \cdot F_1$ and read "R_2 followed by F_1." In the last item we found that $R_2 \cdot F_1$ had the same result as a single manipulation F_3. So we write $R_2 \cdot F_1 = F_3$. Find the single manipulation equal to $F_2 \cdot R_1$.

▼

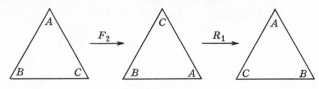

$$\therefore F_2 \cdot R_1 = \underline{\hspace{1cm}}$$

F_1

754 $R_1 \cdot F_3$ means R_1 followed by F_3.

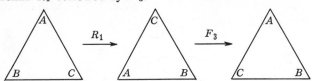

The single manipulation which will transform 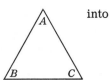 into

 is, according to Panel 8, F_1.

So we write $R_1 \cdot F_3 = F_1$. Similarly, find $R_2 \cdot F_1 = \underline{\hspace{1cm}}$.

F_3

755 $F_2 \cdot F_1$ means to perform F_2 and then F_1. To find the single manipulation which will give the same result (if there is one), take your triangle and first do F_2 and then do F_1. You should obtain this:

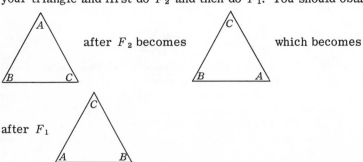

Now, check Panel 8 (or experiment with your triangle) to find a single manipulation which will transform into

. There is one, namely ____.

R_1

---

756   Since R_1 will produce the same result as F_2 followed by F_1, we write $F_2 \cdot F_1 = R_1$. Now find the following: $R_2 \cdot F_2 =$ ____.

F_1

---

757   Let $S = \{R_0, R_1, R_2, F_1, F_2, F_3\}$ and let $\cdot$ mean "followed by." (For example, $R_1 \cdot F_2$ means R_1 followed by F_2.) In all of the examples worked so far there has been a single element of S which will produce the same result as the "product" of two elements. If we find this to hold for all $x, y \in S$, that is, if for every $x, y \in S$, $x \cdot y$ is a unique element of S, then $\cdot$ represents a(n) _____ in S.

---

binary operation

---

758   Determine if $\cdot$ represents a binary operation in S by completing the following multiplication table (on a separate sheet of paper).

		Second factor				
		R_0	R_1	R_2	F_1	F_2	F_3
	R_0	R_0	R_1	R_2	F_1	F_2	F_3
First factor	R_1	R_1	R_2	R_0	F_2	F_3	F_1
	R_2	R_2	R_0	R_1	F_3	F_1	F_2
	F_1						
	F_2						
	F_3						

Answer on Panel 9

759 From Panel 9, for each ordered pair of elements from
$S = \{R_0, R_1, R_2, F_1, F_2, F_3\}$ there is, under $\cdot$, a unique element of
S; that is, if $x, y \in S$, $x \cdot y$ is a unique element of S where $\cdot$ means
"followed by." So we have a binary operation (called "followed
by") in S. Look at the table. Is $\cdot$ commutative? Why?

No, $x \cdot y$ is not necessarily equal to $y \cdot x$. For example,
$R_1 \cdot F_2 = F_3$, $F_2 \cdot R_1 = F_1$. (Use any other example.)

760 Look at Panel 9. Does S have an identity element with respect to $\cdot$?
If so, what is it?

yes, R_0
Note: For all $x \in S$, $x \cdot R_0 = R_0 \cdot x = x$.

761 Thus R_0 is the identity element. Recall that an inverse of an element x is an element, say x^{-1}, such that $x \cdot x^{-1} = x^{-1} \cdot x = e$, the
identity element. For example, does F_1 have an inverse? Look at
Panel 9 and try to find an element, call it F_1^{-1}, such that
$F_1 \cdot F^{-1} = F^{-1} \cdot F_1 = R_0$, the identity element. The answer is F_1;
that is, F_1 is its own inverse. Find an inverse of R_2.

R_1 ($R_2 \cdot R_1 = R_0$ and $R_1 \cdot R_2 = R_0$)

762 Symbolically, R_1^{-1} means the inverse of R_1. Since R_0 is the
identity element, then R_1^{-1}, if it exists, must be an element such
that:

$R_1 \cdot R_1^{-1} = R_0$ and $R_1^{-1} \cdot R_1 = R_0$

Look at Panel 9. Find R_1^{-1}, if it exists.

R_2

763 A close look at Panel 9 will show that every element of S has a
unique inverse.

$R_0^{-1} = R_0$ $R_1^{-1} = R_2$ $R_2^{-1} = R_1$
$F_1^{-1} = $ _____ $F_2^{-1} = $ _____ $F_3^{-1} = $ _____

F_1, F_2, F_3

764 R_0, F_1, F_2, and F_3 are their own inverses. Let S be the set of rational numbers under multiplication. The identity element is 1.

    (1) The inverse of 5 is ___ , since _____. Using the usual notation for inverse 5^{-1} = ___.

    (2) Find 1^{-1}.

    (1) $\frac{1}{5}$, $5 \cdot \frac{1}{5} = 1$ and $\frac{1}{5} \cdot 5 = 1$ (or $5 \cdot \frac{1}{5} = \frac{1}{5} \cdot 5 = 1$), $\frac{1}{5}$

    (2) 1

Note: 1 is its own inverse under $\cdot$.

765 If additive notation is used for a binary operation in a set S, then an inverse of an element a is usually indicated by $(-a)$ instead of a^{-1}. Let S be the set of integers under addition. The identity element under addition is 0.

    (1) The inverse of 10 under addition is ___ since _____.

    (2) Find the additive inverse of -5.

    (1) -10, $10 + (-10) = 0$ and

    $(-10) + 10 = 0$ [or $10 + (-10)] = (-10) + 10 = 0$

    (2) 5 [since $-5 + 5 = 0$ and $5 + (-5) = 0$]

766 The presence (or absence) of _____ is immediately evident from a table of the binary operation (symmetry about the diagonal). However, associativity cannot be easily determined from the table.

commutativity

767 It can be proved that the binary operation of Panel 9 (manipulations of a triangle) is associative. You *could* prove it by trying every $x, y, z \in S$ and showing that for all $x, y, z \in S$ it follows that $(x \cdot y) \cdot z =$ _____. This would be a tremendous job. There exist easier ways of proving that associativity holds in this structure.

$x \cdot (y \cdot z)$

II. Group

768 We have the following information about the set S of manipulations
     of a triangle $\{R_0, R_1, R_2, F_1, F_2, F_3\}$.
     1. There is a binary operation $(\cdot)$ in S.
     2. The binary operation $(\cdot)$ is associative, that is, **(1)** _____.
     3. There is an identity element $R_0 \in S$ such that for all $x \in S$,
        (2) _____.
     4. For *each* $x \in S$ there exists a unique element $x^{-1} \in S$ called the
        inverse of x such that **(3)** _____.

     (1) $x \cdot (y \cdot z) = (x \cdot y) \cdot z$ for all $x, y, z \in S$
     (2) $x \cdot R_0 = R_0 \cdot x = x$
     (3) $x \cdot x^{-1} = x^{-1} \cdot x = R_0$

769 Look at Panel 7. We have multiplication of the permutations of
     degree 3. Here again there is a set S with a binary operation $(\cdot)$
     such that:
     (1) The binary operation is _____; that is, $x \cdot (y \cdot z) = (x \cdot y) \cdot z$
              for all $x, y, z \in S$.
     (2) There exists a(n) _____ a, such that $x \cdot a = a \cdot x = x$ for
              all $x \in S$.
     (3) For each $x \in S$ there exists a unique _____ $x^{-1} \in S$, such
              that $x \cdot x^{-1} = x^{-1} \cdot x = a$.

     (1) associative   **(2)** identity element   **(3)** inverse

770 Let $S = \{1, -1, i, -i\}$. Construct a multiplication table for S.
     (1) Is multiplication a binary operation in S?
     (2) Is this operation associative?
     (3) Is there an identity element with respect to multiplication?
              If so, what is it?
     (4) Does each $x \in S$ have a unique inverse?

$\cdot$	1	-1	i	$-i$
1	1	-1	i	$-i$
-1	-1	1	$-i$	i
i	i	$-i$	-1	1
$-i$	$-i$	i	1	-1

     (1) yes   **(2)** yes   **(3)** yes, (1)   **(4)** yes

771   Let S be the set of integers with respect to ordinary addition. From your past experience,
  (1)   Is addition a binary operation in S? If not, why not?
  (2)   Is addition in S associative? If not, why not?
  (3)   Is there an identity element for addition in S? If so, what is it?
  (4)   Does each element of S have a unique inverse with respect to addition?

(1)   yes   (2)   yes   (3)   yes,   ∘   (4)   yes

772   Once again we are in a position of finding an underlying theme which encompasses a great number of seemingly dissimilar structures. In all of these past problems *we have found a set having a binary operation which is* (1) _____, *for which there is a(n)*
(2) _____ , *and such that each element has a unique*
(3) _____. Therefore, it will be profitable for us to study such a structure in general, for all the examples we have seen are simply particular cases, and whatever we find about the structure in general will be true for the particular cases. In studying the more general case, we will gain a greater insight whenever we see a particular example.

(1)   associative   (2)   identity element   (3)   inverse

773   *Definition*: A set S having a binary operation $*$ is a *group with respect to that binary operation* if and only if:
  (1)   the _____ $*$ is associative in S.
  (2)   there exists a(n) _____ element in S with respect to $*$.
  (3)   every element of S has a(n) _____ inverse with respect to $*$.

(1)   binary operation   (2)   identity   (3)   unique

774   Let S be the set of integers with respect to addition (+).
  1. Addition of integers is associative.
  2. There is an identity element in S, (0), with respect to +.
  3. Every element of S has an inverse with respect to +. The inverse of a is $(-a)$. Therefore the set of integers is a(n) _____ with respect to _____.

group,   addition

775   The set S of integers is not a group with respect to multiplication since one of the properties of a group is not satisfied.
  (1)   Is multiplication a binary operation in S?

▼

(2) Is multiplication in S associative?
(3) Is there an identity element? If so, what is it?
(4) Does every element of S have an inverse in S?

---

(1) yes   (2) yes   (3) yes, (1)
(4) No; for example, find the inverse of 5. It is *not* an integer.

---

776 An inverse of an element under a binary operation having an identity is an element which, operating on x, will give you back the identity element. In frame 775 (the integers under multiplication) the identity element is 1. Note that 5 has no inverse in S because there is no *integer* x such that _____. Therefore the set of integers under multiplication _____ (is or is not) a group.

$5 \cdot x = x \cdot 5 = 1,$ is not

---

777 Perhaps we can enlarge the last set so that it will be a group with respect to multiplication. We want to include fractions, so let S be the set of rational numbers under multiplication.
(1) Is multiplication a binary operation in S?
(2) Is multiplication of rational numbers associative?
(3) Is there an identity element in S? If so, what is it?
(4) Does every element of S have an inverse in S? If not, exhibit such an element.

---

(1) yes   (2) yes   (3) yes, (1)
(4) No, 0 does not have an inverse with respect to multiplication.

---

778 If S is the set of rational numbers under multiplication, the identity element is 1. $0 \in S$, but there is no $x \in S$ such that $0 \cdot x = x \cdot 0 = 1$. Every other element of S does have an inverse; but still, the property demanding that every element of S have an inverse is not satisfied. Therefore the set of rational numbers _____ (is or is not) a group with respect to multiplication.

---

is not

---

779 Suppose we get rid of the one element which gave us trouble. Let S be the set of rational numbers excluding 0 (nonzero rational numbers).
(1) Is multiplication a binary operation in S?
(2) Is multiplication associative in S?
(3) Is there an identity element in S? If so, what is it?
(4) Does every element of S have an inverse in S?

---

(1) yes   (2) yes   (3) yes, (1)   (4) yes

780   From frame 779, then, the set of nonzero rational numbers is a(n)
_____ with respect to multiplication.

group

781   The definition of a group can be written symbolically as follows:
If S is a set of elements having a binary operation $*$, then S is a
group if and only if:
(1)   for all $x, y, z \in S$, _____.
(2)   there exists an identity element $e \in S$ such that for all $x \in S$,

_____.

(3)   for each $x \in S$, there is an inverse x^{-1} such that _____.

(1) $(x * y) * z = x * (y * z)$
(2) $x * e = x$ and $e * x = x$
(3) $x * x^{-1} = e$ and $x^{-1} * x = e$

782   The *group* concept is so important that you should be certain that
you know its properties. A set S having a binary operation $*$ which
is (1) _____ and having a(n) (2) _____ with respect to
that binary operation and such that every element of S has a(n)
(3) _____ in S is called *a group with respect to that binary
operation*.

(1)   associative   (2)   identity element   (3)   inverse

•783   Complete the following definition: A set S having a(n) (1) _____
is a group if and only if,
(2)   _____.
(3)   _____.
(4)   _____.

(1)   binary operation $*$
(2) $*$ is associative [or for all $x, y, z \in S, (x * y) * z = x * (y * z)$]
(3)   there exists an identity element in S with respect to $*$ (or
there exists $e \in S$ such that $x * e = e * x = x$ for all $x \in S$)
(4)   Every $x \in S$ has an inverse in S with respect to $*$ (or for all
$x \in S$, there exists an $x^{-1} \in S$ such that $x * x^{-1} = e$ and
$x^{-1} * x = e$)

784   In order to have a group, we must have a set S and a binary oper-
      ation $*$ in that set. Then the three conditions—associativity,
      identity element, and existence—of an inverse for each $x \in S$ must
      be satisfied. Is the set of even integers a group under addition?
      If not, why not?

      yes

785   Is the set S of integers a group under multiplication? Check the
      properties of a group.
      (1)   binary operation?
      (2)   associative?
      (3)   identity?
      (4)   inverse?
      (5)   Therefore the set of integers _____ (is or is not) a group
             with respect to multiplication.

      (1)   yes   **(2)**   yes   **(3)**   yes $(e = 1)$
      (4)   No, except for +1 and −1, no element of S has an inverse under
             multiplication.
      (5)   is not

COMMENT

Frames 786 to 796 will ask whether certain sets form a group with
respect to certain binary operations. The answers will ordinarily
consist simply of "no" or "yes," but do not just make a quick guess.
Check carefully, one by one, the properties of a group. Ask yourself:

1. Is this a binary operation in the set? (If not, the problem is
   finished, because a group must have a binary operation.)
2. Is the operation associative?
3. Is there an identity element?
4. Does *every* element of the set have an inverse?

If the answer to any one of these questions is "no," then the set is
not a group with respect to the binary operation. If you forget the
properties, you may look at Panel 10. If you are asked to define a
group, however, do not use Panel 10.

786   Is the set of odd integers a group under multiplication? If not, what
      properties are not satisfied?

      No, not every odd integer has an inverse under multiplication.

787 Do the *nonnegative* integers form a group with respect to addition? If not, why not?

No, except for 0, no element of S has an inverse under +.

788 Do the *positive rational numbers* form a group with respect to multiplication? If not, why not?

Yes

789 Let $S = \{1, -1, i, -i\}$. Is S a group with respect to multiplication ($\cdot$)? If not, why not? (You may want to construct a table for $\cdot$.)

yes

790 Look at Panel 7. We have mentioned that permutation multiplication is associative. If so, does S form a group with respect to multiplication? If not, why not?

yes

791 Look at Panel 9. Assuming that the binary operation is associative, does S form a group with respect to $\cdot$? If not, why not?

yes

792 Let $S = \{\ldots, -9, -6, -3, 0, 3, 6, 9, 12, \ldots, 3n, \ldots\}$.
  (1) Is ordinary addition a binary operation in S?
  Addition is associative in S since S is a subset of the set of integers in which addition is associative.
  (2) Does S contain an identity element with respect to addition? If so, what is it?
  (3) Does every element of S have a unique inverse in S? If so, what is the inverse of 12?
  (4) Therefore S _____ (is or is not) a group with respect to addition.

  (1) yes, note that if $a, b \in S$, $a + b \in S$.
  (2) yes, 0
  (3) yes, -12, since $12 + (-12) = 0$ and $(-12) + (12) = 0$.
  (4) is

793 Let $S = \{0, 1, 2, 3\}$ have a binary operation + given in the table. Assuming that the binary operation + is associative, is S a group with respect to +? If not, why not?

+	0	1	2	3
0	0	1	2	3
1	1	2	3	0
2	2	3	0	1
3	3	0	1	2

yes

794 Let $S = \{1, 2, 3, 4\}$ and have a binary operation ∘ given in the table.
  (1) Assume that the binary operation is associative; is S a group with respect to ∘? If not, why not?
  (2) Find 2^{-1} in this example.

∘	1	2	3	4
1	1	2	3	4
2	2	4	1	3
3	3	1	4	2
4	4	3	2	1

(1) yes   (2) 3
Note: 2^{-1} means the inverse of 2, that is, an element x such that $2 \cdot x = x \cdot 2 = 1$, the identity element. From the table $2 \circ 3 = 1$ and $3 \circ 2 = 1$.

795 Let $S = \{1, 3, 5, 7\}$ have a binary operation ∘ as given. Assuming the binary operation is associative, is S a group with respect to ∘? If not, why not?

∘	1	3	5	7
1	1	3	5	7
3	3	1	7	5
5	5	7	1	3
7	7	5	3	1

yes

796 Let $S = \left\{1, \dfrac{-1 + i\sqrt{3}}{2}, \dfrac{-1 - i\sqrt{3}}{2}\right\}$ under ordinary multiplication. The multiplication table is shown below. Is S a group with respect to multiplication?

▼

$\cdot$	1	$\dfrac{-1+i\sqrt{3}}{2}$	$\dfrac{-1-i\sqrt{3}}{2}$
1	1	$\dfrac{-1+i\sqrt{3}}{2}$	$\dfrac{-1-i\sqrt{3}}{2}$
$\dfrac{-1+i\sqrt{3}}{2}$	$\dfrac{-1+i\sqrt{3}}{2}$	$\dfrac{-1-i\sqrt{3}}{2}$	1
$\dfrac{-1-i\sqrt{3}}{2}$	$\dfrac{-1-i\sqrt{3}}{2}$	1	$\dfrac{-1+i\sqrt{3}}{2}$

If not, why not?

yes
Note that S is the set of cube roots of 1.

•797 A set G having a binary operation $*$ is a group if and only if:
  (1) for all $x, y, z \in S$, _____ = _____.
  (2) there exists in S an element e called the identity element,
       such that for all $x \in S$, ____ = ____ = ____.
  (3) for each $x \in S$, there exists an element $x^{-1} \in S$ called an in-
       verse of x such that ____ = ____ = ____.

  (1) $(x * y) * z = x * (y * z)$
  (2) $x * e = e * x = x$
  (3) $x * x^{-1} = x^{-1} * x = e$

798 Frame 797 states, in general, the properties of a group. However,
    other facts must be considered. It is understood that a group G has
    an equivalence relation which will be indicated by "=." Hence "="
    will have the three properties of an equivalence relation: namely,
    for all $x, y, z \in G$,
    (1) $x = x$ (_____ property)
    (2) If $x = y$, then $y = x$ (_____ property)
    (3) If $x = y$ and $y = z$, then $x = z$ (_____ property)

    (1) reflexive   (2) symmetric   (3) transitive

799 If the equivalence relation "=" is simply that of identity, an *element*
    is equal to *itself* and no other. In such a case, the statement $x = y$
    means that two different symbols have been assigned to the same

    _____.

    element

800   Let G have an equivalence relation of identity. Then $x = y$ means
that x and y are different symbols for the same element. Thus
(a,x) and (a,y) represent a single element of $G \times G$, and if $*$ is a
binary operation in G, $*$ maps (a,x) and (a,y) into the _____ element of G.

same

801   Assume that the equivalence relation is that of identity. From $x = y$,
we obtain that $a * x =$ ____, since the symbols x and y represent
the same _____.

$a * y$,   element

802   Assume that the equivalence relation is that of identity. If the x of
$x * a$ is replaced by y (keep in mind the symbols x and y represent the same element), the result $y * a$ must be the same. So
$x * a =$ ____.

$y * a$

803   However, suppose that "=" is an *arbitrary* equivalence relation.
(1)   Then $x = y$ _____ (does or does not) necessarily imply
that x and y are the same element. This is much like the
relationship between similar triangles.
(2)   They _____ (are or are not), however, members of the same
equivalence class.

(1)   does not   (2)   are

804   Assume that "=" is an *arbitrary* equivalence relation and $x = y$.
There is no guarantee that (1) ____ $= a * y$ or (2) ____ $= y * a$,
since $*$ could map (a,x) and (a,y) into two (3) _____ elements
of G. (a,x) and (a,y) are distinct ordered pairs of (4) ____.

(1) $a * x$ (2) $x * a$ (3)   different   (4) $G \times G$
For an example of the situation described in frames 802 and 803
see Appendix A.

805   If $*$ is a binary operation in G, and an element is equal to itself and
no other, then the equivalence relation "=" is simply that of _____.

identity

806   If $*$ is a binary operation in G, and $x = y$ does not necessarily imply that x and y are the same element, then it is a(n) _____ equivalence relation.

arbitrary

807   In order to avoid complications it will be understood that the binary operation in G does "fit in" with the equivalence relation "=." That is, if $x = y$ and a is any element of G, then (1) $a * x =$ ____ and (2) ____ = ____ .

(1) $a * y$ (2) $x * a = y * a$

808   A(n) _____ which satisfies the properties whenever $x = y$
1. $a * x = a * y$ and
2. $x * a = y * a$
is said to be well-defined with respect to "=."

binary operation

III. Proofs of Some Theorems on Groups

In the last section of Part Three we will establish *some* of the properties of a group. The form of the work will be similar to that of plane geometry. Each step of a proof will be justified in one of three ways: (1) as being part of the hypothesis, (2) by one of the properties listed on Panel 10, (3) by a previously proved theorem.

Look at Panel 10. On it are listed the definition of a group G and the other properties implied by the definition. They are labeled G_1, G_2, G_3, E_1, E_2, E_3, B_1, B_2, Definition 1, and Definition 2. For brevity, we will identify the group properties by these labels. This is simply for convenience *in this program* but these labels will not be understood by all teachers and students of mathematics. On the other hand, the terms "reflexive," "identity element," "transitivity of an equivalence relation," etc., *are* meaningful and these are terms which will be understood by mathematicians. Therefore, if you prefer to give as a reason, "$*$ is an associative binary operation" instead of simply "G_1," you will be correct and you will become more familiar with the terminology normally used.

Some of the assertions are labeled as theorems and listed on Panel 11. You may refer to Panels 10 and 11 for your work. Do not use a theorem from Panel 11, however, until it has been proved. Beginning with frame 818 our proofs become more formal. As you read the proofs, be sure that you understand why each reason given is a justification for the corresponding statement. Keep in mind that eventually you should be able to construct such proofs. There is no set of rules whose use will guarantee the construction of a proof for any theorem in mathematics. One of the best suggestions is to look carefully at the conclusion, and to keep it in mind while working.

There is no reason to believe that any proof you read is the *only* correct proof. The only requirements for a correct proof are that each step can be justified and that the proper conclusion is reached. If you are not certain about one of your proofs, check with your instructor or discuss it with other students.

---

809   Let G be a group and $p \in G$. Why does $p = p$? (Refer to Panel 10.)

E_1 (or reflexive property of "=")

•810   Let G be a group; $x, y, p \in G$, and $x = y$. Why does $p * x = p * y$?

B_1

---

811   Let $p, q \in G$, where G is a group. If $p = q$, why does $q = p$?

E_2

---

812   Let $p, q, r \in G$, where G is a group and $p = q$ and $q = r$. Justify the statement $p = r$.

E_3

---

813   Let G be a group and $p, q, r \in G$. Why does $(p * q) * r = p * (q * r)$?

G_1

---

814   Let G be a group and $p \in G$. Now p^{-1} represents an inverse of p with respect to $*$. How do you know that there exists a $p^{-1} \in G$?

G_3

---

815   Let G be a group and $p \in G$. Using G_3, we know that there exists $p^{-1} \in G$. Why does $p * p^{-1} = e$?

Definition 2

---

816   Let G be a group, with $m, n, p, q \in G$, and $n * p = n * q$. Why does $m * (n * p) = m * (n * q)$?

B_1
Note: $n * p \in G$, and $n * q \in G$, so we are using B_1 where x is $n * p$ and y is $n * q$ and a is m.

817   Let $p, q \in G$, where G is a group. Then, since $*$ *is* a binary operation in $G, p * q \in G$. Why does $e * (p * q) = p * q$?

Definition 1 (where x is $p * q$)

818   *Prove*: In a group G, if $p = q$ and $q = r$, then $r = p$.
Proof:
1. $p = q, q = r$ 1. Hypothesis
2. $\therefore p = r$ 2. _____
3. $\therefore r = p$ 3. _____

(2) E_3 (3) E_2

819   Consider frame 818. Here is a slightly different proof.
Prove: In a group G, if $a = b$ and $b = c$, then $c = a$.
Proof:
1. $b = c, a = b$ 1. Hypothesis
2. $\therefore c = b, b = a$ 2. _____
3. $\therefore c = a$ 3. _____

(2) E_2 (3) E_3

•820   *Prove*: In a group G, if $a = b$ and $c = b$, then $a = c$.
Proof:
1. $a = b$ 1. Hypothesis
2. $c = b$ 2. Hypothesis
3. $\therefore b = c$ 3. _____
4. $\therefore a = c$ 4. _____

(3) E_2 (4) E_3 (using statements 1 and 3)

•821　*Prove*: In a group G, if $a = b$ and $c = b$, then $c = a$

Here are the two most obvious proofs. You may have some other proof which is correct.

1. $a = b$, $c = b$　　1. Hypothesis
2. $b = c$　　　　　　 2. E_2
3. $a = c$　　　　　　 3. E_3 (using the first part of statements 1 and 2)
4. $\therefore c = a$　　　　 4. E_2

1. $a = b$, $c = b$　　1. Hypothesis
2. $b = a$　　　　　　 2. E_2
3. $\therefore c = a$　　　　 3. E_3 (using the second part of statements 1 and 2)

822　*Prove*: In a group G, if $a = b$, $b = c$, and $c = d$, then $a = d$.
　　Proof:
1. $a = b$, $b = c$　　1. _____
2. $\therefore a = c$　　　　 2. _____
3. $c = d$　　　　　　 3. _____
4. $\therefore a = d$　　　　 4. _____

Note: It is customary, as above, to use the information from the hypothesis as needed, not to use the entire hypothesis in one statement.

(1) Hypothesis　　　(2) E_3　　　(3) Hypothesis　　　(4) E_3

823　*Prove*: In a group G, if $a = b$, $b = c$, and $d = c$, then $a = d$.

Proof:
1. $a = b$, $b = c$　　1. Hypothesis
2. $\therefore a = c$　　　　 2. E_3
3. $d = c$　　　　　　 3. Hypothesis
4. $\therefore c = d$　　　　 4. E_2
5. $a = d$　　　　　　 5. E_3 (using statements 2 and 4)

824　*Prove*: Let G be a group; $b, x, y, z \in G$. If $x = y$ and $b * y = z$, then $z = b * x$.

Proof:
1. $x = y$, $b \in G$　　1. Hypothesis
2. $b * x = b * y$　　　 2. B_1
3. $b * y = z$　　　　　 3. Hypothesis
4. $\therefore b * x = z$　　 4. E_3 (using statements 2 and 3)
5. $z = b * x$　　　　　 5. E_2

Note: In statement 1 only two statements were chosen from the hypothesis in order to obtain statement 2: $b * x = b * y$. This was done because the conclusion, $z = b * x$, contains the expression $b * x$ and $b * x$ does not occur in any part of the hypothesis.

825   Let G be a group; $b, x, y, z \in G$. If $x = y$ and $y * z = b$, then
      $x * z = b$.

Proof:
1. $x = y$, $z \in G$ 1. Hypothesis
2. $x * z = y * z$ 2. B_2
3. $y * z = b$ 3. Hypothesis
4. $\therefore x * z = b$ 4. E_3 (using statements 2 and 3)

826   Read note 2, Panel 10, carefully. In using B_1 or B_2, you must op-
      erate on the *left* of *both* sides of the equation or on the *right* of *both*
      sides of the equation. There is no property of Panel 10 which justi-
      fies the following: In a group, if $x = y$ and $z \in G$, then $z * x = y * z$.
      This is not correct. Look at the group of permutations of degree 3
      on Panel 7. Although $d = d$, does $e \cdot d = d \cdot e$?

No, $e \cdot d = b, d \cdot e = c$.

827   Of course, if $*$ were a(n)   **(1)**   binary operation, then order
      of the operation would make no difference. But in this section we
      are working with a group in general, and   **(2)**   is not one of
      the properties listed. Therefore in a group G, if $a = b$ and $x \in G$,
      using B_1, $x * a = x * b$
      using B_2,   **(3)**

(1) commutative   (2) commutativity   (3) $a * x = b * x$

•828 *Prove*: If G is a group and $a, b, c, d \in G$, and if $a = b$ and
      $b * c = d$, then $a * c = d$.

Proof:
1. $a = b$, $c \in G$ 1. Hypothesis
2. $a * c = b * c$ 2. B_2
3. $b * c = d$ 3. Hypothesis
4. $a * c = d$ 4. E_3

COMMENT

From this point, we will no longer specify in the hypothesis that
various elements are members of a group. If an element is involved
in the hypothesis, you are to assume that it $\in G$.

In a proof, you no longer need specify that such elements are members of G. However, if you introduce any other element into a proof,
you should justify that this element is, in fact, a member of the group.

(For example, G_2 guarantees that there exists an identity element e in *any* group; or, if $x \in G$, G_3 guarantees that there is an $x^{-1} \in G$.)

---

829   *Prove*: In a group G, if $x = y$ and $z * y = w$, then $z * x = w$.

Proof:

1. $x = y$ 1. Hypothesis
2. $z * x = z * y$ 2. B_1
3. $z * y = w$ 3. Hypothesis
4. $\therefore z * x = w$ 4. E_3

830   *Prove*: In a group G, if $x = y$ and $y = z$, then $a * x = a * z$.

Here are the two most obvious proofs:

1. $x = y, y = z$ 1. Hypothesis
2. $x = z$ 2. E_3
3. $a * x = a * z$ 3. B_1

1. $x = y, y = z$ 1. Hypothesis
2. $a * x = a * y, a * y = a * z$ 2. B_1
3. $\therefore a * x = a * z$ 3. E_3

831   *Prove*: In a group, if $x = y$ and $y = z$, then $x * b = z * b$.

Here are two obvious proofs:

1. $x = y, y = z$ 1. Hypothesis
2. $x = z$ 2. E_3
3. $x * b = z * b$ 3. B_2

1. $x = y, y = z$ 1. Hypothesis
2. $x * b = y * b, y * b = z * b$ 2. B_2
3. $x * b = z * b$ 3. E_3

832   *Prove*: In a group, if $a = x$ and $a * b = c * d$, then $x * b = c * d$.

Proof:

1. $a = x$ 1. Hypothesis
2. $\therefore a * b = x * b$ 2. B_2
3. $x * b = a * b$ 3. E_2
4. $a * b = c * d$ 4. Hypothesis
5. $x * b = c * d$ from statements 3 and 4   5. E_3

833   *Prove*: In a group, if $b = x$ and $a * b = c * d$, then $a * x = c * d$.

Proof:
1. $b = x$ 1. Hypothesis
2. $a * b = a * x$ 2. B_1
3. $a * x = a * b$ 3. E_2
4. $a * b = c * d$ 4. Hypothesis
5. $\therefore a * x = c * d$ 5. E_3

834   *Prove*: In a group, if $a = x$ and $c = y$ and $a * b = c * d$, then $x * b = y * d$.

Proof:
1. $a = x$ 1. Hypothesis
2. $a * b = x * b$ 2. B_2
3. $x * b = a * b$ 3. E_2
4. $a * b = c * d$ 4. Hypothesis
5. $\therefore x * b = c * d$ 5. E_3
6. $c = y$ 6. Hypothesis
7. $c * d = y * d$ 7. B_2
8. $\therefore x * b = y * d$ 8. E_3

835   *Theorem* 1. In a group G, if $a = b$ and $c = d$, then $a * c = b * d$.
Proof:
1. $a = b$ 1. _____
2. $a * c = b * c$ 2. _____
3. $c = d$ 3. _____
4. $b * c = b * d$ 4. _____
5. $a * c = b * d$ 5. _____

(1) Hypothesis   (2) B_2 (3) Hypothesis
(4) B_1 (5) E_3 (using statements 2 and 4)
Any result which will be particularly useful in further work and which can be applied in a large number of subsequent proofs will be labeled *Theorem*. Note Panel 11. Of course, you may not use any theorem until it has been proved.

836   *Prove*: In a group, if $a = b$ and $c = d$, then $a * d = b * c$. (You will save steps by using Theorem 1.)

1. $a = b, c = d$ 1. Hypothesis
2. $d = c$ 2. E_2
3. $a * d = b * c$ 3. Theorem 1 (using the first part of statement 1 and statement 2)

837 (1) In Theorem 1, the order of the operation _____ (is or is not) important. Look at Panel 7. (2) $e = e$, $d = d$, but does $e \cdot d = d \cdot e$?

(1) is   (2) no ($e \cdot d = b$, $d \cdot e = c$)

•838 *Prove*: In a group, if $x = y$, $z = w$, and $z * y = b$, then $b = w * x$.

1. $z = w$ 1. Hypothesis
2. $w = z$ 2. E_2
3. $x = y$ 3. Hypothesis
4. $w * x = z * y$ 4. _____
5. $z * y = b$ 5. _____
6. $w * x = b$ 6. _____
7. $b = w * x$ 7. _____

(4) Theorem 1   (5) Hypothesis   (6) E_3 (7) E_2

839 *Prove*: In a group, if $x = y$, $z = w$, and $y * w = d$, then $x * z = d$.

This proof uses Theorem 1.
1. $x = y$, $z = w$ 1. Hypothesis
2. $x * z = y * w$ 2. Theorem 1
3. $y * w = d$ 3. Hypothesis
4. $x * z = d$ 4. E_3 (using statements 1 and 2)

This proof does not use Theorem 1.
1. $x = y$ 1. Hypothesis
2. $x * z = y * z$ 2. B_2
3. $z = w$ 3. Hypothesis
4. $y * z = y * w$ 4. B_1
5. $x * z = y * w$ 5. E_3
6. $y * w = d$ 6. Hypothesis
7. $x * z = d$ 7. E_3

840 We have proved that in a group:
(1) if $a * b = c * d$ and $a = x$, then ____ $= c * d$.
(2) if $a * b = c * d$ and $b = x$, then ____ $= c * d$.
(3) if $a * b = c * d$ and $c = x$, then ____ $=$ ____.
(4) if $a * b = c * d$ and $a = x$ and $c = y$, then ____ $=$ ____.
These items illustrate various expressions in which an element may be replaced by an equivalent.

(1) $x * b$
(2) $a * x$
(3) $a * b = x * d$
(4) $x * b = y * d$

841   In subsequent proofs, we will simply replace an element directly without the added statement about the equivalence. Instead we will give the reason for the equivalence. For example, suppose:

1. $(a * a^{-1}) * b = (c * c^{-1}) * d$ 1. Hypothesis
2.   __(1)__ $* b =$ __(2)__ $* d$ 2. Definition 2
3.   __(3)__   3. Definition 1

In two places, steps 2 and 3, we have immediately replaced an element by a(n)   __(4)__   and given the reason for the   __(5)__ .

(1) e **(2)** e **(3)** $b = d$
(4)   equivalent   **(5)**   equivalence

842   *Prove*: In a group G, $a^{-1} * (a * b) = b$.
Proof:

1. $a^{-1} * (a * b) = (a^{-1} * a) * b$ 1. G_1
2. $\therefore a^{-1} * (a * b) = e * b$ 2. Definition 2
3. $\therefore a^{-1} * (a * b) = b$ 3. _____

In statement 2, the $a^{-1} * a$ was replaced immediately by e, and the reason given is Definition 2, namely that $a^{-1} * a = e$

(3)   Definition 1

843   *Prove*: In a group G, $(x * y) * y^{-1} = x$.

Proof:

1. $(x * y) * y^{-1} = x * (y * y^{-1})$ 1. G_1
2. $\therefore (x * y) * y^{-1} = x * e$ 2. Definition 2
3. $\therefore (x * y) * y^{-1} = x$ 3. Definition 1

844   Suppose we wish to prove: In a group G, if $x * y = x * z$ then $y = z$. In this case, we start with products ($x * y$ and $x * z$) and work toward elimination of the x elements. This will leave the single elements (y and z). First recall that in a group every element has an inverse. Operating on both sides on the left of $x * y = x * z$ with x^{-1}, we get $x^{-1} * (x * y) =$ _____.

$x^{-1} * (x * z)$

845   We now have $x^{-1} * (x * y) = x^{-1} * (x * z)$. Using _____ on both sides of the equation, we get $(x^{-1} * x) * y = (x^{-1} * x) * z$.

associativity

846 We now have $(x^{-1} * x) * y = (x^{-1} * x) * z$. Using Definition 2, we obtain _____ , and then by _____ we reach $y = z$.

$e * y = e * z$,   Definition 1

847 *Prove*: In a group G, if $x * y = x * z$, then $y = z$.

Proof:
1. $x * y = x * z$ 1. Hypothesis
2. $x^{-1} \in G$ 2. G_3
3. $x^{-1} * (x * y) = x^{-1} * (x * z)$ 3. B_1
4. $(x^{-1} * x) * y = (x^{-1} * x) * z$ 4. G_1
5. $e * y = e * z$ 5. Definition 2
6. $\therefore y = z$ 6. Definition 1
This is Theorem 2 on Panel 11.

848 *Prove*: In a group G, if $a * b = a * c$ and $b = d$, then $c = d$. (Theorem 2 will help you.)

1. $a * b = a * c$ 1. Hypothesis
2. $b = c$ 2. Theorem 2
3. $c = b$ 3. E_2
4. $b = d$ 4. Hypothesis
5. $\therefore c = d$ 5. E_3

849 *Prove*: In a group G, if $x * y = x * z$ and $a * z = a * w$, then $y = w$.

Here is a proof using Theorem 2.
1. $x * y = x * z, a * z = a * w$ 1. Hypothesis
2. $y = z, z = w$ 2. Theorem 2
3. $y = w$ 3. E_3

850 *Theorem* 3 (right cancelation law). In a group G, if $y * x = z * x$, then $y = z$. (*Suggestion*: Operate with x^{-1} on both sides of the equation.)

1. $y * x = z * x$ 1. Hypothesis
2. There exists $x^{-1} \in G$ 2. G_3
3. $(y * x) * x^{-1} = (z * x) * x^{-1}$ 3. B_2
4. $y * (x * x^{-1}) = z * (x * x^{-1})$ 4. G_1
5. $y * e = z * e$ 5. Definition 2
6. $y = z$ 6. Definition 1

•851 *Prove*: In a group G, if $a * b = c * b$ and $c = d$, then $a = d$.
(*Suggestion*: Use Theorem 3.)

1. $a * b = c * b$ 1. Hypothesis
2. $a = c$ 2. Theorem 3
3. $c = d$ 3. Hypothesis
4. $a = d$ 4. E_3

852 *Prove*: In a group G, if $a * x = a * y$ and $z * b = w * b$, then
$x * z = y * w$. (*Suggestion*: Use Theorem 2, Theorem 3, and then
Theorem 1.)

Proof:
1. $a * x = a * y$ 1. Hypothesis
2. $x = y$ 2. Theorem 2
3. $z * b = w * b$ 3. Hypothesis
4. $z = w$ 4. Theorem 3
5. $x * z = y * w$ 5. Theorem 1

853 *Prove*: In a group G, if $a * b = c * b$ and $x * c = x * d$, then $d = a$.

Proof:
1. $a * b = c * b$ 1. Hypothesis
2. $a = c$ 2. Theorem 3
3. $x * c = x * d$ 3. Hypothesis
4. $c = d$ 4. Theorem 2
5. $a = d$ 5. E_3 (using statements 2 and 4)
6. $d = a$ 6. E_2

854 *Prove*: In a group G, if $a * b = c * b$ and $x = y$, then $a * x = c * y$.

Proof:
1. $a * b = c * b$ 1. Hypothesis
2. $a = c$ 2. Theorem 3
3. $x = y$ 3. Hypothesis
4. $a * x = c * y$ 4. Theorem 1

855 *Note*: In the two cancelation laws (Theorems 2 and 3) the order
again is important. We *cannot* prove: in a group, if $x * a = b * x$,
then $a = b$. For example, look at the group of Panel 7.
    $d \cdot c =$ _____ and $b \cdot d =$ _____
$\therefore d \cdot c = b \cdot d$ but $c \neq b$
If $*$ were commutative, we would not have this difficulty.

    $e,$ e

856 *Theorem* 4. In a group, if $a = b$, then $a^{-1} = b^{-1}$.
    Proof:

1. $a = b$	1. Hypothesis
2. There exists $a^{-1} \in G$	2. _____
3. $a^{-1} * a = a^{-1} * b$	3. B_1
4. There exists $b^{-1} \in G$	4. _____
5. $(a^{-1} * a) * b^{-1} = (a^{-1} * b) * b^{-1}$	5. _____
6. $\therefore (a^{-1} * a) * b^{-1} = a^{-1} * (b * b^{-1})$	6. _____
7. $e * b^{-1} = a^{-1} * e$	7. _____
8. $b^{-1} = a^{-1}$	8. Definition 1
9. $a^{-1} = b^{-1}$	9. _____

(2) G_3 (4) G_3 (5) B_2 (6) G_1
(7)   Definition 2   (9) E_2

857 *Prove*: In a group, if $a * b = c * d$ and $a = c$, then $b = d$.
(*Suggestion*: Use Theorem 4 and then Theorem 1.)

1. $a = c$	1. Hypothesis
2. $a^{-1} = c^{-1}$	2. Theorem 4
3. $a * b = c * d$	3. Hypothesis
4. $a^{-1} * (a * b) = c^{-1} * (c * d)$	4. Theorem 1
5. $(a^{-1} * a) * b = (c^{-1} * c) * d$	5. G_1
6. $e * b = e * d$	6. Definition 2
7. $b = d$	7. Definition 1

858 *Prove*: In a group, if $a * b = c * d$ and $b = d$, then $a = c$.

Proof:	
1. $b = d$	1. Hypothesis
2. $b^{-1} = d^{-1}$	2. Theorem 4
3. $a * b = c * d$	3. Hypothesis
4. $(a * b) * b^{-1} = (c * d) * d^{-1}$	4. Theorem 1
5. $a * (b * b^{-1}) = c * (d * d^{-1})$	5. G_1
6. $a * e = c * e$	6. Definition 2
7. $a = c$	7. Definition 1

859 In frames 860 to 868 we shall recall some terminology and ideas from elementary algebra. Consider the *conditional* equation: $3x + 2 = 7$. We say that $x = $ ____ is a solution to the _____ equation.

$\frac{5}{3}$, conditional

---

860 We call $x = \frac{5}{3}$ a(n) _____ to the conditional equation because, if $x = \frac{5}{3}$, then $3x + 2 = 3(\frac{5}{3}) + 2 = $ ____ .

---

solution, 7

---

861 So, if $x = \frac{5}{3}$, then $3x + 2 = 7$ is true. If there is no other value of x for which this is true, we say that the solution $x = \frac{5}{3}$ is _____ .

---

unique

---

862 If $x \neq \frac{5}{3}$, then $3x + 2$ ____ 7. This contradicts our first hypothesis that $3x + 2 = 7$. Therefore, the _____ $x = \frac{5}{3}$ is unique.

$\neq$, solution

---

863 Consider the _____ equation $2x - 4 = 9$. If there is a solution, then $x = $ ____ .

---

conditional, $\frac{13}{2}$

---

864 So, if $2x - 4 = 9$, then $x = \frac{13}{2}$ or, equivalently, if $x \neq \frac{13}{2}$, then _____ .

$2x - 4 \neq 9$

---

865 We have shown that *if* there is a solution to $2x - 4 = 9$, then that solution is $\frac{13}{2}$. It remains for us to show that $x = \frac{13}{2}$ *is* a solution. We do that in this manner:
  (1) if $x = \frac{13}{2}$, then $2x - 4 = 2(\frac{13}{2}) - 4 = $ ____
  (2) if $x = \frac{13}{2}$, then $2x - 4 = $ ____ .

---

(1) 9   (2) 9

866 Thus the work which is usually exhibited in finding a solution to a(n)
     _____(1)_____ equation,
     e.g.: $2x - 3 = 5$
             $x = $ __(2)__
     is mostly exploratory. It merely proves that *if* there is a solu-
     tion to $2x - 3 = 5$, that solution is $x = $ __(3)__ .

     (1) conditional   **(2)** 4   **(3)** 4

867 So far we have eliminated a great number of possibilities, but it
     remains to show that $x = 4$ *is* a(n) _____(1)_____ . We do that in this
     manner:
     If $x = 4$, $2x - 3 = $ __(2)__

     (1) solution   **(2)** 5

868 Eventually it should be proved that certain operations on conditional
     equations yield conditional equations that have the same solutions.
     (Two conditional equations having the same set of solutions are called
     equivalent.) It can be proved that $ax + b = c$ where a, b, c are real
     numbers and $a \neq 0$ has a(n) _____(1)_____ solution, namely, $x = $ __(2)__

     (1) unique   **(2)** $\dfrac{c - b}{a}$

     We will now prove two similar theorems concerning groups.

869 *Theorem* 5. In a group G, $a * x = b$ has a unique solution,
     $x = a^{-1} * b$. We must prove two things:
     1. If $a * x = b$, then $x = $ _____(1)_____ .
     2. If $x = a^{-1} * b$, then _____(2)_____ .
     3. Statement 1 will show that *if* there is a solution, that solution
        is _____(3)_____ .
     4. Statement 2 will show that $x = a^{-1} * b$ _____(4)_____ (is or is not)
        a solution.

     (1) $a^{-1} * b$
     (2) $a * x = b$
     (3) $x = a^{-1} * b$
     (4) is

870 *Prove*: If $a * x = b$, then $x = a^{-1} * b$.

1. $a * x = b$	1. Hypothesis
2. There exists $a^{-1} \in G$	2. G_3
3. $a^{-1} * (a * x) = a^{-1} * b$	3. B_1
4. $(a^{-1} * a) * x = a^{-1} * b$	4. G_1
5. $e * x = a^{-1} * b$	5. Definition 2
6. $\therefore x = a^{-1} * b$	6. Definition 1

871 We have shown that *if* $a * x = b$ has a solution, the solution is $x = a^{-1} * b$. It remains to show that $x = a^{-1} * b$ *is* a solution. *Prove*: If $x = a^{-1} * b$, then $a * x = b$.

1. $x = a^{-1} * b$	1. Hypothesis
2. $a * x = a * (a^{-1} * b)$	2. B_1
3. $a * x = (a * a^{-1}) * b$	3. G_1
4. $a * x = e * b$	4. Definition 2
5. $a * x = b$	5. Definition 1

872 *Theorem 6*. In a group G, $y * a = b$ has a unique solution, namely, $y = b * a^{-1}$. Again you must prove:
(1) If _____ , then _____ .
(2) If _____ , then _____ .

(1) $y * a = b$, $y = b * a^{-1}$
(2) $y = b * a^{-1}$, $y * a = b$

•873 *Theorem 6*. In a group G, $y * a = b$ has a unique solution, namely, $y = b * a^{-1}$.

Part 1:

1. $y * a = b$	1. Hypothesis
2. There exists $a^{-1} \in G$	2. G_3
3. $(y * a) * a^{-1} = b * a^{-1}$	3. B_2
4. $y * (a * a^{-1}) = b * a^{-1}$	4. G_1
5. $y * e = b * a^{-1}$	5. Definition 2
6. $y = b * a^{-1}$	6. Definition 1

Part 2:

1. $y = b * a^{-1}$	1. Hypothesis
2. $y * a = (b * a^{-1}) * a$	2. B_2
3. $y * a = b * (a^{-1} * a)$	3. G_1
4. $y * a = b * e$	4. Definition 2
5. $y * a = b$	5. Definition 1

Self-test VI (Answers to Self-test VI appear on page 316)

1 Let S and T be nonempty sets. Any subset of $S \times T$ is called a(n) _____.

2 Let R be a binary relation in $S \times T$. If dom $R = S$, R is called _____.

3 Let R be a binary relation from S *into* T. If for each $x \in S$ there is exactly one $y \in T$ such that $(x, y) \in R$, R is called _____.

4 Let f be a function from S into T. Then for each $x \in S$ there is a unique $y \in T$ such that $(x, y) \in f$. This unique $y \in T$ is called the _____ of x under the function f and is denoted by _____.

5 As a simple example, let $S = \{1, 2, 3\}$ and $T = \{2, 4, 6, 8\}$. Suppose $f = \{(1,4), (2,4), (3,2)\}$. Pictorially, we can show:

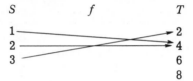

(1) dom $f =$ _____.
(2) for each $x \in S$ there is a unique _____ such that $(x, y) \in f$.
(3) f _____ (is or is not) a function from S into T.
(4) $f(1) =$ _____.

6 If f is a function from S into T and ran $f = T$, then f is a(n) _____.

COMMENT

We have now seen some of the elementary theorems which can be proved using the group properties. We have by no means exhausted the study of group theory, but we have done enough to illustrate the idea of an algebraic structure.

In your study of plane geometry you also had a set of assumptions which were used to prove various theorems, but most of the assumptions and theorems applied *only* to geometric figures.

Notice carefully that, in the study of groups, we worked with an unspecified set of elements having an *arbitrary* equivalence relation and an *arbitrary* binary operation satisfying the properties of Panel 10. The theorems we proved can now be applied to any specific set of elements having a binary operation with these properties. For example, we know that the set of integers under ordinary addition is a group. Hence, we could apply our theorems to this set, replacing $*$ by $+$ and a^{-1} by $(-a)$. Similarly, the set of permutations of degree 3 under $\cdot$ ("followed by") is a group, and the theorems can be applied to this particular case.

In fact, whenever we find a set of elements having a binary operation satisfying the properties of an abstract group, we can immediately use the theorems we have already proved (with slight alterations for the symbolism).

This is one important reason for the study of algebraic structures. Another is that, upon determining that a certain set is a group with respect to some binary operation, you can obtain a better concept of its structure, unhampered by the description of the set or the binary operation involved. In other words, no matter how complicated the description or symbolism of the set or its binary operation, if you can determine that it is a group, then you will probably obtain a clearer understanding of the set and its binary operation. Many such particular examples of groups occur in mathematics (and outside mathematics).

IV. Mappings and Transformations

874 Let S be finite, and f be given in roster form. The decision whether (1) dom $f =$ ____ and (2) for each $x \in$ dom f there is _____ $y \in T$ such that $(x,y) \in f$ are satisfied so that f is a function from _____ is merely a matter of observation of the ordered pairs of f.

(1) S
(2) exactly one, S into T

875 However, consider the following:
Let S be the set of integers and $f = \{(x,y) \mid x \in S, y \in S, \text{ and } y = x^2\}$. You should represent part of f pictorially. Complete the following through integer 3.

▼

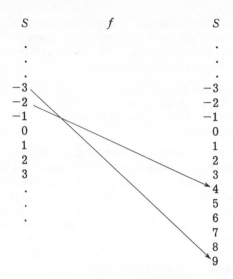

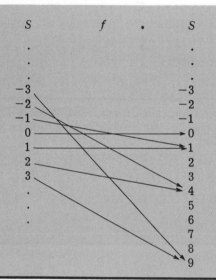

Keep your answer for
frames 876 to 878

876 From our mapping it becomes clear that:
   (1)   For each ____ there is a $y \in S$ such that $(x,y) \in F$; that is,
         ____ = S.
   (2)   The image of each $x \in S$ under f is _____; that is, for each
         $x \in S$, there is _____ (how many) $y \in S$ such that
         $(x,y) \in f$.
   Therefore, you should feel certain that (3)   you can prove f to be
   a(n) _____ from S into S.

   (1) $x \in S$,   dom f (2)   unique,   exactly one
   (3)   function (or mapping)

877   Look at your mapping.
  (1) It becomes fairly obvious that a(n) _____ integer cannot be
      an image of any $x \in S$.
  (2) So f is a function from S into S_1 where S_1 is the set of non-
      negative _____.
  (3) Moreover, f is a mapping from S____S_2 where S_2 is the set
      of perfect squares.

(1) negative   **(2)** integers   **(3)** onto

878   A sketch does not prove anything, but it does help you to obtain a
      clearer idea of the mapping. In order to prove that f is a mapping
      of S into S, we need only appeal to the fact that multiplication *is*
      a(n) _____ in the set of integers.

binary operation

879   Let S be the set of *positive integers*.
      Let $R = \{(x,y) \mid x \in S, y \in S,$ and $y = x - 1\}$. Is R a function from
      S to S? (Make a sketch of a mapping from S into S for the first
      three elements of S.)

No, as seen in the sketch, 1 has no image in S under f.

880   Would f be a function from S into T where T is the set of non-
      negative integers?

Yes, for then $1 \in S$ has 0 as its image, and $0 \in T$.

881   Let S be the set of positive integers.
      Let $R = \{(x,y) \mid x \in S, y \in S,$ and $y = 1$ if x is odd and $y = \frac{x}{2}$ if x
          is even.$\}$

▼

(1)   Make a sketch of a mapping from S into S for the first six
       elements of S.
(2)   Is f a function from S into S?
(3)   Is f a function from S onto S?

(1) S f S

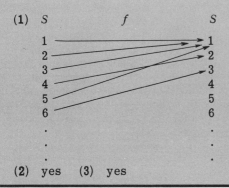

(2) yes   (3) yes

---

882   Although a function from S into T is a set of ordered pairs, it is
       sometimes more convenient to think in terms of the rule of corre-
       spondence which associates with each $x \in S$ a unique $y \in T$. We
       speak of the rule which "maps" each $x \in S$ into a unique $y \in T$.
       Thus, if $(a,17) \in f$, we say that a is mapped into _____ by f.

17

---

883   In making a map of the United States, each geographic "element"
       of the United States is associated with a unique "element" on a piece
       of paper. Similarly, if f is a function from S into T, each $x \in S$ is
       mapped into a unique $y \in T$. For example, if $f(3) = 71$, $3 \in S$ is
       mapped into _____ $\in T$ by f.

71

---

884   The word "mapping" is often used instead of "function" when the
       rule of correspondence rather than the set of ordered pairs is under
       consideration. Thus, if f is a function from S into T, we might say
       instead that f is a _____.

mapping from S into T

---

885   If f maps S into T, we write $f : S \rightarrow T$ and read "f is a mapping
       from S into T" or "f maps S into T." Notice that the notation
       emphasizes the correspondence between elements of S and elements

▼

of T. If $(a,17) \in f$, f maps a into 17, and we write $f : a \to 17$. Similarly, if f maps 3 into 8, we write _____.

$f : 3 \to 8$ [or $f(3) = 8$]

---

886   Let $S = \{1, 2, 3\}$, $T = \{a, b\}$ and $f = \{(1,a), (2,a), (3,b)\}$, $f : S \to T$; that is, f maps S into T. Referring to specific elements,
$f : 1 \to$ ____
$f : 2 \to$ ____

---

a, a

---

887   $f : S \to T$ is read _____.

---

f maps S into T or f is a mapping from S into T

---

888   If $f : S \to T$, then f is a(n) _____ of S into T. Under f, each $x \in S$ is made to correspond to a *unique* $y \in T$.

---

mapping

---

889   Given $\alpha : S \to T$: α is a mapping from S into T.
Therefore α is a rule of correspondence which assigns to each element $s \in S$ a(n) _____ element, $t \in T$.

---

unique

---

890   S α T

Under the rule shown above,
        a is mapped by α into 1
(1) b is mapped by α into ____
(2) c is mapped by α into ____
(3)   Each $x \in S$ is mapped by α into a unique $y \in T$. Therefore α is a(n) _____.

---

(1) 4   (2) 2   (3) mapping of S into T

891

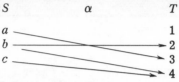

$$S \qquad \alpha \qquad T$$

(1) α is not a mapping of S into T since _____.
(2) α is a mapping of S_1 into T where $S_1 =$ _____.

(1) $b \in S$, but b has no image under α (or dom $\alpha \neq S$)
(2) $\{a, c, d\}$

892

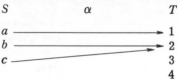

$$S \qquad \alpha \qquad T$$

α is not a mapping of S into T since _____.

$b \in S$, but there is no *unique* $y \in T$ such that $\alpha : b \rightarrow y$ (or equivalent)

893

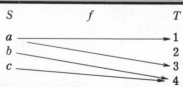

$$S \qquad \alpha \qquad T$$

Here is a pictorial representation of a mapping α from a set S into a set T. Under the rule α,

   a corresponds under α to 1,
   b corresponds under α to 2,

(1) c corresponds under α to ____.
(2)   Each $s \in S$ corresponds to a unique $t \in T$; therefore α is a

   _____.

(1)   2   (2)   mapping (or function) of S into T

894

$$S \qquad f \qquad T$$

a ——————— 1
b 2
c ——————— 3
4

Is f a mapping of S into T? Why?

No, a does not correspond under f to a unique element of T [or $a \in S$, but there is no unique $y \in T$ such that $(a, y) \in f$].

895

$$S \qquad f \qquad T$$

1 ———————————→ a
2 ——————→ b
3 ——————

Is f a mapping from S into T? Why?

No, $2 \in S$, but there is no $y \in T$ such that $f : 2 \to y$ (or equivalent).

•896 Let $f : S \to T$. The symbolism indicates that f is a(n) _____ .

mapping (or function) of S into T

897 Let $F : S \to T$.
    (1) Then for _____ $x \in S$ there is a(n) _____ $y \in T$ such that
    _____ .
    (2) y is called the _____ and is denoted by _____ .

    (1) each,   unique, $(x,y) \in f$ (or $f : x \to y$)
    (2) image of x under f, $f(x)$ [or $(x)f$]

898 Let $\alpha : S \to T$. *In this section of the program we are going to indi-*
cate the image of $x \in S$ under α by $(x)\alpha$ rather than $\alpha(x)$. For our
purpose this notation will be handier. We will read $(x)\alpha$ as "the
image of x under (the mapping) α." Suppose $(2,10) \in \alpha$; then, using
the notation just described, the image of 2 under α is 10 is written

_____ .

$(2)\alpha = 10$

899

$$S \qquad \alpha \qquad S$$

a ———————→ a
b ——————→ b
c ———————→ c

α is a mapping of S into S.
    (1) $(a)\alpha = $ _____
    (2) $(b)\alpha = $ _____
    (3) $(c)\alpha = $ _____

    (1) b (2) a (3) b

900 Let S be the set of integers and $f : x \to 2x$.
   (1) $(3)f = $ _____.
   (2) Suppose $a \in S$; then $(a)f = $ _____.
   (3) (___)$f = -18$.

   (1) 6   (2) $2a$ (3) -9

901 Let S be the set of rational numbers and $\alpha : x \to x + 1$ be the rule of correspondence. This rule tells us that the image of any $s \in S$ is to be $s + 1$, that is, $(s)\alpha = s + 1$.
   (1) $\therefore (5)\alpha = $ _____   (2) $(\frac{1}{8})\alpha = $ _____   (3) $(0)\alpha = $ _____
   (4) $(-2)\alpha = $ _____   (5) $(1.6)\alpha \doteq $ _____   (6) $(a + 3)\alpha = $ _____

   (1) 6   (2) $\frac{9}{8}$ (3) 1   (4) -1 (5) 2.6   (6) $a + 4$

902 Let S be the set of rational numbers and $f : x \to x + 1$. Then,
   (1) $(-7)f = $ _____   (2) (___)$f = \frac{3}{8}$
   (3) (___)$f = a$ (4) (___)$f = \frac{1}{t}$ (if $t \neq 0$)

   (1) -6 (2) $-\frac{5}{8}$ (3) $a - 1$ (4) $\frac{1}{t} - 1$ or $\frac{1-t}{t}$

903 Let S be the set of *nonzero* rational numbers and $f : x \to 1/x$. Then,
   (1) $(s)f = $ _____   (2) (___)$f = \frac{1}{8}$ (3) (___)$f = \frac{2}{3}$
   (4) (___)$f = t$ (5) (___)$f = a + 1$ (6) (___)$f = \frac{3}{s} + 1$

   (1) $\frac{1}{s}$ (2) 8   (3) $\frac{3}{2}$ (4) $\frac{1}{t}$ (5) $\frac{1}{a + 1}$
   (6) $\frac{1}{3/s + 1}$ or $\frac{s}{3 + s}$

904 Let S be the set of rational numbers and $\alpha : x \to x^2$. Then,
   (1) $(-3)\alpha = $ _____   (2) $(s_1)\alpha = $ _____
   (3) (___)$\alpha = \frac{9}{4}$ (4) (___)$\alpha = t_1{}^2$

   (1) 9   (2) $s_1{}^2$ (3) $\frac{3}{2}$ or $-\frac{3}{2}$ (4) t_1 or $-t_1$

905 Let S be the set of *integers* and $\alpha : x \to x^2$. Then,
(1) $(-3)\alpha = $ ____   (2) $(3)\alpha = $ ____
(3) (____)$\alpha = 16$ (4) (____)$\alpha = 5$

(1) 9   (2) 9   (3) 4 or -4
(4) 5 is not an image of any $s \in S$, so there is no answer.

906 We have shown a variety of symbolism and terminology to represent the same concepts. This has been done because no symbols or
terms are universally accepted. Thus we use either function or
_____ of S into T.

mapping

907 Similarly, $(x,y) \in f$ is equivalent to $(x)f = y$ or _____, where
f is a function from S into T. Each indicates that y is the _____
of x under f.

$f(x) = y$,   image

908 We have defined a(n) _____ or _____ from S into T. In this
section we will need to prove that from time to time some binary
relation f in $S \times T$ is a function from S into T.

function,   mapping

909 We know that a binary relation f in $S \times T$ is a function from S into
T if and only if:
(1) dom $f = S$. This means we must show that for each $x \in S$

_____ .

(2) for each $x \in S$, the $y \in T$ is _____. This means we must
show that if $(x,y_1) \in f$ and $(x,y_2) \in f$, then _____.

(1) there is a $y \in T$ such that $(x,y) \in f$
(2) unique, $y_1 = y_2$

910 Let S be the set of integers and $\alpha : x \to 2x$ for each $x \in S$. Let us
prove that α is a mapping of S into S.
(1) Illustrate part of f.
(2) In order to prove that α is a function:
(a) let $p \in S$, $2 \in S$, and multiplication be a binary operation in
the set of integers. Thus $2p \in S$. Then for each $p \in S$
there is a ____ (namely, $2p$) such that $(p,y) \in \alpha$.

▼

(b)   Suppose $(p, y_1) \in \alpha$ and $(p, y_2) \in \alpha$. Then $y_1 = 2p$ and
$y_2 = 2p$, but, since multiplication is a(n) _____ in
S, $2p$ is a unique element of S, so $y_1 = y_2$.

(3)   From (a) and (b) we have proved that α is _____ .

(1) S α S

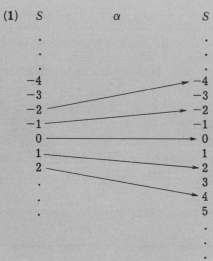

(2)(a) $y \in S$ (b) binary operation
(3) a function (or mapping) of S into S

911

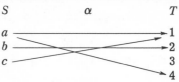

Is α a mapping from S into T? Why?

No, the image of a is not unique; that is, it is not true that for each
$x \in S$, if $(x, y_1) \in \alpha$ and $(x, y_2) \in \alpha$, then $y_1 = y_2$. In this case,
$(a, 1) \in a$ and $(a, 2) \in a$, but $1 \neq 2$.

912

Is f a mapping from S into T?

yes

913

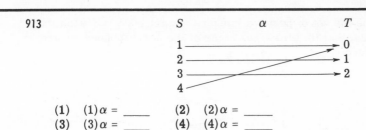

$$S \qquad \alpha \qquad T$$

(1) (1)α = ____   (2) (2)α = ____
(3) (3)α = ____   (4) (4)α = ____

---

(1) 0   (2) 1   (3) 2   (4) 0

---

914 If $\alpha : S \to T$ and $(s)\alpha = t$, then t is _____.

---

the image of s under α

---

915 Let S be the set of *even* integers and $\alpha : x \to x/2$ is *not* a mapping
of S into S since it is not true that for each $s \in S$ there is a $t \in S$
such that $(s)\alpha = t$. If $s \in S$, $\frac{s}{2}$ is not necessarily an element of S
(remember what S is). For example, let $s = 6$. Suppose T is the
set of integers. Does $\alpha : S \to T$? If you have difficulty, you should
draw a picture of part of the mapping.

---

yes

---

916 If possible, rather than representing a mapping pictorially or in a
table, a formula is given indicating the image of each $s \in S$. For
example, let S be the set of integers and T be the set of even integers. Let $\alpha : S \to T$ such that $(s)\alpha = 2s$ for all $s \in S$. Thus we
have a rule which associates with each element of S a unique element of T. For example, $(5)\alpha = 10$, that is, the image of 5 under the
mapping is 10. $(-4)\alpha = $ ____.

-8

---

917 Let S be the set of real numbers and T be the set of nonnegative
real numbers. Let $f : S \to T$ such that $(s)f = s^2$ for all $s \in S$. Thus
the image of 2 under f is 4, or $(2)f = 4$.
(1) The image of -11 under f is ____ or $(-11)f = $ ____.
(2) $(\sqrt{2})f = $ ____.   (3) $\left(-\frac{\pi}{2}\right)f = $ ____.

---

(1) 121,   121   (2) 2   (3) $\dfrac{\pi^2}{4}$

918   Let S be the set of positive integers and let $\alpha : S \rightarrow S$ such that
$\alpha : a \rightarrow 2a$, that is, $(a)\alpha = 2a$. Some of the correspondences are
shown here.

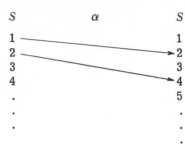

Thus $\alpha : 1 \rightarrow 2$ or $(1)\alpha = 2$,
$\alpha : 2 \rightarrow 4$ or $(2)\alpha = 4$,
(1) $\alpha : 3 \rightarrow$ ____ or (3)____.
(2)   Thus α is a mapping of _____.

(1) 6, $\alpha = 6$ (2) S into S

919   Let S be the set of integers and let $\alpha : a \rightarrow 2a$. The image of 4 under α is 8, that is, $(4)\alpha = 8$. Similarly, the image of 10 under α
is ____, that is, ____.

20, $(10)\alpha = 20$

920   Let S be the set of positive integers and $\beta : \begin{cases} n \rightarrow 1 \text{ if } n \text{ odd} \\ n \rightarrow \dfrac{n}{2} \text{ if } n \text{ even} \end{cases}$

Part of the mapping is shown.

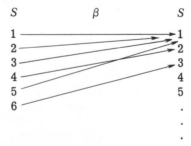

Thus every $s \in S$ corresponds under β to a unique $t \in S$. If s odd,
$(s)\beta = 1$. If s even, $(s)\beta = \dfrac{s}{2}$. Every $s \in S$ has a unique image
under β. Therefore β is a(n) _____.

mapping of S into S (or mapping of S onto S)

921   Let S be the set of integers and $\beta : S \to S$ such that if $a \in S$,
      $\beta : a \to a + 1$.
      The image of 1 under β is 2, that is, $(1)\beta = 2$.
      The image of 2 under β is 3, that is, $(2)\beta = 3$.
      The image of 10 under β is ____, that is, ____.

      11, $(10)\beta = 11$

922   Let S be the set of real numbers and $\alpha : S \to S$ such that if $s \in S$,
      $\alpha : s \to \dfrac{s}{2}$.
      Then **(1)** $(5)\alpha =$ ____   **(3)** $(\frac{3}{8})\alpha =$ ____
            (2) $(0)\alpha =$ ____   **(4)** $(-\pi)\alpha =$ ____

      (1) $\frac{5}{2}$ **(2)** 0   **(3)** $\frac{3}{16}$ **(4)** $\dfrac{-\pi}{2}$

923   Let $\beta : W \to V$. W is called the domain of the mapping, and V is
      called its codomain, and $(W)\beta$, the set of all images of W under β,
      is called the range of the mapping.

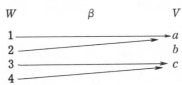

      (1)   dom $\beta =$ _____
      (2)   codomain $\beta =$ _____
      (3)   ran $\beta =$ _____

      (1) W or $\{1, 2, 3, 4\}$ **(2)** V or $\{a, b, c\}$ **(3)** $\{a, c\}$

924

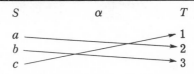

      $\alpha : S \to T$.
      dom $\alpha = S$ codomain $\alpha = T$ ran $\alpha =$ ____

      T or $\{1, 2, 3\}$

•925

$$S \qquad \beta \qquad T$$

$$
\begin{array}{lcr}
a & & 1 \\
b & & 2 \\
c & & 3 \\
& & 4
\end{array}
$$

(1)   dom β = _____
(2)   codomain β = _____
(3)   ran β = _____

(1) S or $\{a, b, c\}$ (2) T or $\{1, 2, 3, 4\}$ (3) $\{2, 4\}$
Note: codomain $\beta \neq$ ran β

•926   Let S be the set of integers and $\alpha : S \to S$ be a mapping from S into
S such that if $s \in S$, $\alpha : s \to 2s$, that is, $(a)\alpha = 2a$.
Thus, $(1)\alpha = 2$
   (1) $(2)\alpha =$ _____
   (2) $(3)\alpha =$ _____
   (3) $(0)\alpha =$ _____
   (4)   dom $\alpha =$ _____
   (5)   codomain $\alpha =$ _____
   (6)   ran $\alpha =$ _____
An illustration of part f will help you.

(1)   4   (2)   6   (3)   0   (4) S or set of integers
(5) S or set of integers   (6)   set of even integers

927   We see, then, that the range of a mapping $\alpha : S \to T$ need not be T;
that is, every element of T is not necessarily an image of some
element of S.

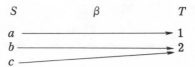

$$S \qquad \beta \qquad T$$

In this example every $x \in T$ is the image of at least 1 $y \in S$ so
range β = _____.

T

928 Whenever the range of a mapping $\alpha : S \to T$ is T, that is, whenever every element of T is the image under α of some element of S, we say that α is a mapping of S onto T.

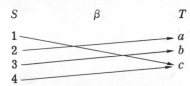

ran β = ____, so β ____ (is or is not) a mapping of S onto T.

T,   is

929 If $\alpha : S \to T$, α is a mapping of S *onto* T if and only if for each $t \in T$ there is an $s \in S$ such that $(s)\alpha = t$. Roughly speaking, every element of T must be the image of some element of S. Suppose:

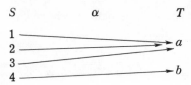

(1) Is α a mapping of S into T?
(2) Is α a mapping of S onto T?

(1) yes   (2) yes

930 α is a mapping of S *into* T if and only if
(1) for each $s \in S$, there is a $t \in T$ such that _____.
(2) if $(s)\alpha = t_1$ and $(s)\alpha = t_2$, then _____.

(1) $(s)\alpha = t$ (2) $t_1 = t_2$

931 If $\alpha : S \to T$, α maps S *onto* T if and only if for every $t \in T$ there is an $s \in S$ such that _____.

$(s)\alpha = t$ (in other words, ran $\alpha = T$)

932   S α T

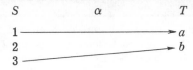

(1) Is α a mapping of S into T?
(2) Is α a mapping of S onto T?

(1) No, there is no $t \in T$ such that $(2)\alpha = t$.
(2) No, in order to be *onto*, α first must be *into*. Since α is not
     even a mapping, it cannot be an *onto* mapping.

933   S α T

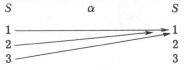

α is a mapping of S_1 onto T where $S_1 = $ ____ .

$\{1, 3\}$

934   S α S

1 ———————————→ 1
2 ————————————→ 2
3 ————————————— 3

(1) Is α a mapping of S into S?
(2) Is α a mapping of S onto S?

(1) yes   (2) no
It is not true that for every $t \in S$ there is an $s \in S$ such that
$(s)\alpha = t$. For example, there is no $s \in S$ which has 2 as its image.
In short, ran $\alpha \neq S$.

935 Let S be the set of integers and $\alpha : x \to x + 1$; that is, $(s)\alpha = s + 1$.
     α is a mapping of S into S since:
     1. for all $s \in S$, $s + 1 \in S$, so there is a $t \in S$, namely $s + 1$, such
        that $(s)\alpha = t$.
     2. if $(s)\alpha = t_1$ and $(s)\alpha = t_2$, then $t_1 = s + 1$ and $t_2 = s + 1$.
        (1) $\therefore$ _____ . (2) Hence α is a _____ .

(1) $t_1 = t_2$ (2) mapping of S into S
Note: We have not proved that α is *onto*.

936 Consider again: S is the set of integers and $\alpha : x \to x + 1$. In frame
935 we proved that α is a mapping of S into S. Is α also an *onto*
mapping? Let us see. Suppose $t \in S$. We must show that there is
an $s \in S$ such that $(s)\alpha = t$. In fact, let $s = t - 1$. $t - 1 \in S$ since
subtraction is a binary operation in the set of integers and
$(t - 1)\alpha =$ ____. Therefore S ____ (is or is not) a mapping of
S *onto* S.

$t,$ is

937 Let S be the set of positive integers and $\alpha : x \to 2x$.
(1) Is α a mapping of S into S?
(2) Is α a mapping of S onto S?
Note: You should represent some of the mapping using typical elements from S before answering the question.

S	α	S
1		1
2		2
.		3
.		4
.		.

(1) yes
(2) No, if, for example, we take $3 \in S$, there is no $s \in S$ such that
$(x)\alpha = 3$; that is, 3 is not an image of any s under α.

938

S	α	S
1	⟶	1
2	⟶	2
3	⟶	3

(1) Is α a mapping of S into S?
(2) Is α a mapping of S onto S?

(1) yes   (2) yes

●939

S	α	S
1	⟶	1
2		2
3	⟶	3

(1) Is α a mapping of S into S?
(2) Is α a mapping of S onto S?
(3) Could you describe α as a mapping?

(1) no   (2) No, α is not a mapping since (3)α is not indicated.
(3) Yes, α is a mapping of S_1 into S where $S_1 = \{1, 2\}$.

940 *Note*: Every mapping of S onto T must be an into mapping, but every into mapping is not onto. α is a mapping of S into T if and only if:
(1) for each $s \in S$ there is a $t \in T$ such that _____.
(2) if $(s)\alpha = t_1$ and $(s)\alpha = t_2$, then _____.
(3) α is a mapping of S onto T if and only if α is a mapping of S into T and, in addition, for every $t \in T$ there is an $s \in S$ such that _____.

(1) $(s)\alpha = t$ [or $(s,t) \in \alpha$]   (2) $t_1 = t_2$
(3) $(s)\alpha = t$ [or $(s\ t) \in \alpha$]

941 Let S be the set of integers, T be the set of real numbers, and $\alpha : x \to \dfrac{x}{2}$. For each $s \in S$, $\dfrac{s}{2} \in T$ (since the real numbers contain the rational numbers) such that $(s)\alpha = \dfrac{s}{2}$. Suppose $(s)\alpha = t_1$ and $(s)\alpha = t_2$; then $t_1 = \dfrac{s}{2}$ and $t_2 = \dfrac{s}{2}$. $\therefore t_1 = t_2$. Therefore α is a _____.

mapping of S *into* T
Note: α is not onto T. For example $\frac{1}{3} \in T$, but there is no integer s such that $(s)\alpha = \frac{1}{3}$.

942 α is a mapping of S into T if and only if:
(1) _____.
(2) _____.

(1) for each $s \in S$ there is a $t \in T$ such that $(s)\alpha = t$, [or $(s,t) \in \alpha$]
(2) if $(s,t_1) \in \alpha$ and $(s,t_2) \in \alpha$, then $t_1 = t_2$

943   Let S be the set of integers and $\alpha : x \rightarrow x + 5$.
    (1)   If $s \in S$, $s + 5 \in S$ such that $(s)\alpha =$ ____.
    (2)   If $(s)\alpha = t_1$ and $(s)\alpha = t_2$, then $t_1 =$ ____ and $t_2 =$ ____.
    ∴ ____ = ____.
    (3)   We have proved that α is a(n) _____.

    (1) $s + 5$ (2) $s + 5$, $s + 5$, $t_1 = t_2$
    (3)   mapping of S into S
    Note: α is an onto mapping, but we have not proved it.

944   We have just proved that $\alpha : x \rightarrow x + 5$ is a mapping of S into S
    where S is the set of integers. To prove that α is *onto*, let $t \in S$;
    then ____ $\in S$ and ($\_\_\_$)$\alpha = t$. Therefore for each $t \in S$ there is
    an $s \in S$ such that $(s)\alpha = t$. Therefore α is onto.

    $t - 5$, $t - 5$

945

$$S \qquad \alpha \qquad S$$

By inspection:
    (1)   for each $s \in S$, there is a $t \in S$ such that ____. Specifically,
        $(1)\alpha =$ ____
        $(2)\alpha =$ ____
        $(3)\alpha =$ ____
    (2)   If $(s)\alpha = t_1$ and $(s)\alpha = t_2$, then ____.
    (3)   Therefore α is a(n) _____.

    (1) $(s)\alpha = t$,   1,   1,   3   (2) $t_1 = t_2$
    (3)   mapping from S into S
    Note: α is not onto.

946   α is a mapping of S onto T if and only if: α is a mapping of S
    into T and for each $t \in T$, _____.

    there is an $s \in S$ such that $(s)\alpha = t$

947

S	α	T

$$
\begin{array}{ccc}
1 & \longrightarrow & a \\
2 & \longrightarrow & b \\
3 & \diagdown & c \\
 & & d
\end{array}
$$

α is a mapping of S into T. Is α a mapping of S onto T? Why?

No, there is a $t \in T$ such that there is no $s \in S$ for which $(s)α = t$, namely, $t = c$.

948　α is a mapping of S *onto* T if and only if α is an *into* mapping and

_____.

for each $t \in T$ there is an $s \in S$ such that $(s)α = t$

949　Let S be the set of integers and T be the set of even integers. Consider α : $x \rightarrow 2x$. Copy this information on a separate sheet of paper. We shall use frames 950 to 952 to prove that α is a mapping of S onto T. It would also be a good idea for you to illustrate part of the mapping by listing some elements of S and T and drawing the arrows.

This is not an answer, but you should have something like this for your illustration.

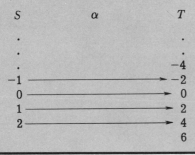

950　Let $s \in S$. s is an integer. $2s$ is an even integer by definition of even integers. $\therefore 2s \in$ ____ and $(s)α = 2s$. Thus we have found for each $s \in S$ there is a $t \in T$ such that ____.

T
$(s)α = t$　　So each $s \in S$ has an image under α.

951 To prove that each image is unique, suppose some s has two images; that is, suppose $(s)\alpha = t_1$ and $(s)\alpha = t_2$.
$\therefore t_1 = 2s$ and $t_2 = 2s$.
$\therefore$ _____.

Therefore the image of each $s \in S$ is unique.

$t_1 = t_2$

952 As a result of frames 950 and 951, α is a mapping of S _____ T.

into
Note: To prove *onto*, we must show that every $t \in T$ is the image of some $s \in S$ under α

953 Now we show that each $t \in T$ is an image of some $s \in S$ under α.
Suppose $t \in T$. t is an even integer, so $\frac{t}{2}$ is an integer. Therefore,

$\frac{t}{2} \in S$ and $\left(\frac{t}{2}\right)\alpha =$ _____. So for each $t \in T$, there is an $s \in S$ for which $(s)\alpha = t$; that is, each element of T is the image of some element of S. Therefore, α is a mapping of S _____ T.

t,   onto

954 Informally, α is a mapping of S into T if and only if every $s \in S$ has a unique image $t \in T$. To prove α is a mapping, then, we must show that:

every element of s has an image under α and
no element $s \in S$ has more than one distinct image under α.

Formally translated, then, we must show:

for every $s \in S$, there exists a $t \in T$ such that _____.
if $(s)\alpha = t_1$ and $(s)\alpha = t_2$, then _____.

$(s)\alpha = t$, $t_1 = t_2$

955 Informally, a mapping α of S into T is an onto mapping if every $t \in T$ is the image of at least one element of S. Formally, then, we must show that for each $t \in T$ there exists an $s \in S$ such that _____.

$(s)\alpha = t$

956 Sometimes a mapping $\alpha : S \rightarrow T$ is such that no two distinct elements of S have the same image. In this case, we say that α is *a one-to-one mapping of S into T*. For example:

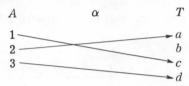

No element of T is the image of more than one element of S, so α is a(n) _____.

one-to-one mapping of S into T

957 *Definition:* $\alpha : S \rightarrow T$ is one-to-one if and only if whenever $(x_1)\alpha = y$ and $(x_2)\alpha = y$, then _____.

$x_1 = x_2$

958 Note that a one-to-one mapping of S into T does not imply that *every* element of T is an image, but that no element of T is the image of more than one element of S; that is, that no two distinct elements of S are mapped into the same element of T.

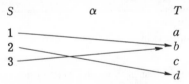

Is α a one-to-one mapping of S into T? Why?

No, b is the image under α of more than one element of S (1 and 3).

959 The phrase one-to-one will be written 1-1.

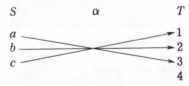

Is α a 1-1 mapping of S into T?

yes

•960 *Definition*: A mapping $\alpha : S \rightarrow T$ is 1-1 if and only if _____.

whenever $(x_1)\alpha = y$ and $(x_2)\alpha = y$, then $x_1 = x_2$

961 (1) By definition, in a 1-1 mapping of S into T, no element of T is the _____ under α of more than one element of S.

(2)

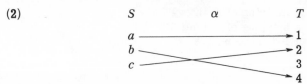

Is α a 1-1 mapping of S into T?

(1) image   (2) yes

962

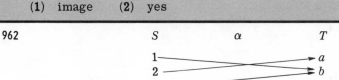

Is α a 1-1 mapping of S into T? Why?

No, $(1)\alpha = b$, $(3)\alpha = b$, but $1 \neq 3$.

963

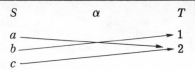

(1) Is α a mapping of S into T?
(2) Is α a mapping of S onto T?
(3) Is α a 1-1 mapping?

(1) yes
(2) yes
(3) no $[(a)\alpha = 2$ and $(c)\alpha = 2$, but $a \neq c]$

964   Note that in frame 963 α was an onto mapping, but not 1-1.

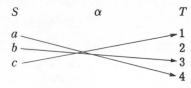

(1)   Is α a mapping of S into T?
(2)   Is α a mapping of S onto T?
(3)   Is α a 1-1 mapping?

(1)   yes   (2)   no
(3)   yes (No element of t is the image under α of more than one element of S.)

965   Note that in frame 964 α was a 1-1 mapping but not onto.

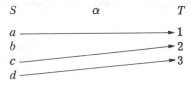

(1)   Is α a mapping of S into T?
(2)   Is α a mapping of S onto T?
(3)   Is α a 1-1 mapping?

(1)   No, b has no image under α (2)   no   (3)   no
Note: to be onto or 1-1, you must have a mapping to begin with.

966

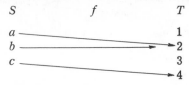

(1)   Is f a mapping of S into T?
(2)   Is f a mapping of S onto T?
(3)   Is f a 1-1 mapping?

(1)   yes
(2)   No, 1 and 3 are not images.
(3)   No, 2 is the image of more than one element under f.

967

(1) Is f a mapping of S into T?
(2) Is f a mapping of S onto T?
(3) Is f a 1-1 mapping?

(1) yes   (2) yes   (3) yes

968 Suppose S is the set of integers and $(x)f = x + 1$, f is a mapping of S onto S. Let us prove that f is 1-1. You should sketch part of the mapping to see what is happening.
Suppose $(s_1)f = t$ and $(s_2)f = t$.
  then $s_1 + 1 = t$ and $s_2 + 1 = t$
  $\therefore s_1 + 1 = s_2 + 1$
    $s_1 = s_2$
Therefore no two elements of S are mapped onto the same element of S. Therefore f is a(n) _____ mapping.

1-1

969 Remember, to prove that f is a 1-1 mapping, you must show that no two distinct elements of s are mapped into the same $t \in T$; that is, if $(s_1)f = t$ and $(s_2)f = t$, then _____.

$s_1 = s_2$

970 Suppose S is the set of integers and $\alpha : x \rightarrow x^2$. α is a mapping of S into S. Again you should draw part of the mapping. α is not 1-1 since:
if $(s_1)\alpha = t$ and $(s_2)\alpha = t$,
then $s_1^2 = t$ and $s_2^2 = t$.
  $\therefore s_1^2 = s_2^2$.
Does this imply that $s_1 = s_2$?

No, $(-5)^2 = 5^2$, for example, so $(-5)\alpha = 25$ and $(5)\alpha = 25$.

•971

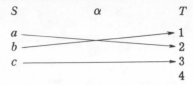

(1) Is α a mapping of S into T?
(2) Is α a mapping of S onto T?
(3) Is α a 1-1 mapping?

(1) yes   (2) no   (3) yes

•972 Let S be the set of integers. Let $\alpha : S \to S$ such that if $s \in S$,
$(s)\alpha = 2s$. *Draw part of the mapping.*
(1) Is α a mapping of S into S?
(2) Is α a mapping of S onto S?
(3) Is α 1-1?

(1) yes   (2) No, for example, 3 is not the image of any $s \in S$.
(3) yes

973 We shall be concerned with mappings of a set S into (or onto)
itself. We have just seen examples of such mappings of S into S
which were:
1. 1-1 and onto
2. onto but not 1-1
3. 1-1 but not onto
4. neither 1-1 nor onto

Let S be the set of integers and $\alpha : S \to S$ such that $(a)\alpha = a$.
(1) Is α 1-1?
(2) Is α onto?

(1) yes   (2) yes

974 Let S be the set of positive integers and $\alpha : S \to S$ such that
$$(s)\alpha = \begin{cases} 1 \text{ if } s \text{ is odd} \\ \dfrac{s}{2} \text{ if } s \text{ is even} \end{cases}$$

You should sketch part of the mapping before answering.
(1) Is α a mapping of S into S?
(2) Is α a mapping of S onto S?
(3) Is α 1-1?

(1) yes   (2) yes
(3) No, 1 is the image of more than one element of S.

975 **(1)** A mapping $\alpha : S \rightarrow T$ is a rule of correspondence which associates with _____ $s \in S$ a(n) _____ $t \in T$. That is:
  (2) for each $s \in S$, there exists a $t \in T$ such that _____.
  (3) if $(s)\alpha = t_1$ and $(s)\alpha = t_2$, then _____.

---

(1) each (or every),   unique   **(2)** $(s)\alpha = t$ **(3)** $t_1 = t_2$

---

976 For example, let S be the set of integers and $\alpha : x \rightarrow 3x$. Let us prove that α is a mapping from S into S. (Sketch part of the mapping.)
  (1) For each $s \in S$, there is a $3s \in S$ (since multiplication is a binary operation in S) such that _____. Suppose $(s)\alpha = t_1$ and $(s)\alpha = t_2$. $\therefore 3s = t_1$ and $3s = t_2$.
  (2) $\therefore$ _____.
  (3) Therefore S is a(n) _____.

---

(1) $(s)\alpha = 3s$ **(2)** $t_1 = t_2$ **(3)** mapping of S *into* S

---

977 Suppose S is the set of rational numbers and $\alpha : x \rightarrow 1/x$. Is $\alpha : S \rightarrow S$?
Note: for *every* $s \in S$, is there a $\frac{1}{s} \in S$?

Not necessarily, if $s = 0$, $\frac{1}{s}$ not defined; therefore α is not a mapping of S into S.

---

978 If we alter frame 977 and take S as the nonzero rational numbers and $\alpha : x \rightarrow \frac{1}{x}$, let us see if $\alpha : S \rightarrow S$.

For all $s \in S$, there is a $\frac{1}{s} \in S$ (since division is a binary operation in the set of nonzero rational numbers) such that $(s)\alpha = \frac{1}{s}$.

If $(s)\alpha = t_1$ and $(s)\alpha = t_2$, then ____ $= t_1$ and ____ $= t_2$
Therefore α is a mapping of S into S.

$\frac{1}{s}$, $\frac{1}{s}$

---

979 A mapping of S into T is an onto mapping if every element of T is the image of some element of S; that is, if for each $t \in T$, _____.

---

there exists an $s \in S$ such that $(s)\alpha = t$

980   For example, consider the mapping of frame 979: $\alpha : x \rightarrow \dfrac{1}{x}$ where S is the set of nonzero rationals. We proved that α is a mapping of S into S. Let us prove that α is an onto mapping: for each $t \in S$, there is a $\dfrac{1}{t} \in S$ and $\left(\dfrac{1}{t}\right)\alpha = $ ____. Therefore each t is the image of some s and α is an onto mapping.

$\dfrac{1}{1/t}$ or t

981   A mapping $\alpha : S \rightarrow T$ is 1-1 if and only if no $t \in T$ is the image of more than one $s \in S$, that is: if $(s_1)\alpha = t$ and $(s_2)\alpha = t$, then ____.

$s_1 = s_2$

982   For example, let S be the set of nonzero rational numbers and $\alpha : x \rightarrow \dfrac{1}{x}$ as in frames 977 and 981. We have established that α is an onto mapping. Let us prove that α is 1-1, that is, prove that no $t \in T$ is (1) ____.
Further, suppose $(s_1)\alpha = t$ and $(s_2)\alpha = t$
$$(s_1)\alpha = \frac{1}{s_1} \text{ and } (s_2)\alpha = \frac{1}{s_2}$$
$$\therefore \frac{1}{s_1} = t \text{ and } \frac{1}{s_2} = t$$
$$s_1 = \frac{1}{t} \text{ and } s_2 = \frac{1}{t}$$
(2)   so, $s_1 = $ ____
(3)   Therefore α is ____.

(1)   the image of more than one $s \in S$
(2) s_2 (3)   a 1-1 mapping

983   *Definition*: a mapping α from S into T is *reversible* if it is onto and 1-1.
For example, let S be the set of nonzero rationals and $\alpha : x \rightarrow \dfrac{1}{x}$.
We have shown that α is a 1-1 mapping of S onto S, so α is _____.

reversible

984

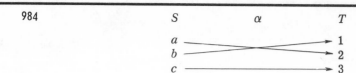

(1) Is α a mapping from S into T?
(2) Is α an onto mapping?
(3) Is α 1-1?
(4) Is α a reversible mapping? Why?

(1) yes   (2) yes   (3) yes
(4) Yes, it is a 1-1 and onto mapping.

985 A mapping $\alpha : S \rightarrow T$ is a reversible mapping if it is ____ and ____.

1-1,   onto

986

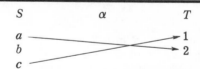

Is α a reversible mapping? Why?

No, α is not 1-1.

987

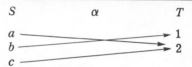

Is α a reversible mapping of S to T? Why?

No, α is not even a mapping of S into T.

988

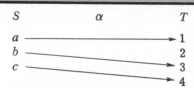

Is α a reversible mapping of S into T? Why?

No, α is not *onto*.

989

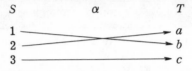

α can be considered a reversible mapping of S into T_1, where
$T_1 =$ _____ .

$\{1, 3, 4\}$

•990

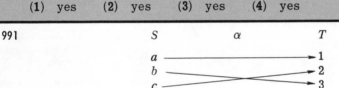

(1) Is α a mapping of S into T?
(2) Is α an onto mapping?
(3) Is α 1-1?
(4) Is α reversible?

---

(1) yes   (2) yes   (3) yes   (4) yes

991

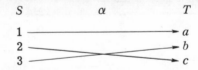

α is a mapping of S into T since for all $s \in S$ there is a unique
$t \in T$ such that $(s)\alpha = t$. α is not onto since _____ . α is 1-1
since if $(s_1)\alpha = t$ and $(s_2)\alpha = t$, then $s_1 = s_2$.

$4 \in T$, and there is no $s \in S$ such that $(s)\alpha = 4$

•992

$$S \qquad \alpha \qquad T$$

Is α reversible? Why?

Yes, α is 1-1 and onto.

993 Let S be the set of integers and $\alpha : x \rightarrow x + 2$. Copy this problem on a separate sheet of paper. In frames 994 to 996 we will prove that α is a reversible mapping of S into S.
   (1) $(3)\alpha = $ _____   (2) $(n - 5)\alpha = $ _____
   (3) $(\_\_\_)\alpha = -7$ (4) $(\_\_\_)\alpha = r$

---

(1) 5   (2) $n - 3$ (3) -9 (4) $r - 2$

---

994 α is a mapping from S into S because:
   (1) for each $s \in S$, $s + 2 \in S$ (since addition is a binary operation in S) such that $(s)\alpha = $ _____.
   (2) If $(s)\alpha = t_1$ and $(s)\alpha = t_2$, $s + 2 = t_1$, $s + 2 = t_2$ $\therefore$ _____.
   (3) Therefore α is a _____.

---

(1) $s + 2$ (2) $t_1 = t_2$ (3) mapping of S into S

---

995 α is a 1-1 mapping because: if $(s_1)\alpha = t$ and $(s_2)\alpha = t$,
   then $s_1 + 2 = t$ and $s_2 + 2 = t$,
   $s_1 = t - 2$ $s_2 = t - 2$
   $\therefore$ _____. And thus α is _____.

$s_1 = s_2$,   1-1

---

996 α is an *onto* mapping because: let $t \in S$; then $t - 2 \in S$ (since subtraction is a binary operation in S) and $(t - 2)\alpha = $ _____. Therefore α is _____.

---

t,   an *onto* mapping

---

997 We have proved that α is a 1-1 mapping of S onto S, so α is a _____ mapping.

---

reversible

998

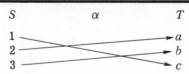

α is a reversible mapping of S to T.

▼

Define $\alpha^{-1}: T \to S$ as follows:
$\qquad \alpha^{-1}: x \to y$ if $(y)\alpha = x$.
For example, $(b)\alpha^{-1} = 3$ since $(3)\alpha = b$. Similarly, $(a)\alpha^{-1} = $ ____
since ____ $\alpha = a$.

2,   (2)

---

999 Consider another reversible mapping α:

S	α	T	T	α^{-1}	S
1		a	a		1
2		b	b		2
3		c	c		3

α is a reversible mapping of S to T.
Define $\alpha^{-1}: T \to S$ by: $(y)\alpha^{-1} = x$ if and only if $(x)\alpha = y$.
For example, $(c)\alpha^{-1} = 2$ since $(2)\alpha = c$.
(1)   Since $(3)\alpha = b$, we have that $(\_\_\_)\alpha^{-1} = \_\_\_\_$.
(2)   Draw the arrows in the representation of α^{-1}. Is α^{-1} a mapping
of T into S?

---

(1) b,   3
(2) α^{-1}

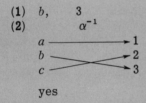

yes

1000 In frames 998 and 999 we have had a reversible mapping $f: S \to T$
and have defined a mapping f^{-1} of T into S by mapping each $t \in T$
into the $s \in S$ of which t was the image under f. For example, if
$f: x \to y$ where $x \in S$ and $y \in T$, then $f^{-1}: \_\_\_ \to \_\_\_$.

$y \to x$

1001 S f T T f^{-1} S

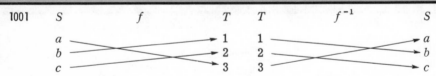

Note: f is a reversible mapping of S into T and f^{-1} is defined
by: $(t)f^{-1} = s$ if and only if $(s)f = t$.

▼

Thus (1) $f^{-1} = b$ because ____ f = ____.
  (2) $f^{-1} =$ ____ because _____.
  (3) $f^{-1} =$ ____ because _____.
  (4) Is f^{-1} a mapping of T into S?

---

(1) b,   1   (2) c, $(c)f = 2$
(3) a, $(a)f = 3$ (4)   yes

1002

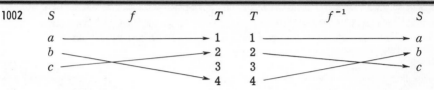

(1) Is f a mapping of S into T?
(2) Is f^{-1} a mapping of T into S?

---

(1)   Yes   (2)   No, 3 has no image under f^{-1}.

1003

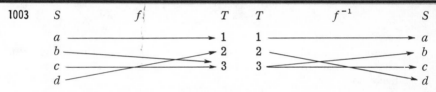

(1) Is f a mapping of S into T?
(2) Is f^{-1} a mapping of T into S?

---

(1)   yes
(2)   No, $(3)f^{-1}$ is not unique; that is, $(3)f^{-1} = b$ and $(3)f^{-1} = c$
   but $b \neq c$

1004   From frames 1002 and 1003 you see that given $f : S \to T$ and defining $f^{-1} : y \to x$ if and only if $(x)f = y$, f^{-1} is not necessarily a
mapping of T into S.

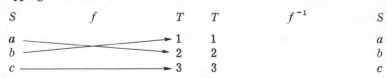

▼

Draw the arrows representing the mapping defined by f^{-1} and note that in this case f^{-1} is a mapping of T into S.

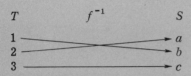

1005 *Note*: If $f : S \to T$ is *not* onto, then if we define f^{-1} as above, there will be some $t \in T$ for which $(t)f^{-1}$ does not exist, so f^{-1} _____ (will or will not) be a mapping of T into S.

will not

1006 For example:

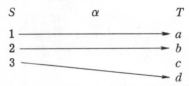

α is a 1-1 mapping of S into T, but α is not an *onto* mapping. Suppose we define $\alpha^{-1} : y \to x$ if and only if $(x)\alpha = y$. Then $(b)\alpha^{-1} = 2$ because _____.

Note that there is no $s \in S$ such that $(s)\alpha = c$. Therefore $(c)\alpha^{-1}$ does not exist, so α^{-1} is not a mapping of T into S.

$(2)\alpha = b$

1007 Note also that if $\alpha : S \to T$ is *not* 1-1, then for at least one $t \in T$, there exist s_1 and $s_2 \in S$ such that $(s_1)\alpha = t$ and $(s_2)\alpha = t$ and $s_1 \neq s_2$; so $(t)\alpha^{-1}$ will not be unique; so α^{-1} _____ (will or will not) be a mapping of $T \to S$.

will not

1008 For example:

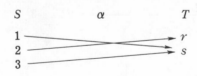

▼

α is a mapping from S *onto* T but is not 1-1. If we define
$\alpha^{-1}: y \rightarrow x$ if and only if $(x)\alpha = y$, we see that $(1)\alpha = s$ and $(3)\alpha = s$.
Therefore we would have
(1) $(s)\alpha^{-1} = $ ____ and
(2) $(s)\alpha^{-1} = $ ____, so α^{-1} is not a mapping of T into S.

---

(1) 1   **(2)** 3

1009   Suppose:

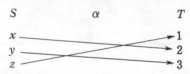

α is a 1-1 mapping of S onto T, that is, α is a reversible mapping.
Again define $\alpha^{-1}: y \rightarrow x$ if and only if $(x)\alpha = y$.
Then **(1)** $(1)\alpha^{-1} = $ ____
      (2) $(2)\alpha^{-1} = $ ____
      (3) $(3)\alpha^{-1} = $ ____
      (4) Is α^{-1} a mapping of T into S?

---

(1) z **(2)** x **(3)** y **(4)** yes

1010   The question we are trying to answer is this: suppose $\alpha: S \rightarrow T$ and
we try to map T into S by mapping each $t \in T$ into the $s \in S$ of
which t is the image under α; that is, $(t)\alpha^{-1} = s$ if and only if
(1) _____.

(2) What kind of a mapping must α be in order that α^{-1} also be a
mapping? Take a guess.

---

(1) $(s)\alpha = t$ **(2)** α must be a reversible mapping.

1011   Suppose:

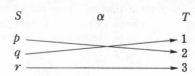

α is a *reversible* mapping of S into T.

▼

(1) Draw α^{-1} where $\alpha^{-1} : y \to x$ if and only if $(x)\alpha = y$.
(2) Is α^{-1} a mapping of T into S?
(3) Is α^{-1} reversible?

(1) T α S

$$
\begin{array}{ccc}
1 & & p \\
2 & & q \\
3 & & r
\end{array}
$$

(2) yes
(3) yes

1012   *Theorem*: If $\alpha : S \to T$ is a reversible mapping, then $\alpha^{-1} : T \to S$
where $\alpha^{-1} : y \to x$ if and only if $(x)\alpha = y$ is a reversible mapping.
To prove this theorem, we must show that:
α^{-1} is a mapping of T into S.
α^{-1} is onto.
α^{-1} is ____ .

1-1

1013   We have given that $\alpha : S \to T$ is a reversible mapping, so we know:
1. α is a mapping so (1) for each $s \in S$ there exists a $t \in T$ such
   that _____ .
2. α is a mapping so (2) if $(s)\alpha = t_1$ and $(s)\alpha = t_2$, then _____ .
3. α is onto, so (3) for each $t \in T$, there is an $s \in S$ such that

   _____ .
4. α is 1-1, so (4) if $(s_1)\alpha = t$ and $(s_2)\alpha = t$, then _____ .
Copy these four statements (with correct answers) on another sheet
of paper and save.

(1) $(s)\alpha = t$ (2) $t_1 = t_2$ (3) $(s)\alpha = t$ (4) $s_1 = s_2$

1014   We wish to show first that α^{-1} is a mapping of T into S.
1. Suppose $t \in T$. There is an $s \in S$ such that $(s)\alpha = t$ from statement 3. Therefore by definition $(t)\alpha^{-1} =$ ___(1)___ .
2. Suppose $(t)\alpha^{-1} = s_1$ and $(t)\alpha^{-1} = s_2$.
   Then $(s_1)\alpha = t$ and $(s_2)\alpha = t$.
   Then by statement 4 ___(2)___ .
From statements 1 and 2, α^{-1} is a ___(3)___ .

(1) s
(2) $s_1 = s_2$
(3) mapping of T into S

1015 α^{-1} is a mapping of T *onto* S.

  Proof: Suppose $s \epsilon S$; then by statement 1 there is a $t \epsilon T$ such that $(s)\alpha = t$. Then by definition $(\underline{})\alpha^{-1} = \underline{}$, so each $s \epsilon S$ is an image of some $t \epsilon T$ under α^{-1}. Therefore α^{-1} is a mapping of $\underline{}$.

  $t,$ $s,$ T onto S

1016 α^{-1} is a 1-1 mapping:

  Proof: Suppose $(t_1)\alpha^{-1} = s$ and $(t_2)\alpha^{-1} = s$. Then $(s)\alpha = t_1$ and $(s)\alpha = t_2$. By statement 2, then, $\underline{}$. Therefore α^{-1} is a 1-1 mapping.

  $t_1 = t_2$

1017 If α is a reversible mapping from S to T, $(s)\alpha = t$, then the mapping $\alpha^{-1} : T \rightarrow S$ defined by $(t)\alpha^{-1} = s$, is called the *inverse of* α. In frames 1014 to 1016 we have proved that α^{-1} is a 1-1 mapping of T onto S. Therefore α^{-1} is a $\underline{}$ mapping.

  reversible

1018 Let S be the set of positive integers and T be the set of even positive integers. Let $\alpha : x \rightarrow 2x$.

  For example, $(1)\alpha = 2$
       $(5)\alpha = \underline{\quad (1) \quad}$

  Obviously, α is a reversible mapping. (Illustrate part of the mapping.) Then α^{-1}, as defined above, is the inverse mapping and is a reversible mapping from T to S.

  Thus $(4)\alpha^{-1} = 2$ because $(2)\alpha = 4$.
     $(8)\alpha^{-1} = \underline{\quad (2) \quad}$ because $\underline{\quad (3) \quad}$.

  (1) 10 **(2)** 4 **(3)** **(4)**$\alpha = 8$

1019 *Definition*: A mapping from a set S into S is called a *transformation* of S. Thus, if S is the set of integers and $\alpha : x \rightarrow x + 1$, α maps S into S; so we call α a(n) $\underline{}$.

  transformation of S

1020 Suppose $\alpha : S \rightarrow S$ is a reversible mapping from S to S. We call it a reversible transformation of S. α^{-1}, the inverse of α, is also a reversible mapping from S to S; so it also is a(n) $\underline{}$.

  reversible transformation of S

1021   Let S be the set of integers and $\alpha : x \rightarrow x + 1$ and $\beta : x \rightarrow 2x$ be two transformations of S. Thus $(3)\alpha =$ ____ , $(-5)\beta =$ ____ .

4, -10

1022   Again let S be the set of integers and $\alpha : x \rightarrow x + 1$ and $\beta : x \rightarrow 2x$ be two transformations of S. $[(3)\alpha]\beta$ indicates the image under β of the image of 3 under α. Since $(3)\alpha = 4$, $[(3)\alpha]\beta = [4]\beta$.

But $[4]\beta = 8$
$\therefore [(3)\alpha]\beta = 8$
Similarly, $[(-2)\alpha]\beta = [$____$]\beta =$ ____ .

-1, -2

1023   Again let S be the set of integers and $\alpha : x \rightarrow x + 1$ and $\beta : x \rightarrow 2x$ be two transformations of S.

Note: $[(5)\alpha]\beta = [6]\beta = 12$,
    but $[(5)\beta]\alpha = [$____$]\alpha =$ ____ .

10,   11

V. Transformation Group

1024   If S is a nonempty set and α and β are two transformations of S, then $[(s)\alpha]\beta$ indicates the mapping of s under α followed by the mapping of this image under β. The result will be to map each $s \in S$ into some image. The result will be a transformation of S which we will denote by $\alpha \cdot \beta$. For example:

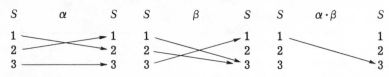

$(1)\alpha \cdot \beta = [(1)\alpha]\beta = (2)\beta = 3$
Complete the arrows for $\alpha \cdot \beta$.

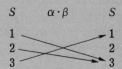

1025   Once again, given a nonempty set S and two transformations of S, say α and β, then by $\alpha \cdot \beta$ we mean the transformation: $(s)\alpha \cdot \beta = [(s)\alpha]\beta$; that is:

map s into its image under ____, then map the result into its image under ____ .

$\alpha, \quad \beta$

1026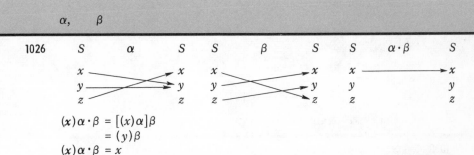

$(x)\alpha \cdot \beta = [(x)\alpha]\beta$
$\qquad\qquad = (y)\beta$
$(x)\alpha \cdot \beta = x$

Under the transformation $\alpha \cdot \beta$ x is mapped into x. Complete the arrows for $\alpha \cdot \beta$.

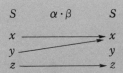

1027   Given a nonempty set S, if we let M_S be the set of *all* transformations of S, $\alpha, \beta \in M_S$, then $\alpha \cdot \beta$ is a transformation of S. Thus to each ordered pair of elements of M_S there is assigned a unique element of M_S called their product. If we call this process multiplication, you see that multiplication is a(n) _____ .

binary operation in M_S

1028   Let S be a nonempty set and $I : S \rightarrow S$ according to the rule $(x)I = x$ for all $x \in S$. Obviously, I is a reversible transformation. Note that it maps every element of S into itself. Thus, if $7 \in S$, $(7)I =$ ____ .

7

1029   Suppose:

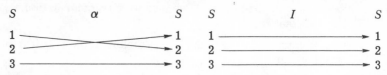

Show a representation of $\alpha \cdot I$.

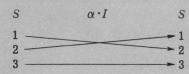

Compare $\alpha \cdot I$ and α.

1030

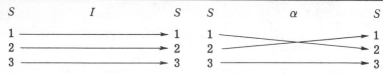

Show a representation of $I \cdot \alpha$.

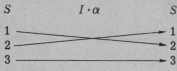

Compare $I \cdot \alpha$ with α.

1031   Let S be the set of integers and $\alpha : x \to x + 3$ and $I : a \to a$ be two transformations of S.

Then $(7)\alpha \cdot I = [(7)\alpha]I$
$\qquad\qquad = [10]I$
$\qquad\qquad = 10$
$\quad(-5)\alpha \cdot I = \underline{\qquad(1)\qquad}$
$\qquad\qquad = \underline{\qquad(2)\qquad}$
$\qquad\qquad = \underline{\qquad(3)\qquad}$

(1) $[(-5)\alpha]I$
(2) $[-2]I$
(3) -2

1032 Recall that if α is a reversible transformation, α^{-1} exists and is a reversible transformation:

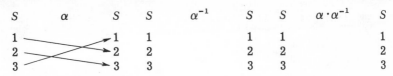

Draw the remaining arrows.

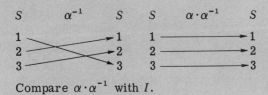

Compare $\alpha \cdot \alpha^{-1}$ with I.

1033 Suppose α is a reversible transformation of S. Then α^{-1} is a reversible transformation of S.

Suppose $(s)\alpha = t$; then $(t)\alpha^{-1} = \underline{\quad (1) \quad}$.
$$(s)\alpha \cdot \alpha^{-1} = [(s)\alpha]\alpha^{-1}$$
$$= [\underline{\quad (2) \quad}]\alpha^{-1}$$
so $(s)\alpha \cdot \alpha^{-1} = \underline{\quad (3) \quad}$
Note: $(s)I = \underline{\quad (4) \quad}$

(1) s
(2) t
(3) s
(4) s

1034 If α and β are two transformations on a nonempty set S, then by $\alpha \cdot \beta$ is meant the result of mapping each $s \in S$ into its unique image, say t, under α and then mapping t into its unique image, say u, under β. Then $(s)\alpha \cdot \beta = [(s)\alpha]\beta$
$$= [t]\beta$$
$$= u$$
Since each $s \in S$ is mapped into a unique $u \in S$ under $\alpha \cdot \beta$, then $\alpha \cdot \beta$ is also a(n) _____.

transformation of S or mapping of S into S

1035   For example, suppose S is the set of integers and $\alpha : x \rightarrow x^2$ and
        $\beta : x \rightarrow x - 2$ are two transformations of S.

        Then $(3)\alpha \cdot \beta = [(3)\alpha]\beta$
                         $= [9]\beta$
             $\therefore (3)\alpha \cdot \beta = 7$

        Find $(3)\beta \cdot \alpha$

        $(3)\beta \cdot \alpha = [(3)\beta]\alpha$
                      $= [1]\alpha$
                      $= 1$
        Note: $(3)\alpha \cdot \beta \neq (3)\beta \cdot \alpha$

1036   Let S be the set of integers and $\alpha : x \rightarrow 2x$ and $\beta : x \rightarrow x + 1$ for all
        $x \in S$ be two transformations. $\alpha \cdot \beta$ is also a transformation of S.

        $(3)\alpha \cdot \beta = [(3)\alpha]\beta$ $(3)\beta \cdot \alpha = \underline{\quad (3) \quad}$
                      $= [\underline{\quad (1) \quad}]\beta$ $= \underline{\quad (4) \quad}$
                      $= \underline{\quad (2) \quad}$ $= \underline{\quad (5) \quad}$

        (1) 6   **(2)** 7   **(3)** $[(3)\beta]\alpha$ **(4)** $[4]\alpha$ **(5)** 8

1037   Given a nonempty set S, let M_S be the set of all transformations of
        S, and for all α, β, $\in M_S$, let $\alpha \cdot \beta : x \rightarrow [(x)\alpha]\beta$. Then $\alpha \cdot \beta$ is a trans-
        formation on S and is an element of M_S. Therefore each ordered
        pair of elements of M_S is associated with a unique element of M_S
        called their product. Thus this multiplication of transformations is
        a(n) _____ in M_S.

        binary operation

1038   For example, let S be the set of integers.

        $\alpha : x \rightarrow x + 1$, $\beta : x \rightarrow 2x$, $\gamma : x \rightarrow 2x + 2$ for all $x \in S$

        Suppose $s \in S$; then $(s)\alpha \cdot \beta = [(s)\alpha]\beta$
                                          $= [\underline{\quad (1) \quad}]\beta$
                                          $= \underline{\quad (2) \quad}$
        Note also that $(s)\gamma = \underline{\quad (3) \quad}$

        (1) $s + 1$ **(2)** $2s + 2$ **(3)** $2s + 2$

1039   Let $f : S \rightarrow T$ and $g : S \rightarrow T$. Suppose that for each $x \in S$, $(x)f = (x)g$.
        Then, as a subset of $S \times T$, $f = g$. In frame 1038 you saw that for
        each $s \in S$, $(s)\alpha \cdot \beta = (s)\gamma$. Thus _____.

        $\alpha \cdot \beta = \gamma$

1040 Suppose S is the set of integers and $\alpha : x \to x^2$, $\beta : x \to x + 2$, $\gamma : x \to x^2 + 2$ for all $x \in S$.

Let $s \in S$; then $(s)\alpha \cdot \beta = [(s)\alpha]\beta$
$$= [s^2]\beta$$
$$= s^2 + 2$$
But $(s)\gamma = s^2 + 2$. So for all $s \in S$, $(s)\alpha \cdot \beta = (s)\gamma$

(1) $\therefore$ ____ = ____.
(2) Find $(s)\beta \cdot \alpha$.
(3) Does $\beta \cdot \alpha = \gamma$?

(1) $\alpha \cdot \beta = \gamma$
(2) $(s)\beta \cdot \alpha = [(s)\beta]\alpha$
$$= [s + 2]\alpha$$
$$= s^2 + 4s + 4$$
(3) no

1041 If α, β are two mappings of S into T and $(s)\alpha = (s)\beta$ for each $s \in S$, then ____.

$\alpha = \beta$

1042 If S is a nonempty set and M_S is the set of all transformations of S, then with each α, $\beta \in S$ there is associated a unique element of S, $\alpha \cdot \beta$, called the product of α and β. Therefore $\cdot$ is a(n) ____ in M_S.

binary operation

1043 Given any set, an equivalence relation, and a binary operation, we are at once interested in the properties which hold in the set. For example, we have seen examples of transformations α and β for which $(s)\alpha \cdot \beta \neq (s)\beta \cdot \alpha$. Therefore $\alpha \cdot \beta \neq \beta \cdot \alpha$; so multiplication of transformations is *not* a(n) ____ binary operation.

commutative

1044 Recall that if $*$ is a binary operation in a set S, then $*$ is associative if and only if ____.

$x * (y * z) = (x * y) * z$ for all $x, y, z \in S$

1045   Let us take a specific example: Let S be the set of integers, and
$\alpha : x \to x + 1$, $\beta : x \to 2x$, $\gamma : x \to 2x - 3$ for all $x \in S$ be three transformations of S.

Let $s \in S$ under $\alpha \cdot (\beta \cdot \gamma)$:

$$(s)\alpha \cdot (\beta \cdot \gamma) = (s + 1)\beta \cdot \gamma$$
$$= [(s + 1)\beta]\gamma$$
$$= [\underline{\quad (1) \quad}]\gamma$$
$$= \underline{\quad (2) \quad}$$

Under $(\alpha \cdot \beta)\gamma$:

$$(s)\alpha \cdot \beta = [(s)\alpha]\beta$$
$$= (s + 1)\beta$$
$$= 2s + 2$$

so $(s)(\alpha \cdot \beta) \cdot \gamma = [(s)\alpha \cdot \beta]\gamma$
$$= [\underline{\quad (3) \quad}]\gamma$$
$$= \underline{\quad (4) \quad}$$

$\therefore \alpha \cdot (\beta \cdot \gamma) = \alpha \cdot (\beta \cdot \gamma)$

(1) $2s + 2$ **(2)** $4s + 1$ **(3)** $2s + 2$ **(4)** $4s + 1$

1046   Let us see if $\cdot$ is an associative binary operation in M_s, the set of
all transformations of a nonempty set S. Let $\alpha, \beta, \gamma \in M_s$ and suppose $(s)\alpha = t$, $(t)\beta = u$, $(u)\gamma = v$.

$(s)(\alpha \cdot \beta) \cdot \gamma = [(s)(\alpha \cdot \beta)]\gamma$ and $(s)\alpha \cdot (\beta \cdot \gamma) = (t)\beta \cdot \gamma$
$ = [((s)\alpha)\beta]\gamma$ $ = [(t)\beta]\gamma$
$ = [(t)\beta]\gamma$ $ = (u)\gamma$
$ = (u)\gamma$ $ = v$
$ = v$

$\therefore (s)(\alpha \cdot \beta) \cdot \gamma = v$ and $(s)\alpha \cdot (\beta \cdot \gamma) = v$
Therefore $(\alpha \cdot \beta) \cdot \gamma = $ _____ **(1)** _____ and $\cdot$ is a(n) _____ **(2)** _____ binary
operation.

(1) $\alpha \cdot (\beta \cdot \gamma)$ **(2)**   associative

1047   Given a nonempty set S, let M_s be the set of all transformations of
S. Multiplication of transformations is a binary operation in M_s and
it is associative but not commutative. Let us see what other properties the set M_s has (under multiplication). Recall that, given a set
T and a binary operation $*$ in T, if there exists an $I \in T$ such that
$I * a = a * I = a$ for all $a \in T$, then I is called the _____
element.

unit or identity

1048   Let S be a nonempty set and $I : x \to x$ for all $x \in S$. Obviously I is
a transformation of S. I simply maps each $s \in S$ into itself. In
fact, I is a 1-1 mapping of S *onto* S, so we would say that I is a(n)
_____ transformation.

reversible

1049 Let S be a nonempty set and $I : x \to x$ be a transformation of S.
  (1) If $s \in S$, $(s)I =$ ____ .
  (2) If $a \in S$, $(a)I =$ ____ .
  (3) If $7 \in S$, $(7)I =$ ____ .

(1) s **(2)** a **(3)** 7

1050 Consider a nonempty set S and let M_S be the set of all transformations of S. Let $I : x \to x$ for all $x \in S$. We found that I is a reversible transformation of S, so $I \in M_S$. Moreover, suppose $\alpha \in M_S$ and
  let $s \in S$. Then there exists a $t \in S$ such that $(s)\alpha = t$.

  Now consider: $(s)\alpha \cdot I = [(s)\alpha]I$ and $(s)I \cdot \alpha = [(s)I]\alpha$
  $\qquad\qquad\qquad\quad = [t]I \qquad\qquad\qquad\qquad\qquad = [\underline{\quad(1)\quad}]\alpha$
  $\qquad\qquad\qquad\quad = t \qquad\qquad\qquad\qquad\qquad\quad = \underline{\quad(2)\quad}$
  So $(s)\alpha \cdot I = (s)\alpha$; $\therefore \underline{\quad(3)\quad} = \alpha$ and $(s)I \cdot \alpha = (s)\alpha$

  $\therefore \alpha \cdot I = I \cdot \alpha = \alpha \qquad\qquad\qquad\qquad \therefore \underline{\quad(4)\quad} = \alpha$

(1) s **(2)** t **(3)** $\alpha \cdot I$ **(4)** $I \cdot \alpha$

1051 *Recall*: Let S be a set having a binary operation $*$ and an identity
  element e. Let $a \in S$. If there exists an element $a^{-1} \in S$ such that
  $a * a^{-1} = a^{-1} * a = e$, then a^{-1} is called the _____ of a under $*$.

inverse

1052 Recall that we proved, if α is a reversible mapping of S to T, then
  $a^{-1} : y \to x$ if and only if $(x)\alpha = y$ is a reversible transformation.
  Note that if $(a)\alpha = b$, then $(\underline{\quad(1)\quad})\alpha^{-1} = \underline{\quad(2)\quad}$.

(1) (b) **(2)** a

1053 Consider

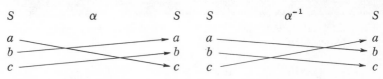

$\qquad S \qquad\qquad \alpha \qquad\qquad S \quad S \qquad\qquad \alpha^{-1} \qquad\qquad S$

$\blacktriangledown$

α is a reversible transformation of S; and therefore α^{-1} as defined previously exists. Show a representation of $\alpha \cdot \alpha^{-1}$.

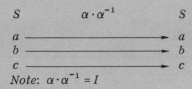

Note: $\alpha \cdot \alpha^{-1} = I$

1054   Consider

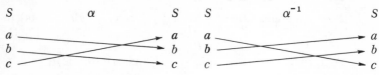

Show a representation of $\alpha^{-1} \cdot \alpha$.

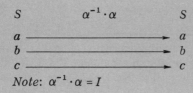

Note: $\alpha^{-1} \cdot \alpha = I$

1055   The question is, if α is any *reversible* transformation of S, is $\alpha \cdot \alpha^{-1} = \alpha^{-1} \cdot \alpha = I$ the identity transformation? Suppose $s \in S$; then there exists a $t \in T$ such that $(s)\alpha = t$. Thus $(t)\alpha^{-1} = s$.
Let $s \in S$: $(s)\alpha \cdot \alpha^{-1} = [(s)\alpha]\alpha^{-1}$
$= (t)\alpha^{-1}$
$\therefore (s)\alpha \cdot \alpha^{-1} = s$ for all $s \in S$.
But also $(s)I = s$ for all $s \in S$
$\therefore$ _____.

$\alpha \cdot \alpha^{-1} = I$

1056   Suppose $s \in S$ and $(s)\alpha^{-1} = t$. Then $(t)\alpha = s$.
Now: $(s)\alpha^{-1} \cdot \alpha = [(s)\alpha^{-1}]\alpha$
$= [t]\alpha$
$(s)\alpha^{-1} \cdot \alpha = s$ for all $s \in S$
Also $(s)I = s$ for all $s \in S$
$\therefore$ _____.

$\alpha^{-1} \cdot \alpha = I$

1057   Therefore, for each reversible transformation α of a nonempty set
        S, there exists a unique α^{-1} which is also reversible and such that
        $\alpha \cdot \alpha^{-1} = \alpha^{-1} \cdot \alpha = \underline{\quad}$.

        I

1058   By now you should have guessed.
        Theorem: Let S be a nonempty set and T_S be the set of all *reversible*
        transformations of S. T_S forms a(n) _____ with respect to mul-
        tiplication of transformations. We shall prove this in frames 1059
        to 1070.

        group

1059   Given a set S having a binary operation $*$, S is a group with respect
        to $*$ if and only if:
        (1)   for all $x, y, z \in S$ _____ (associative law).
        (2)   there exists an $e \in S$ such that _____ for all $x \in S$.
        (3)   for each $a \in S$, there is a unique $a^{-1} \in S$ such that _____.

        (1) $(x * y) * z = x * (y * z)$
        (2) $e * x = x * e = x$
        (3) $a * a^{-1} = a^{-1} * a = e$

1060   If S is a nonempty set and M_S is the set of all transformations of
        S, let T_S be the set of all *reversible transformations* of S. Then
        T_S is a group with respect to multiplication. M_S is not a group since
        a mapping which is not reversible does not have a(n) _____.

        inverse

1061   So, our theorem says that the set T_S of _____ transformations of
        a nonempty set S is a group with respect to multiplication.

        reversible

1062   To begin the proof, we must show that multiplication is a binary
        operation in T_S the set of all reversible mappings; that is, if
        $\alpha, \beta \in T_S$, then _____.

        $\alpha \cdot \beta \in T_S$

1063　In frames 1041 and 1042 we proved *only* that multiplication of transformations is a binary operation; that is, the product of two transformations is a transformation. We need to show that the product of
two reversible transformations is a(n) _____.

reversible transformation

1064　To show that a transformation is reversible, we must prove that it
is ____ and ____.

1-1,　　onto

1065　Suppose α, β are *reversible* transformations of S; then $\alpha \cdot \beta$ is a
transformation of S as seen earlier. Moreover, because β is onto,
if $t \in S$, there is an $s \in S$ such that $(s)\beta = t$ and because α is onto,
there is a $u \in S$ such that $(u)\alpha = s$. So, if $t \in S$, there is a $u \in S$
such that
$$(u)\alpha \cdot \beta = [(u)\alpha]\beta$$
$$= [s]\beta$$
$$= t$$
So for each $t \in S$ there is a $u \in S$ such that $(u)\alpha \cdot \beta = t$; therefore
$\alpha \cdot \beta$ is a(n) _____ transformation.

onto

1066　Now let us prove $\alpha \cdot \beta$ is 1-1. Suppose $(s_1)\alpha \cdot \beta = (s_2)\alpha \cdot \beta$.
Then $[(s_1)\alpha]\beta = [(s_2)\alpha]\beta$
$$\therefore (s_1)\alpha = (s_2)\alpha \text{ since } \beta \text{ is 1-1.}$$
$$\therefore s_1 = s_2 \text{ since } \alpha \text{ is 1-1.}$$
So, if $(s_1)\alpha \cdot \beta = (s_2)\alpha \cdot \beta$, we have that $s_1 = s_2$. Therefore $\alpha \cdot \beta$ is
a(n) ____ transformation.

1-1

1067　In frames 1065 and 1066 we have proved that if α and β are two
reversible transformations in S, then $\alpha \cdot \beta$ is a reversible transformation in S. Therefore multiplication of reversible transformations is a(n) _____.

binary operation in T_S

1068 So, if T_s is the set of all reversible transformations of a nonempty set S, then multiplication is a binary operation in T_s. Moreover, we have shown that multiplication of all transformations of S is associative; and we have seen that there is a reversible transformation $I \in T_s$ such that _____ for all $\alpha \in T_s$.

$I \cdot \alpha = \alpha \cdot I = a$

1069 Finally, we have seen that if $\alpha \in T_s$, there is a reversible transformation $\alpha^{-1} \in T_s$ such that _____.

$\alpha \cdot \alpha^{-1} = \alpha^{-1} \cdot \alpha = I$

1070 So, finally, we see that if T_s is the set of all reversible transformations on a set S, then multiplication of transformations is a binary operation in T_s; and, moreover,
(1) $(\alpha \cdot \beta) \cdot \gamma =$ _____ for all $\alpha, \beta, \gamma \in T_s$.
(2) There is an $I \in T_s$ such that ____ = ____ = ____.
(3) For each $\alpha \in T_s$ there is a ____ $\in T_s$ such that
(4) ____ = ____ = ____.
(5) Therefore T_s is a(n) _____ with respect to multiplication.

(1) $\alpha \cdot (\beta \cdot \gamma)$ (2) $\alpha \cdot I = I \cdot \alpha = \alpha$ (3) α^{-1}
(4) $\alpha^{-1} \cdot \alpha = \alpha \cdot \alpha^{-1} = I$ (5) group

1071 *Definition*: If G is a group with respect to a binary operation $*$, and $*$ is a commutative binary operation, then G is called a *commutative group* (or an Abelian group). Is the transformation group on a set S a commutative group?

No, transformation multiplication is not commutative.

1072 The set S of integers is a group with respect to addition. Also for all $a, b, \in S$ $a + b = b + a$.
Therefore the set of integers is a(n) _____ group with respect to addition.

commutative

1073   Actually you have already seen the transformation group of a cer-
       tain set S. Look at Panel 7. Each permutation of degree 4 is a re-
       versible transformation on S where $S = \{1, 2, 3\}$. So, if we had
       proved the theorem on the transformation group, we would have
       known immediately that the set of all permutations of degree 4 is a
       group with respect to permutation multiplication.
       (1)   In Panel 7 which permutation is really the identity transfor-
             mation?
       (2)   Which permutation is really b^{-1}?

       (1) a
       (2) c

VI. Review Test for Part Three (Answers on page 317)

1 Prove: If G is a group with respect to a binary operation $*$ and $a, b \in G$, then the equation $a * x = b$ has a unique solution in G.

2 If G is a group with respect to a binary operation $*$ and $a, b \in G$, prove that the inverse of $a * b$ is $b^{-1} * a^{-1}$ [or $(a * b)^{-1} = b^{-1} * a^{-1}$].

3 Let $T = \{A, B, C, D\}$ where $A = \{0, 1\}$, $B = \{0\}$, $C = \{1\}$, $D = \phi$. (This is the same as saying "T is the set of all the subsets of $\{0, 1\}$.") Now, if $R, S \in T$, we define the *difference* of R and S, denoted by $R - S$, as follows:

$$R - S = \{x \mid x \in R \text{ and } x \notin S\}$$

Assume that $-$ is a binary operation in T, and prove that it is not commutative.

4 In a group G, if $x * a = x * b$, prove that $a = b$.

5 Let $S = \{5, 6, 7, 8\}$ have a binary operation 0 given in this table.
   (1) Assuming the binary operation is associative, is S a group with respect to 0? If not, why not?
   (2) What is the identity element in this problem?
   (3) What is 7^{-1} in this problem?

0	5	6	7	8
5	8	5	6	7
6	5	6	7	8
7	6	7	8	5
8	7	8	5	6

6 Let N be the set of negative integers and $\alpha : N \rightarrow N$ a mapping as follows: $n(\alpha) = 3n$ for all $n \in N$.
   (1) Is α actually a mapping of N into N? If not, why not?
   (2) Is α a mapping of N onto N? If not, why not?
   (3) Is α a 1-1 mapping of N into N? If not, why not?

7 Let $S = \{1, 2, 3, 4\}$ and
   $\alpha = \{(1,2), (2,2), (3,4), (4,4)\}$
   $\beta = \{(1,3), (2,4), (3,1), (4,2)\}$
   $\gamma = \{(1,1), (2,3), (3,4), (4,2)\}$
   be transformations of S, where the mapping is indicated by ordered pairs. For example, $(3)\gamma = 4$, etc.
   (1) Which of the mappings are reversible?
   (2) Find β^{-1} if it exists.

8 Suppose α is a reversible transformation, so that α^{-1} exists and is also a reversible transformation. Draw the remaining arrows:

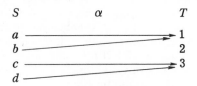

S	α	S	S	α^{-1}	S	S	$\alpha \cdot \alpha^{-1}$	S
1		1	1		1	1		1
2		2	2		2	2		2
3		3	3		3	3		3
4		4	4		4	4		4
5		5	5		5	5		5

9 Let S be the set of integers and $\alpha : x \to 2x + 3$ and $\beta : x \to x - 4$ for all $x \in S$ be two transformations. Assume $\alpha \cdot \beta$ and $\beta \cdot \alpha$ are transformations of S.
   (1) Find $(4)\alpha \cdot \beta$.
   (2) Find $(4)\beta \cdot \alpha$.
   (3) From the preceding answers in this problem, what statement can you make about multiplication of transformations?

10 Suppose:

S	α	T
a		1
b		2
c		3
d		

   (1) Is α a mapping of S into T? of S onto T?
   (2) Is α a 1-1 mapping?
   (3) Is α^{-1} a mapping of T into S? If not, why not?

Part Four   FIELDS

As you know from previous experience, the real numbers form a group with respect to addition and the nonzero real numbers form a group with respect to multiplication. The real numbers are far richer in structure, however, than simply a set which is a group with respect to one operation and a set which is "almost" a group with respect to another operation. An examination of any algebra book will show equations involving both operations. Moreover, you will see that in the set of real numbers, there are interrelationships between the two operations.

In Part Four, we shall consider an algebraic structure called a *field*. This structure has two binary operations and satisfies a set of axioms (essentially, those for a group) under the two operations separately. In addition, a field satisfies an axiom which "meshes" the two operations and produces a structure rich in properties.

I. Review of Binary Relations and Properties

1074   Given a set S and a binary relation R in S, R is reflexive in S if and only if _____ .

for all $x \in S$, $x\,R\,x$ or $(x,x) \in R$

1075   For example, let S be the set of real numbers and $x\,R\,y$ if and only if $x \cdot y \geq 0$, where $\cdot$ is ordinary multiplication. Show that R is reflexive in S.

For all real numbers x, $x^2 \geq 0$. (The square of any real number is ≥ 0.) $\therefore x\,R\,x$ for all $x \in S$.

1076   A binary relation R in a set S is not reflexive in S if and only if

_____ .

there exists an $x \in S$ such that $x\,\not{R}\,x$ or $(x,x) \notin R$

251

1077   Let $S = \{a, b, c\}$
$R = \{(a,a),\ (a,b),\ (b,b),\ (c,b)\}$.
R is not reflexive in S since _____.

$c \in S$, but $(c,c) \notin R$

1078   Given a set S and a binary relation R in S, R is symmetric if and only if _____.

whenever $(x,y) \in R$, then $(y,x) \in R$

1079   For example, suppose S is a set each of whose elements is a set and $X\ R\ Y$ if and only if $X \cap Y = \phi$. Show that R is symmetric.

Suppose $(X,Y) \in R$; then $X \cap Y = \phi$. It follows that $Y \cap X = \phi$, so $(Y,X) \in R$

1080   A binary relation R in a set S is not symmetric if and only if
_____.

there exists an $(x,y) \in R$ such that $(y,x) \notin R$

1081   Let $S = \{1,\ a,\ 17\}$
$R = \{(1,1),\ (a,17),\ (1,a),\ (a,1)\}$.
R is not symmetric since _____.

$(a,17) \in R$ but $(17,a) \notin R$

1082   Given a set S and a binary relation R in S, R is transitive if and only if _____.

whenever $x\ R\ y$ and $y\ R\ z$, then $x\ R\ z$
[or whenever $(x,y) \in R$ and $(y,z) \in R$, then $(x,z) \in R$]

1083   For example, let S be the set of real numbers and $x\ R\ y$ if and only if $x < y$. R _____(is or is not) transitive since _____.

is
if $x < y$ and $y < z$, then $x < z$ (or if $x\ R\ y$ and $y\ R\ z$, then $x\ R\ z$)

1084 A binary relation R in a set S is *not* transitive if and only if
_____.

there exist $(x,y) \in R$ and $(y,z) \in R$ such that $(x,z) \notin R$

1085 Let $S = \{a, b, 17, \Delta\}$
$R = \{(a,a), (a,b), (b,\Delta), (a,\Delta), (\Delta,17), (a,17)\}$.
Is R transitive? Why?

No, $(b,\Delta) \in R$ and $(\Delta,17) \in R$, but $(b,17) \notin R$.

1086 A binary relation "$=$" is an equivalence relation in a set S if and
only if the following properties are satisfied: For all $x, y, z \in S$,
(1) _____ (2) _____ (3) _____

(1) $x = x$
(2) if $x = y$, then $y = x$
(3) if $x = y$ and $y = z$, then $x = z$

1087 For every $x \in S$, $x = x$.   (1) _____ property
If $(x,y) \in R$, then $(y,x) \in R$.   (2) _____ property
If $(x,y) \in R$ and $(y,z) \in R$, then $(x,z) \in R$.   (3) _____ property

(1) reflexive   (2) symmetric   (3) transitive

1088 For example, let S be the set of triangles and congruence $\cong$ be the
relation. $\cong$ represents an equivalence relation in S since:
(1) for all $x \in S$, _____ .
(2) if $x \cong y$, then _____ .
(3) if $x \cong y$ and $y \cong z$, then _____ .

(1) $x \cong x$ (2) $y \cong x$ (3) $x \cong z$

II. Review of Binary Operations and Properties

1089 If S is a set and $*$ is a mapping, $* : S \times S \to S$, then with each
$(x,y) \in S \times S$, there is associated a unique z called the (1) _____ .
Then, if $* : (x,y) \to z$, we write (2) _____ .

(1) image of (x,y) under $*$ (2) $(x,y) * = z$

1090   Such a mapping of $S \times S$ into S is called a binary operation in S; and
       if $(x,y) * = z$, that is, if the (1) _____ of (x,y) under $*$ is z, in-
       stead of writing $(x,y) * = z$, we usually write (2) _____.

---

   (1)   image   (2) $x * y = z$

1091   A binary operation $*$ in S is a mapping of (1) _____, and
       if the unique image of (a,b) under the mapping $*$ is c, instead of
       writing $(a,b) * = c$, we write (2) _____. Suppose S is the set of
       integers and $(x,y) * = x + 2y$. Then $(2,3) * = 8$ would be written
       (3) _____.

---

   (1) $S \times S$ into S (2) $a * b = c$ (3) $2 * 3 = 8$

1092   Let S be the set of integers and $x * y = x + (2 \cdot y)$ where $+$ and $\cdot$
       mean ordinary addition and multiplication. Then $3 * 5 = 3 + 2 \cdot 5$
       so $3 * 5 = 13$. Find $5 * 3$.

   $11 \; [5 * 3 = 5 + (2 \cdot 3) = 11]$

1093   If $*$ is a binary operation in a set S and for all $a,\ b \in S$,
       $a * b = b * a$, then the binary operation is called (1) _____.
       For example, if T is a set of integers, for all $x,\ y \in T$,
       $x + y = y + x$, so addition of integers is a(n) (2) _____ binary
       operation.

---

   (1)   commutative   (2)   commutative

1094   Let S be the set of integers and $x * y = x + (x \cdot y)$. Prove that $*$ is
       not commutative.

   One example is:
   $2 * 3 = 2 + (2 \cdot 3) = 8$
   $3 * 2 = 3 + (3 \cdot 2) = 9$
   $2 * 3 \neq 3 * 2$
   Therefore $*$ is not commutative.

1095   Let S be the set of integers and ordinary subtraction $(-)$ be the bi-
       nary operation. Is subtraction a commutative binary operation in S?
       Why?

   No, for example, $8 - 3 \neq 3 - 8$.

•1096   Let S be the set of integers and $a * b = a^2 + ab$. Prove that $*$ is not commutative.

One example is:
$4 * 3 = 4^2 + 4 \cdot 3 = 28$
$3 * 4 = 3^2 + 3 \cdot 4 = 21$
$4 * 3 \neq 3 * 4$
Therefore $*$ is not commutative.

•1097   Let S be the set of integers and $a * b = a^2 + b^2$. Prove that $*$ is commutative.

$x * y = x^2 + y^2$
$y * x = y^2 + x^2$
In the set of integers, $+$ is commutative, so $x^2 + y^2 = y^2 + x^2$
$\therefore x * y = y * x$ for all x, $y \in S$

1098   Let $S = \{\square, \triangle, \bigcirc\}$ have a binary operation $*$ as given in the following table:

$*$	$\square$	$\triangle$	$\bigcirc$
$\square$	$\bigcirc$	$\square$	$\triangle$
$\triangle$	$\square$	$\triangle$	$\bigcirc$
$\bigcirc$	$\triangle$	$\bigcirc$	$\square$

From the table, for example, $\square * \triangle = \square$
$\triangle * \bigcirc = \bigcirc$
Is $*$ a commutative binary operation in S? Why?

Yes, $x * y = y * x$ for all x, $y \in S$.
(Note the symmetry about the diagonal.)

•1099   Let $S = \{\triangle, \square, \bigcirc\}$ have a binary operation $*$ as shown:

$*$	$\triangle$	$\square$	$\bigcirc$
$\triangle$	$\triangle$	$\bigcirc$	$\square$
$\square$	$\bigcirc$	$\square$	$\bigcirc$
$\bigcirc$	$\square$	$\triangle$	$\bigcirc$

Is $*$ a commutative binary operation in S? Why?

No, $\bigcirc * \square \neq \square * \bigcirc$

1100   If $*$ is a binary operation in a set S and for all $a, b, c \in S$,
$a * (b * c) = (a * b) * c$, we say that $*$ is a(n) _____ binary operation. For example, suppose T is the set of integers and the binary

▼

operation is addition $(+)$. For all x, y, $z \in T$, $(x + y) + z = x + (y + z)$, so addition is a(n) _____ binary operation.

associative,   associative

1101   Let S be the set of integers and $*$ a binary operation such that
$a * b = a + 2b$.
$(3 * 2) * 4 = (3 + 2 \cdot 2) * 4 = 7 * 4$
$= (7 + 2 \cdot 4) = 15$
(1)   Find $3 * (2 * 4)$.
(2)   Is $*$ associative?

(1) $3 * (2 * 4) = 3 * (2 + 2 \cdot 4) = 3 * 10$
$= (3 + 2 \cdot 10) = 23$
(2)   no

1102   Let S be the set of integers and $a * b = a^2 + b^2$. Prove that $*$ is not associative.

One example is:
$(2 * 3) * 4 = (2^2 + 3^2) * 4 = 13 * 4 = 13^2 + 4^2 = 185$
$2 * (3 * 4) = 2 * (3^2 + 4^2) = 2 * 25 = 2^2 + 25^2 = 629$
$(2 * 3) * 4 \neq 2 * (3 * 4)$
Therefore $*$ is not associative.

•1103   Let S be the set of integers and $a * b = 2ab$. Prove that $*$ is commutative.

Let x, $y \in S$
$x * y = 2xy$
$y * x = 2yx$
In the set of integers, ordinary multiplication is commutative, so
$2xy = 2yx$.
$\therefore x * y = y * x$ for all x, $y \in S$
$*$ is commutative.

1104   Let $a * b = 2ab$ be a binary operation in the set of integers. Prove that $*$ is associative.

Let x, y, $z \in S$.
$(x * y) * z = (2xy) * z = 2 \cdot 2xy \cdot z = 4xyz$
$x * (y * z) = x * (2yz) = 2x \cdot 2yz = 4xyz$
$\therefore (x * y) * z = x * (y * z)$ for all x, y, $z \in S$
So $*$ is associative.

1105 If $*$ is a binary operation in a set S and there exists an $e \in S$ such that $e * x = x * e = x$, for all $x \in S$, e is called the (1) _____ element with respect to $*$. Thus, let T be the set of real numbers and multiplication ($\cdot$) be the binary operation. (2) _____is the (3) _____element with respect to $\cdot$ because (4) _____.

(1) identity (or unit)
(2) 1
(3) identity (or unit)
(4) $1 * x = x * 1 = x$ for all $x \in S$

•1106 Let S be the set of real numbers and ordinary addition ($+$) be the binary operation. Then the identity element with respect to addition is (1) _____since (2) _____.

(1) 0   (2) $x + 0 = 0 + x = x$ for all $x \in S$

1107 Let S be the set of permutations of degree 3. Then if
$\begin{pmatrix} 1 & 2 & 3 \\ a & b & c \end{pmatrix} \in S$, where a, b, c are the numbers 1, 2, and 3 in some order,
$\begin{pmatrix} 1 & 2 & 3 \\ 1 & 2 & 3 \end{pmatrix} \cdot \begin{pmatrix} 1 & 2 & 3 \\ a & b & c \end{pmatrix} = \begin{pmatrix} 1 & 2 & 3 \\ a & b & c \end{pmatrix} \cdot \begin{pmatrix} 1 & 2 & 3 \\ 1 & 2 & 3 \end{pmatrix} = \begin{pmatrix} \text{_____} \end{pmatrix}$
So _____is the identity element with respect to permutation multiplication of permutations of degree 3.

$\begin{pmatrix} 1 & 2 & 3 \\ a & b & c \end{pmatrix}, \quad \begin{pmatrix} 1 & 2 & 3 \\ 1 & 2 & 3 \end{pmatrix}$

1108 Let S be any set and M_S be the set of all transformations of S. Let $I : a \to a$ for all $a \in S$. Then if $\phi \in S$, $I \cdot \phi = \phi \cdot I = \phi$. So I is the _____ element with respect to multiplication of transformations.

identity

•1109 Let $S = \{\triangle, \square, \bigcirc\}$ have a binary operation $*$ as shown:

$*$	$\triangle$	$\square$	$\bigcirc$
$\triangle$	$\square$	$\bigcirc$	$\triangle$
$\square$	$\bigcirc$	$\triangle$	$\square$
$\bigcirc$	$\triangle$	$\square$	$\bigcirc$

___(1)___ is the identity element with respect to $*$ in S since, for all $x \in S$, _(2)_ $* x = x *$ _(3)_ $= x$.

(1) $\bigcirc$ (2) $\bigcirc$ (3) $\bigcirc$

1110   Let S be the set of integers and $a * b = 2ab$. Is 1 the identity element with respect to $*$? Prove it.

no
One example is:
   $1 * 5 = 2 \cdot 1 \cdot 5 = 10$
$\therefore 1 * 5 \neq 5$
So 1 is not the identity element under $*$.

1111   Let S be the set of rational numbers and $x * y = 2xy$. Prove that $\frac{1}{2}$ is the identity element with respect to $*$.

Let $x \in S$.
$$\frac{1}{2} * x = 2 \cdot \frac{1}{2} \cdot x = x$$
and $x * \dfrac{1}{2} = 2 \cdot x \cdot \dfrac{1}{2} = x$
$$\frac{1}{2} * x = x * \frac{1}{2} = x \text{ for all } x \in S$$
So $\dfrac{1}{2}$ is the identity element with respect to $*$.

1112   Let $S = \{A, B, C, D\}$ where
$A = \{1, 2\}, \qquad B = \{1\}, \qquad C = \{2\}, \qquad D = \phi$
have a binary operation $\cap$ (ordinary intersection). Does S have an identity element with respect to $\cap$? If so, what is it? (A table will help you.)

Yes, A since for all $X \in S$, $A \cap X = X \cap A = X$.

1113   Let S be the set of *even integers* under ordinary multiplication ($\cdot$). Does S have an identity element under $\cdot$? If so, what is it?

no
Note: $1 \notin S$

1114   Recall that we proved in Part Two that *if* a set S has an identity element e with respect to a binary operation $*$, then e is unique, that is, only one element of S having the properties of an identity element. Therefore we are justified in referring to the identity element e with respect to the binary operation $*$ in S. e is the identity element in S with respect to the binary operation $*$ if and only if

_____ .

$e * x = x * e = x$ for *all* $x \in S$ (or $e * x = x$ and $x * e = x$ for all $x \in S$)

1115 Of course, a set S having more than one binary operation can have more than one identity element, but each is the identity element with respect to a particular binary operation. For example, let S be the set of real numbers.
(1) _____ is the identity element in S with respect to multiplication since _____.
(2) _____ is the identity element in S with respect to addition since _____.

(1) 1, $1 \cdot x = x \cdot 1 = x$ for all $x \in S$
(2) 0, $0 + x = x + 0 = x$ for all $x \in S$

1116 (1) Let S be a set having a binary operation $*$ and an identity element e. If $x \in S$ and there exists an $x^{-1} \in S$ such that $x * x^{-1} = x^{-1} * x = e$, x^{-1} is called a(n) _____.
(2) For example, 0 is the identity element with respect to addition in the set of integers. Consider $5 \in S$. -5 is a(n) _____ of 5 under $+$ because _____ .

(1) inverse of x with respect to $*$
(2) inverse, $5 + (-5) = 0$ and $(-5) + 5 = 0$

1117 In Part Two we proved that if $*$ is an *associative* binary operation in S having an identity element e, then if $x \in S$ has an inverse x^{-1}, then x^{-1} is (1) _____ . That is, x^{-1} is the only element of x having the property of an inverse of x. So, if $*$ is associative, we are justified in calling x^{-1} the (2) _____ of x.

(1) unique   (2) inverse

1118 Let S be the set of rational numbers with respect to multiplication. The identity element with respect to multiplication is (1) _____. The inverse of 7 with respect to multiplication is (2) _____ because (3) _____ .

(1) 1
(2) $\dfrac{1}{7}$
(3) $7 \cdot \dfrac{1}{7} = \dfrac{1}{7} \cdot 7 = 1$ (the identity element)

1119   Let S be the set of rational numbers and $a * b = 2ab$. The identity element is $\frac{1}{2}$. Find the inverse of 7, if it exists. (* is associative, so, if it exists, the inverse of 7 is unique.)

The inverse of 7 is $\frac{1}{28}$ because $7 * \frac{1}{28} = 2 \cdot 7 \cdot \frac{1}{28} = \frac{1}{2}$

$$\frac{1}{28} * 7 = 2 \cdot \frac{1}{28} \cdot 7 = \frac{1}{2} \text{ (the identity element)}$$

•1120   Let $S = \{\triangle, \square, \bigcirc\}$ have a binary operation $*$ as shown:

$*$	$\triangle$	$\square$	$\bigcirc$
$\triangle$	$\triangle$	$\square$	$\bigcirc$
$\square$	$\square$	$\bigcirc$	$\triangle$
$\bigcirc$	$\bigcirc$	$\triangle$	$\bigcirc$

(1)   There is an identity element, _____, in S with respect to $*$ since _____ .

(2) $\square$ has an inverse under $*$, namely, _____, since _____ .

(1) $\triangle$, $\triangle * x = x * \triangle = x$ for all $x \in S$
(2) $\bigcirc$, $\bigcirc * \square = \square * \bigcirc = \triangle$

1121   Let S be the set of permutations of degree 4 with respect to permutation multiplication. The identity element with respect to multiplication is $\begin{pmatrix} 1 & 2 & 3 & 4 \\ 1 & 2 & 3 & 4 \end{pmatrix}$.
Find the inverse of $\begin{pmatrix} 1 & 2 & 3 & 4 \\ 2 & 3 & 1 & 4 \end{pmatrix}$.

$\begin{pmatrix} 1 & 2 & 3 & 4 \\ 3 & 1 & 2 & 4 \end{pmatrix}$ since

$$\begin{pmatrix} 1 & 2 & 3 & 4 \\ 2 & 3 & 1 & 4 \end{pmatrix}\begin{pmatrix} 1 & 2 & 3 & 4 \\ 3 & 1 & 2 & 4 \end{pmatrix} = \begin{pmatrix} 1 & 2 & 3 & 4 \\ 3 & 1 & 2 & 4 \end{pmatrix}\begin{pmatrix} 1 & 2 & 3 & 4 \\ 2 & 3 & 1 & 4 \end{pmatrix} = \begin{pmatrix} 1 & 2 & 3 & 4 \\ 1 & 2 & 3 & 4 \end{pmatrix}$$

1122   Let T be the set of all reversible transformations on the set $\{a, b, c\}$ and the operation be multiplications of transformations. Then the identity transformation I is as shown:

$$I$$

$$a \longrightarrow a$$
$$b \longrightarrow b$$
$$c \longrightarrow c$$

▼

For example, let α be as shown:

$$\alpha$$

then complete

I · α   α · I

a   a   and   a   a
b   b   b   b
c   c   c   c

$I \cdot \alpha$ $\alpha \cdot I$

a ⟶ a   a ⟶ a
b ⟶ b   b ⟶ b
c ⟶ c   c ⟶ c

Note: $I \cdot \alpha = \alpha \cdot I = \alpha$

1123   Let T be the set of all reversible transformations on the set $\{a, b, c\}$. The identity transformation is as shown:

$$I$$

a ⟶ a
b ⟶ b
c ⟶ c

Let $\alpha \in T$ be as shown.

$$\alpha$$

a ⟶ a
b ⟶ b
c ⟶ c

Find α^{-1} (the inverse of α).

α^{-1}

a ⟶ a
b ⟶ b
c ⟶ c

Note: $\alpha^{-1} \cdot \alpha = \alpha \cdot \alpha^{-1} = I$

1124 Let S be the set of rational numbers. **(1)** _____ is the identity element with respect to addition $(+)$.

(2) The inverse of $\frac{1}{3}$ with respect to addition $(+)$ is _____ since _____ .

(1) 0   **(2)** $-\frac{1}{3}$, $\frac{1}{3} + \left(-\frac{1}{3}\right) = \left(-\frac{1}{3}\right) + \left(\frac{1}{3}\right) = 0$

1125 Let S be the set of rational numbers.
(1) _____ is the identity element with respect to multiplication $(\cdot)$.

(2) The inverse of $\frac{1}{3}$ with respect to multiplication is _____ since _____ .

(1) 1   **(2)** 3, $\frac{1}{3} \cdot 3 = 3 \cdot \frac{1}{3} = 1$

1126 A binary operation $*$ in a set S is *well-defined* with respect to an equivalence relation $=$ if and only if:
    if $a = b$ and $c \in S$,
then $a * c = b * c$ and $c * a = c * b$
For example, let T be the set of integers with respect to addition.
If $a = b$ and $c \in T$, $a + c = b + c$ and $c + a = c + b$.
So addition is a(n) _____ binary operation in the set integers.

well-defined

1127 A set S having an equivalence relation $=$ and a well-defined binary operation $*$ is called a *group* if the following properties are satisfied: **(1)** _____ . **(2)** _____ . **(3)** _____ .

(1)   for all $x, y, z \in S$, $(x * y) * z = x * (y * z)$
(2)   there exists $e \in S$ such that $e * x = x * e = x$ for all $x \in S$
(3)   for each $x \in S$ there exists $x^{-1} \in S$ such that $x * x^{-1} = x^{-1} * x = e$

1128 If a group G also satisfies the commutative law, that is, if
(1) _____ = _____ for all $x, y \in G$, then G is called a(n)
(2) _____ group.

(1) $x * y = y * x$ **(2)** commutative (or Abelian)

1129 Consider $S = \{\ldots, -6, -4, -2, 0, 2, 4, 6, 8, \ldots\}$ with respect to addition. Addition is a binary operation in S since the sum of any two elements of S is an element of S.

▼

1. For all $x, y, z \in S$, $x + (y + z) = (x + y) + z$.
2. There exists $0 \in S$ such that, $x + 0 = 0 + x = x$ for all $x \in S$.
3. For every $x \in S$ there is $(-x) \in S$ such that $x + (-x) = (-x) + x = 0$.
Therefore S is a(n) **(1)** _____ with respect to addition. Moreover, for all $x, y \in S$, $x + y = y + x$ so S is a(n) **(2)** _____ .

(1)   group
(2)   commutative group (or Abelian group)

III. Examples of Sets with Two Binary Operations

1130   Let $S = \{\ldots, -6, -4, -2, 0, 2, 4, 6, \ldots\}$. We proved that S is a commutative group with respect to addition. S is *not* a group with respect to multiplication. Why?

S has no identity element with respect to multiplication. (Of course, no element has an inverse with respect to multiplication since "inverse" is meaningless where there is not identity.)

1131   Let $S = \{\ldots, -7, -5, -3, -1, 1, 3, 5, \ldots\}$ with respect to multiplication. Is S a group with respect to multiplication? Why?

No, 1 is the identity element, and multiplication is an associative binary operation in S, but no element of S (except 1) has an inverse in S.

1132   The set of integers is not a group with respect to subtraction. Why?

Subtraction is not an associative binary operation.

1133   The set of rational numbers is not a group with respect to division. Why?

$\frac{x}{0}$ is not defined, so $\div$ is not a binary operation in the set of rational numbers.

1134 The set of rational numbers is not a group with respect to multiplication. Why?

0 has no inverse; that is, there is no rational number x such that $x \cdot 0 = 1$.

1135 The set of *nonzero rational numbers* is a group with respect to multiplication. Is it a commutative group? Why?

Yes, $x \cdot y = y \cdot x$ for all $x, y \in S$.

1136 The set S of rational numbers is a group with respect to addition. Is it a commutative group? Why?

Yes, $x + y = y + x$ for all $x, y \in S$.

1137 So the set of rational numbers is a commutative group with respect to addition [with identity element 0 and inverse of x is $(-x)$] and the set of rational numbers excluding zero is a commutative group with respect to multiplication (with identity element _____ and inverse of x is _____.

1, $\dfrac{1}{x}$

1138 Let us look at another set which will turn out to have the same structure.
$$(3 - 2\sqrt{2}) + (5 + 8\sqrt{2}) = (3 + 5) + (-2 + 8)\sqrt{2}$$
$$= 8 + 6\sqrt{2}$$
$$(2 + 4\sqrt{2}) + (-3 + 5\sqrt{2}) = \underline{\hspace{1cm}}.$$

$-1 + 9\sqrt{2}$

1139 $(a + b\sqrt{2}) + (c + d\sqrt{2}) = \underline{\hspace{2cm}}.$

$(a + c) + (b + d)\sqrt{2}$

1140 $(5 + 3\sqrt{2}) + (0 - 5\sqrt{2}) = \underline{\hspace{2cm}}.$
$(0 - 5\sqrt{2}) + (5 + 3\sqrt{2}) = \underline{\hspace{2cm}}.$

$5 + (-2)\sqrt{2}$
$5 + (-2)\sqrt{2}$

1141 $(3 - 2\sqrt{2}) + [(2 + 5\sqrt{2}) + (-3 + \sqrt{2})] = $ _____ .
$[(3 - 2\sqrt{2}) + (2 + 5\sqrt{2})] + (-3 + \sqrt{2}) = $ _____ .

$(3 - 2\sqrt{2}) + (-1 + 6\sqrt{2}) = 2 + 4\sqrt{2}$
$(5 + 3\sqrt{2}) + (-3 + \sqrt{2}) = 2 + 4\sqrt{2}$

1142 $(3 + 5\sqrt{2}) + (0 + 0\sqrt{2}) = $ _____ .
$(0 + 0\sqrt{2}) + (3 + 5\sqrt{2}) = $ _____ .

$3 + 5\sqrt{2}$
$3 + 5\sqrt{2}$

1143 $(a + b\sqrt{2}) + (0 + 0\sqrt{2}) = $ _____ .
$(0 + 0\sqrt{2}) + (a + b\sqrt{2}) = $ _____ .

$a + b\sqrt{2}$
$a + b\sqrt{2}$

1144 $(3 - 5\sqrt{2}) + (-3 + 5\sqrt{2}) = $ _____ .

$0 + 0\sqrt{2}$

1145 $5 + 7\sqrt{2} + ($ _____ $) = 0 + 0\sqrt{2}$

$-5 + (-7)\sqrt{2}$

1146 $(a + b\sqrt{2}) + ($ _____ $) = 0 + 0\sqrt{2}$

$-a + -b\sqrt{2}$

1147 If a and b are rational numbers, then $a + b$ is a(n) _____ .

rational number

1148 The set S of rational numbers is a *commutative* group with respect to addition, so if x, y, z are rational numbers:
(1) _____ (commutative law)
(2) _____ (associative law)
(3) There exists $0 \in S$ such that _____ .
(4) For every $x \in S$ there exists $-x \in S$ such that _____ .

(1) $x + y = y + x$ (2) $x + (y + z) = (x + y) + z$
(3) $x + 0 = 0 + x = x$ for all $x \in S$ (4) $x + (-x) = (-x) + x = 0$

1149   Let S be the set of all numbers of the form $x + y\sqrt{2}$ where x and y are rational numbers. Then, if $(a + b\sqrt{2}) \, \epsilon \, S$ and $(c + d\sqrt{2}) \, \epsilon \, S$, we define addition $(+)$ in S by:
$(a + b\sqrt{2}) + (c + d\sqrt{2}) = (a + c) + (b + d)\sqrt{2}$
But $a + c$ and $b + d$ are rational numbers, so
$(a + c) + (b + d)\sqrt{2} \, \epsilon$ _____. Therefore $+$ is a binary operation in the set S.

S

1150   For example: $3 + \dfrac{5}{3}\sqrt{2} \, \epsilon \, S$ and $-\dfrac{5}{8} + \dfrac{3}{2}\sqrt{2} \, \epsilon \, S$,

$\left(3 + \dfrac{5}{3}\sqrt{2}\right) + \left(-\dfrac{5}{8} + \dfrac{3}{2}\sqrt{2}\right) =$ _____, which is also a member of S.

$\dfrac{19}{8} + \dfrac{19}{6}\sqrt{2}$

1151   Again let S be the set of numbers of the form $x + y\sqrt{2}$ where x and y are rational. Then, if $a + b\sqrt{2}$ and $c + d\sqrt{2} \, \epsilon \, S$,
$(a + b\sqrt{2}) + (c + d\sqrt{2}) = (a + c) + (b + d)\sqrt{2}$
$(c + d\sqrt{2}) + (a + b\sqrt{2}) = (c + a) + (d + b)\sqrt{2}$
but, since $a, b, c,$ and d are rational numbers, $a + c = c + a$ and $b + d = d + b$.
$\therefore \; (a + b\sqrt{2}) + (c + d\sqrt{2}) = (c + d\sqrt{2}) + (a + b\sqrt{2})$
So addition in S is a(n) _____ binary operation.

commutative

1152   For example: $\left(-3 + \dfrac{5}{8}\sqrt{2}\right) + \left(\dfrac{2}{3} - \dfrac{3}{2}\sqrt{2}\right) =$ _____.

and $\left(\dfrac{2}{3} - \dfrac{3}{2}\sqrt{2}\right) + \left(-3 + \dfrac{5}{8}\sqrt{2}\right) =$ _____.

$-\dfrac{7}{3} + \left(-\dfrac{7}{8}\right)\sqrt{2}$

$-\dfrac{7}{3} + \left(-\dfrac{7}{8}\right)\sqrt{2}$

1153   Let S be the set of numbers of the form $x + y\sqrt{2}$ where x and y are rational numbers. If $a + b\sqrt{2}$, $c + d\sqrt{2}$, $e + f\sqrt{2} \, \epsilon \, S$,

$[(a + b\sqrt{2}) + (c + d\sqrt{2})] + (e + f\sqrt{2})$
$\qquad = [(a + c) + (b + d)\sqrt{2}] + (e + f\sqrt{2})$
$\qquad\qquad = [(a + c) + e] + [(b + d) + f]\sqrt{2}$

and

▼

$(a + b\sqrt{2}) + [(c + d\sqrt{2})] + (e + f\sqrt{2})$
$$= (a + b\sqrt{2}) + [(c + e) + (d + f)\sqrt{2})]$$
$$= [\underline{\quad} + \underline{\quad}] + [b + (d + f)]\sqrt{2}$$

But since a, b, c, d, e, f are rational numbers, $(a + c) + e = a + (c + e)$ and $(b + d) + f = b + (d + f)$.

$\therefore [(a + b\sqrt{2}) + (c + d\sqrt{2})] + (e + f\sqrt{2})$
$$= a + b\sqrt{2} + [(c + d\sqrt{2}) + (e + f\sqrt{2})]$$

Therefore addition is a(n) _____ binary operation in S.

$[a + (c + e)]$
associative

1154   Let S be the set of numbers of the form $x + y\sqrt{2}$ where x and y are rational numbers. $0 + 0\sqrt{2} \in S$ and for every $a + b\sqrt{2} \in S$,
(1) $(a + b\sqrt{2}) + (0 + 0\sqrt{2}) = (a + 0) + (b + 0)\sqrt{2} =$ _____
and
(2) $(0 + 0\sqrt{2}) + (a + b\sqrt{2}) = (0 + a) + (0 + b)\sqrt{2} =$ _____ .
(3)   So $0 + 0\sqrt{2}$ is the _____ element with respect to addition in S.

---

(1) $a + b\sqrt{2}$
(2) $a + b\sqrt{2}$
(3)   identity (or unit)

1155   For example: $(3 + 5\sqrt{2}) + (0 + 0\sqrt{2}) =$ _____ .
                        $(0 + 0\sqrt{2}) + (3 + 5\sqrt{2}) =$ _____ .

$3 + 5\sqrt{2}$
$3 + 5\sqrt{2}$

1156   Let S be the set of numbers of the form $x + y\sqrt{2}$ where x and y are rational numbers. Suppose $a + b\sqrt{2} \in S$. Then there exists $-a$ and $-b$ which are rational numbers, and:
(1) $(a + b\sqrt{2}) + (-a - b\sqrt{2}) =$ _____
and
(2) $(-a - b\sqrt{2}) + (a + b\sqrt{2}) =$ _____ .
(3)   Therefore each $x + y\sqrt{2} \in S$ has a(n) _____ with respect to addition in S.

---

(1) $0 + 0\sqrt{2}$
(2) $0 + 0\sqrt{2}$
(3)   inverse

1157   For example, the additive inverse of $-\frac{7}{3} + \frac{5}{8}\sqrt{2}$ is _____, since

_____.

$\frac{7}{3} - \frac{5}{8}\sqrt{2}$

$\left(-\frac{7}{3} + \frac{5}{8}\sqrt{2}\right) + \left(\frac{7}{3} - \frac{5}{8}\sqrt{2}\right) = 0 + 0\sqrt{2}$ and $\left(\frac{7}{3} - \frac{5}{8}\sqrt{2}\right) + \left(-\frac{7}{3} + \frac{5}{8}\sqrt{2}\right) =$

$0 + 0\sqrt{2}$

1158   In frames 1149 to 1157 we have seen that the set S of numbers of the
form $x + y\sqrt{2}$ where x and y are rational numbers has a binary
operation called addition and such that
1. addition is commutative.
2. addition is associative.
3. there exists an identity element, $0 + 0\sqrt{2}$, with respect to addition.
4. for each element of S there is an inverse with respect to addition.
Therefore S is a(n) _____ with respect to $+$.

commutative group (or Abelian group)

1159 $(3 + 5\sqrt{2})(2 + 4\sqrt{2}) = (3 \cdot 2 + 5 \cdot 4 \cdot 2) + (5 \cdot 2 + 3 \cdot 4)\sqrt{2}$
$= 46 + 22\sqrt{2}$
Similarly,
$(2 - 3\sqrt{2})(4 + \sqrt{2}) =$ _____.

$2 - 10\sqrt{2}$

•1160 $(a + b\sqrt{2})(c + d\sqrt{2}) = (ac + 2bd) + (bc + ad)\sqrt{2}$
$(3 - 2\sqrt{2})(7 + 3\sqrt{2}) =$ _____.

$(3 \cdot 7 - 2 \cdot 3 \cdot 2) + (-2 \cdot 7 + 3 \cdot 3)\sqrt{2}$ or $9 - 5\sqrt{2}$

1161 $\left(\frac{2}{3} + \frac{1}{2}\sqrt{2}\right)\left(\frac{3}{4} - \frac{5}{3}\sqrt{2}\right) =$ _____.

$-\frac{7}{6} - \frac{53}{72}\sqrt{2}$

1162 $(2 + 3\sqrt{2})(1 + 0\sqrt{2}) =$ _____.
$(1 + 0\sqrt{2})(2 + 3\sqrt{2}) =$ _____.

$2 + 3\sqrt{2}$
$2 + 3\sqrt{2}$

1163 $(2 + 3\sqrt{2})\left(-\dfrac{1}{7} + \dfrac{3}{14}\sqrt{2}\right) =$ _____ .

$1 + 0\sqrt{2}$

•1164 $\left(-\dfrac{1}{7} + \dfrac{3}{14}\sqrt{2}\right)(2 + 3\sqrt{2}) =$ _____ .

$1 + 0\sqrt{2}$

1165 $\left(-\dfrac{1}{7} + \dfrac{2}{7}\sqrt{2}\right)(1 + 2\sqrt{2}) =$ _____ .

$1 + 0\sqrt{2}$

1166 $(2 - 3\sqrt{2})(5 + 2\sqrt{2}) =$ _____ .
$(5 + 2\sqrt{2})(2 - 3\sqrt{2}) =$ _____ .

$-2 - 11\sqrt{2}$
$-2 - 11\sqrt{2}$

1167 $[(3 + 2\sqrt{2})(2 - 5\sqrt{2})](1 - 3\sqrt{2}) = [-14 - 11\sqrt{2}\,(1 - 3\sqrt{2})] = 52 + 31\sqrt{2}$
$(3 + 2\sqrt{2})[(2 - 5\sqrt{2})(1 - 3\sqrt{2})] =$ _____ .
The _____ law holds for this example.

$52 + 31\sqrt{2}$,　　associative

1168 Let S be the set of numbers of the form $x + y\sqrt{2}$ where x and y are rational numbers. Then, if $a + b\sqrt{2}$ and $c + d\sqrt{2} \in S$,
$(a + b\sqrt{2})(c + d\sqrt{2}) = (ac + 2bd) + (bc + ad)\sqrt{2}$. But $ac + 2bd$ and $bc + ad$ are rational numbers, so the product of two elements of S is an element of S. Therefore multiplication is a(n) _____ in S.

binary operation

1169 Let S be the set of numbers of the form $x + y\sqrt{2}$ where x and y are rational numbers. Then, if $a + b\sqrt{2}$, $c + d\sqrt{2} \in S$,

$(a + b\sqrt{2})(c + d\sqrt{2}) = (ac + 2bd) + (bc + ad)\sqrt{2}$
$(c + d\sqrt{2})(a + b\sqrt{2}) = (ca + 2db) + (cb + da)\sqrt{2}$

and since a, b, c, d are rational numbers, $ac + 2bd = ca + 2db$ and $bc + ad = cb + da$.

▼

$\therefore (a + b\sqrt{2})(c + d\sqrt{2}) = (c + d\sqrt{2})(a + b\sqrt{2})$

So multiplication in S is a(n) _____ binary operation.

---

commutative

1170   Let S be the set of numbers of the form $x + y\sqrt{2}$ where x and y are rational numbers. It can be shown that if $a + b\sqrt{2}$, $c + d\sqrt{2}$, $e + f\sqrt{2} \in S$,

$$[(a + b\sqrt{2})(c + d\sqrt{2})](e + f\sqrt{2}) = (a + b\sqrt{2})[(c + d\sqrt{2})(e + f\sqrt{2})]$$

that is, that multiplication in S is a(n) _____ binary operation.

---

associative

1171   Let S be the set of numbers of the form $x + y\sqrt{2}$ where x and y are rational numbers. $1 + 0\sqrt{2} \in S$ and note: If $a + b\sqrt{2} \in S$,
(1) $(1 + 0\sqrt{2})(a + b\sqrt{2}) = $ _____ .
(2) $(a + b\sqrt{2})(1 + 0\sqrt{2}) = $ _____ .
(3)   Therefore $1 + 0\sqrt{2}$ is the _____ with respect to multiplication in S.

---

(1) $a + b\sqrt{2}$
(2) $a + b\sqrt{2}$
(3)   identity (or unit) element

1172   Let S be the set of numbers of the form $x + y\sqrt{2}$ where x and y are rational numbers. Suppose $a + b\sqrt{2} \in S$ where both a and b are not zero.

$$\frac{a}{a^2 - 2b^2} - \frac{b}{a^2 - 2b^2}\sqrt{2} \in S$$

Then $(a + b\sqrt{2})\left(\dfrac{a}{a^2 - 2b^2} - \dfrac{b}{a^2 - 2b^2}\sqrt{2}\right) = $ _____

and $\left(\dfrac{a}{a^2 - 2b^2} - \dfrac{b}{a^2 - 2b^2}\sqrt{2}\right)(a + b\sqrt{2}) = $ _____

Therefore, except for $0 + 0\sqrt{2}$, every element of S has an inverse with respect to multiplication.

$1 + 0\sqrt{2}$
$1 + 0\sqrt{2}$

1173   Let S be the set of numbers of the form $x + y\sqrt{2}$ with x and y rational numbers. In frames 1168 to 1172 we have seen that multiplication is a binary operation in S and is such that:

▼

1. multiplication is associative and commutative.
2. there exists an identity element $\epsilon\ S$, $1 + 0\sqrt{2}$.
3. every element of S, except $0 + 0\sqrt{2}$, has an inverse with respect to multiplication.

Therefore the set S of the form $x + y\sqrt{2}$ with x and y 'rational and both x and $y \neq 0$ is a(n) _____ with respect to multiplication.

---

commutative group

1174 So we see that the set S of numbers of the form $x + y\sqrt{2}$ is a commutative group with respect to addition where **(1)** _____ is the identity element with respect to addition and the additive inverse of $a + b\sqrt{2}$ is **(2)** _____. Moreover, S, excluding the element $0 + 0\sqrt{2}$, is a commutative group with respect to multiplication where **(3)** _____ is the identity with respect to multiplication and the multiplicative inverse of

$a + b\sqrt{2}$ is $\dfrac{a}{a^2 - 2b^2} - \dfrac{b}{a^2 - 2b^2}\sqrt{2}$

---

(1) $\ 0 + 0\sqrt{2}$ **(2)** $\ -a - b\sqrt{2}$ **(3)** $\ 1 + 0\sqrt{2}$

1175 Let $S = \{0, 1, 2\}$ and define a binary operation in S as follows: if $a, b \epsilon S$, $a \oplus b =$ the remainder found when $a + b$ is divided by 3. Thus, to find $1 \oplus 2$, we find $1 + 2 = 3$. Now the remainder when 3 is divided by 3 is 0, so $1 \oplus 2 = 0$. Similarly, $2 \oplus 0 = 2$ since the remainder when $2 + 0$ is divided by 3 is 2.

(1) $1 \oplus 1 =$ ____ since the remainder when $1 + 1$ is divided by 3 is ____.

(2) $2 \oplus 2 =$ ____ since the remainder when $2 + 2$ is divided by 3 is ____.

---

(1) 2,   2
(2) 1,   1

1176 Using the example of frame 1175 we can construct a table of the binary operation. *Copy it.*

$\oplus$	0	1	2
0	0	1	2
1	1	2	0
2	2	0	1

$\oplus$	0	1	2
0	0	1	2
1	1	2	0
2	2	0	1

1177　Check the table in frame 1176: Is ⊕ a binary operation in S?

Yes, $a \oplus b$ is an element of S for every $a, b \in S$.

1178　Check the table from frame 1176. Is ⊕ a commutative binary operation in S?

Yes, $a \oplus b = b \oplus a$ for all $a, b \in S$.
Note the symmetry about the diagonal.

1179　Check the table from frame 1176. Does S have an identity element for ⊕ in S? If so, what is it?

Yes
0, since $x \oplus 0 = 0 \oplus x = x$ for all $x \in S$.

1180　Check the table from frame 1176. The identity element in S with respect to ⊕ is 0. Does every element have an additive inverse? If so, what is the inverse of 2 under ⊕?

Yes
The inverse of 2 is 1 since $1 \oplus 2 = 2 \oplus 1 = 0$.

1181　The operation ⊕ in frames 1179 and 1180 is associative; so, if $S = \{0, 1, 2\}$ and ⊕ is as defined, we have a binary operation which is commutative and associative; there is an identity element; and each $x \in S$ has an inverse. Thus S is a(n) _____ with respect to ⊕.

commutative group (or Abelian group)

1182　Again let $S = \{0, 1, 2\}$ and define a binary operation in S as follows: If $a, b \in S$, let $a * b =$ the remainder when $a \cdot b$ is divided by 3. Thus, to find $2 * 1$, we find $2 \cdot 1 = 2$; and the remainder when 2 is divided by 3 is 2. $\therefore 2 * 1 = 2$.
Similarly, $2 * 2 =$ ____ since $2 \cdot 2$ when divided by 3 has a remainder of ____.

1,　　1

1183 Let us set up a table of the binary operation
* defined in frame 1182. *Copy it.*

*	0	1	2
0	0	0	0
1	0	1	2
2	0	2	1

*	0	1	2
0	0	0	0
1	0	1	2
2	0	2	1

1184 Look at the table for * from frame 1183. Is * a binary operation
in S?

Yes, for every $x, y \in S$, $x * y \in S$.

1185 Look at the table for * from frame 1183. Is * commutative? Why?

Yes, $a * b = b * a$ for all $a, b \in S$.
Note the symmetry about the diagonal.

1186 Look at the table for * from frame 1183. Is there an identity element in S with respect to *? If so, what is it?

Yes, since $1 * x = x * 1$ for all $x \in S$.

1187 Look at the table for * from frame 1183. The identity element with
respect to * is 1. Does every element of S have an inverse with respect to *?

No, 0 has no inverse with respect to *; that is, there is no $x \in S$
such that $x * 0 = 0 * x = 1$.

1188 However, except for 0, every element of S has an inverse with respect to *. For example, the inverse of 2 with respect to * is ____
since _____.

2
$2 * 2 = 1$

1189   The binary operation $*$ in the set $S = \{0, 1, 2\}$ of frames 1186 to 1188 is commutative, and it can be shown that the operation is associative. There is an identity element, and except for 0 each element has an inverse. So the nonzero elements of S form a(n) _____ with respect to $*$.

commutative group (or Abelian group)

1190   You have seen four examples of a set having two binary operations such that the set was a commutative group with respect to one of the operations and, except for the identity element of that operation, was a commutative group with respect to the other operation. For example, the set S of the form $x + y\sqrt{2}$ with x and y rational is a commutative group with respect to addition, and the same set except for $0 + 0\sqrt{2}$ is a commutative group with respect to multiplication. Recall that $0 + 0\sqrt{2}$ is excluded because it did not have a(n) _____ .

inverse with respect to multiplication

1191   Similarly, the set of rational numbers is a commutative group with respect to addition; and the set of nonzero rational numbers is a commutative group with respect to multiplication. Why must the zero element be excluded?

0 has no inverse with respect to multiplication.

IV. Fields

It might be valuable to consider a set having two binary operations and certain group properties and see what we can discover. We are once again at the point where we can see certain unifying concepts which are applicable to a variety of seemingly unlike structures.

1192   Note, however, that if we were simply to consider a set S having two binary operations, which is a group with respect to each binary operation, we would have nothing richer than two _____ . We must find something which will cause the two operations to be combined in some way. From the set of real numbers, we recall that $a \cdot (b + c) = $ _____ .

groups, $(a \cdot b) + (a \cdot c)$

•1193   In the set of real numbers with the binary operations multiplication and addition, $a \cdot (b + c) =$ _____. This is known as the *distributive law of multiplication over addition*. Does this law indicate a certain relationship between the two binary operations?

$(a \cdot b) + (a \cdot c),$ yes

1194   Looking at the distributive law from the opposite direction, we see $(x \cdot y) + (x \cdot z) =$ _____. In other words this is the law used in "factoring out" a common factor of two terms.

$x(y + z)$

1195   So we are led to the consideration of a set S having two binary operations, say $\oplus$ and $*$ such that S is a commutative group with respect to $\oplus$, a commutative group with respect to $*$, and such that the distributive law of $*$ over $\oplus$ holds; that is, if $a, b, c \in S$, then $a * (b \oplus c) =$ _____.

$(a * b) \oplus (a * c)$

1196   Let us tentatively set up the system and notation. Remember that we are trying to establish the structure in such a way that the examples we have seen in this unit will fit into the pattern. *Roughly,* we have a nonempty set S with *two* binary operations $*$ and $\oplus$. We will let S be a commutative group with respect to $\oplus$. We will let S be a commutative group with respect to $*$. Moreover, in order to create some something richer than two groups, we will let the distributive law of $*$ over $\oplus$ hold; that is, if $a, b, c \in S$, then _____.

$a * (b \oplus c) = (a * b) \oplus (a * c)$

•1197   If S is to be a commutative group with respect to $+$, then the following must hold:

(1) S must have an equivalence relation "$=$," and $\oplus$ must be a binary relation which is _____ with respect to "$=$" (if $a, b, x \in S$ and $a = b$, then $x \oplus a = x \oplus b$).

(2)   The commutative law for $\oplus$ must hold; that is, if $a, b \in S$, then _____.

(3)   The associative law for $\oplus$ must hold; that is, if $a, b, c \in S$, then _____.

(4) S must have a(n) _____ with respect to $\oplus$.

▼

(5) Every $x \in S$ must have a(n) _____ with respect to $\oplus$.

---

(1) well-defined
(2) $a \oplus b = b \oplus a$
(3) $a \oplus (b \oplus c) = (a \oplus b) \oplus c$
(4) identity element
(5) inverse

1198 We need an identity element with respect to $\oplus$. We will indicate it by z. Therefore for all $x \in S$, _____.
Note: For the rest of this section, the set S we refer to will be this set S under discussion.

$x \oplus z = z \oplus x = x$

1199 Recall: We proved in Part Two: A set S can have at most one distinct identity element with respect to a binary operation. Therefore we are justified in saying that z is *the* identity element with respect to $\oplus$. If z is the identity element with respect to $\oplus$, then, if $x \in S$,
$x \oplus z =$ ____
$z \oplus x =$ ____

---

x
x

1200 (1) If a and $b \in S$, then $(a \oplus b) \oplus z =$ ____.
(2) Recall that z is the _____ with respect to $\oplus$.

---

(1) $a \oplus b$ (2) identity element

1201 If $a, b \in S$, then $z \oplus (a \oplus b) =$ ____, because z _____.

$a \oplus b$
is the identity element with respect to $\oplus$

1202 Recall that an inverse of an element with respect to a binary operation is an element which will "take you back" to the identity element with respect to that operation.
For example, in the set of rational numbers, an inverse of $2/3$ with respect to multiplication is $3/2$ since $2/3 \cdot 3/2 = 3/2 \cdot 2/3 = 1$, the identity with respect to multiplication. An inverse of $2/3$ with

▼

respect to addition is _____ since _____ , the identity with respect to addition.

$$-\frac{2}{3}$$
$$\frac{2}{3} + \left(-\frac{2}{3}\right) = \left(-\frac{2}{3}\right) + \frac{2}{3} = 0$$

1203   We have assumed that every element of S has an inverse with respect to $\oplus$. Since z is the identity element with respect to $\oplus$, then if b is an inverse of a with respect to $\oplus$, we have that $b \oplus a = a \oplus b = $ _____.

---

z

1204   We need some sort of notation to indicate an inverse of an element with respect to $\oplus$. For example, if T is the set of rational numbers and $x \in T$, an inverse of x with respect to addition is indicated by $(-x)$. If $x \neq 0$, an inverse of x with respect to multiplication is indicated by $\frac{1}{x}$.

If $x \in S$, we will indicate an inverse of x with respect to $\oplus$ by $\bar{x}$. Since z is the identity element with respect to $\oplus$, we have _____ $= z$.

$x \oplus \bar{x} = \bar{x} \oplus x$

1205   Recall: We proved in Part Two that if a set has an associative binary operation with an identity element, then an element has at most _____ distinct inverse with respect to that operation. Therefore, since $\oplus$ is associative in S and z is the identity element, we are justified in referring to *the* inverse of x with respect to $\oplus$. We indicate the inverse of x with respect to $\oplus$ by $\bar{x}$.
∴ $x \oplus \bar{x} = $ _____
$\bar{x} \oplus x = $ _____

---

one
z, z

1206   In our set S, we assume that *every* element has an inverse with respect to $\oplus$, and we know that an inverse is _____ for that element. If $a \in S$, we indicate the inverse of a with respect to $\oplus$ by $\bar{a}$, and then $a \oplus \bar{a} = \bar{a} \oplus a = $ _____.

---

unique, z

1207   *Note:* There is only one identity in S with respect to $\oplus$ and we have
       called it z. z is the identity with respect to $\oplus$ for every element of
       of S. **(1)**   So, if x is any element of S, $z \oplus x =$ _____ and $x \oplus z =$
       _____. However, each $x \in S$ has its own inverse with respect to $\oplus$.
       There is no single inverse with respect to $\oplus$ for the whole set.
       (2)   If $c \in S$, we indicate the inverse of c with respect to $\oplus$ by _____.

       (1) $x,$ x
       (2) $\bar{c}$

1208   You should have learned the notation and terminology by now.
       (1)   In S, the identity element with respect to $\oplus$ is _____ and if
       $x \in S$, $x \oplus$ _____ $=$ _____ $\oplus x =$ _____.
       (2)   If $x \in S$, the inverse of x with respect to $\oplus$ is _____ and
       $x \oplus$ _____ $=$ _____ $\oplus x =$ _____.

       (1) $z,$ $z,$ $z,$ x
       (2) $\bar{x},$ $\bar{x},$ $\bar{x},$ z

1209   In our set, z is a special symbol representing the _____
       with respect to $\oplus$. We will not use it in any other manner. There-
       fore if a and $b \in S$, then $(a \oplus b) \oplus z =$ _____.

       identity element, $a \oplus b$

1210   If $a, b \in S$, $(a * b) \oplus z =$ _____.

       $a * b$

1211   Similarly, in S, $\bar{a}$ is the notation used for the _____ with
       respect to $\oplus$.
       $a \oplus \bar{a} =$ _____
       $\bar{a} \oplus a =$ _____

       inverse of a
       $z,$ z

1212   Similarly, since $*$ is a(n) _____ in S, $a * b$ is simply an
       element of S. Its inverse with respect to $\oplus$ would be indicated by
       $\overline{(a * b)}$.
       $\therefore (a * b) \oplus \overline{(a * b)} =$ _____.

       binary operation, z

1213 Note the similarity:
    (1) In the set T of rational numbers, 0 is the identity element with respect to addition and if $x \in T$, then _____ $= x$.
    (2) In the set S, z is the identity element with respect to $\oplus$ and if $x \in S$, then _____ $= x$.

    (1) $x + 0 = 0 + x$
    (2) $x \oplus z = z \oplus x$

1214 Similarly:
    (1) In the set T of rational numbers, the inverse of x with respect to addition is $(-x)$ and _____ $= 0$.
    (2) In the set S, the inverse of x with respect to $\oplus$ is $\bar{x}$ and _____ $= z$.

    (1) $x + (-x) = (-x) + x$
    (2) $x \oplus (\bar{x}) = (\bar{x}) \oplus x$

1215 If $x \in S$, $x \oplus z =$ _____.
                $z \oplus x =$ _____.

    x
    x

1216 If $a, b \in S$, $(a * b) \oplus z =$ _____.

    $a * b$

1217 In S, $a \oplus \bar{a} =$ _____.

    z

1218 $\bar{x} \oplus x =$ _____.

    z

1219 If $a, b \in S$, $(a * b) \oplus (\overline{a * b}) =$ _____.

    z

1220 So far we have S as a commutative group with respect to $\oplus$ with identity element with respect to $\oplus$ indicated by _____ and the inverse with respect to $\oplus$ of any $x \epsilon S$ indicated by _____ .

z

$\bar{x}$

1221 In addition to the properties of the identity z and the inverses with respect to $\oplus$ we have that:

(1) The commutative law for $\oplus$ holds; that is, if $a, b \epsilon S$, then

_____ .

(2) The associative law for $\oplus$ holds; that is, if $a, b, c \epsilon S$,

_____ .

(1) $a \oplus b = b \oplus a$
(2) $a \oplus (b \oplus c) = (a \oplus b) \oplus c$

1222 In S, $x \oplus y = y \oplus x$ because the commutative law for $\oplus$ holds in S. In S, $(a \oplus b) \oplus c = a \oplus (b \oplus c)$ because _____ .

the associative law for $\oplus$ holds

1223 Recall also that $=$ is an equivalence relation in S, so the following properties hold:

(1) reflexive property: _____
(2) symmetric property: _____
(3) transitive property: _____

(1) $a = a$ for all $a \epsilon S$
(2) if $a = b$, then $b = a$
(3) if $a = b$ and $b = c$, then $a = c$

1224 We can now prove some simple theorems in S, supplying reasons for each step. If we involve ourselves only with $\oplus$, however, many of our theorems are simply restatements of problems on groups. We will do some of the proofs again for practice and to become more familiar with the notation.

Prove: If $a, b \epsilon S$, then $(\bar{a} \oplus b) \oplus a = b$.

Proof:

1. $(\bar{a} \oplus b) \oplus a = (b \oplus \bar{a}) \oplus a = b$	1. _____ law for $\oplus$
2. $\quad\quad\quad = b \oplus (\bar{a} + a)$	2. _____ law for $\oplus$
3. $\quad\quad\quad = b \oplus z$	3. Definition of inverse
4. $(\bar{a} \oplus b) \oplus a = b$	4. z is the identity with respect to $\oplus$, so $b \oplus z = b$

(1) commutative   (2) associative

1225 *Prove*: If $a, b, c \in S$ and $a \oplus b = a \oplus c$, then $b = c$.
Proof:

1. $a \oplus b = a \oplus c$ 1. Hypothesis
2. $\bar{a} \in S$ 2. Every $x \in S$ has an inverse with respect to $\oplus$
3. $\bar{a} \oplus (a \oplus b) = \bar{a} \oplus (a \oplus c)$ 3. $\oplus$ is well-defined with respect to "$=$"
4. $(\bar{a} \oplus a) \oplus b = (\bar{a} \oplus a) \oplus c$ 4. _____
5. $z \oplus b = z \oplus c$ 5. _____
6. $b = c$ 6. _____

   (4)   associative law for $\oplus$
   (5)   definition of inverse, $\bar{a} \oplus a = z$
   (6) z is the identity with respect to $\oplus$, so for all $x \in S$, $z \oplus x = x$

1226 It would be simpler to list all of the properties of S and to refer to the list for our reasons. We will do that soon, but first we need more notation for the binary operation $*$. Recall that S is also to be a commutative group with respect to $*$, so we must have:

   (1) $*$ is a well-defined _____ with respect to $*$.
   (2)   The commutative law for $*$ holds; that is, if $a, b \in S$, then _____.
   (3)   The associative law for $*$ holds; that is, if $a, b, c \in S$, then _____.
   (4)   There is a(n) _____ with respect to $*$.
   (5)   Every $x \in S$ has a(n) _____ with respect to $*$.

   (1)   binary operation
   (2) $a * b = b * a$
   (3) $a * (b * c) = (a * b) * c$
   (4)   identity
   (5)   inverse

1227 We need a symbol for the identity element with respect to $*$, and we will use u. Therefore for all $x \in S$, $x * u = u * x =$ ____.

   x

1228 The identity element with respect to $\oplus$ is z, so for all $x \in S$, $x \oplus z = z \oplus x =$ ____. The identity element with respect to $*$ is u, so for all $x \in S$, $x * u = u * x =$ ____.

   x
   x

1229   In S, the identity element with respect to $\oplus$ is _____.

z

1230   In S, the identity element with respect to $*$ is _____.

u

1231   In S, $z \oplus u =$ _____ , because z is _____ .

u,   the identity with respect to $\oplus$

1232   In S, $u * z =$ _____ , because u is _____ .

z,   the identity with respect to $*$

1233   If $x \in S$, $x \oplus z =$ _____ .

x

1234   In S, $x * u =$ _____ .

x

1235   If $x \in S$, $x \oplus \bar{x} =$ _____ .

z

1236   We also need some notation for the inverse of $x \in S$ with respect to $*$. We will indicate the inverse by x^{-1}. $\therefore x * x^{-1} =$ _____ and $x^{-1} * x =$ _____ .

u
u (the identity with respect to $*$)

1237   Our notation is as follows:
For $\oplus$:
(1) The identity element with respect to $\oplus$ is _____.
(2) So for every $x \in S$, _____ .
(3) Each $x \in S$ has an inverse, denoted by _____, with respect to $\oplus$ such that _____ .

▼

For ∗

(4) The identity element with respect to ∗ is _____ .
(5) So for every $x \in S$, _____ .
(6) Each $x \in S$ has an inverse, denoted by _____ , with respect to ∗ such that _____ .

---

(1) z
(2) $x \oplus z = z \oplus x = x$
(3) $\bar{x}, \qquad x \oplus \bar{x} = \bar{x} \oplus x = z$
(4) u
(5) $x * u = u * x = x$
(6) $x^{-1}, \qquad x * x^{-1} = x^{-1} * x = u$

1238 For all $x \in S$, $x \oplus z =$ _____
            and $z \oplus x =$ _____

---

x
x

1239 For every $x \in S$, there is an $\bar{x} \in S$ such that $x \oplus \bar{x} =$ _____
               and _____ $=$ _____ .

---

z
$\bar{x} \oplus x = z$

1240 For all $x \in S$, $x * u =$ _____ and _____ .

---

x
$u * x = x$

1241 For every $x \in S$, there is an $x^{-1} \in S$ such that _____ $= u$
               and _____ $= u$.

$x * x^{-1}$
$x^{-1} * x$

1242 $x \oplus z = x$ for every $x \in S$, in particular, $z \oplus z =$ _____ .

---

z

1243 $x * u = x$ for every $x \in S$, in particular, $u * u =$ _____ .

---

u

1244   In S, $x \oplus z = x$ and $z \oplus x = x$ for every $x \in S$. In particular,
$u \oplus z =$ _____ and $z \oplus u =$ _____.

u
u

1245 $x * u = x$ and $u * x = x$ for every $x \in S$. In particular, $z * u =$ _____
and _____ $=$ _____.

z
$u * z,$ z

1246   In S, $u * [a \oplus (b * c)] =$ _____ , since u is _____.

$a \oplus (b * c)$
the identity with respect to $*$

1247   It is to be understood that if parentheses are not used, the operation $*$
is to be thought of as being performed *first*, then the operation $\oplus$.
That is, $a \oplus b * c$ will mean $a \oplus (b * c)$. Similarly, $a * b \oplus c$ will
mean _____.

$(a * b) \oplus c$

1248   Let a, b, $c \in S$. If we wish a to operate by $*$ on $b \oplus c$, we write
$a * (b \oplus c)$. If we wish $a * b$ to operate by $\oplus$ on c, we write
_____ .

$a * b \oplus c$

1249   Let a, b, $c \in S$. If we wish $a * b$ to operate by $\oplus$ on c, we write
_____ . We could write $(a * b) \oplus c$, but since _____ is thought of
as being performed first, the parentheses are not necessary.

$a * b \oplus c,$ $*$

1250   Finally, we assume that S has a property which will "mesh" the
two sets of group properties together.
The distributive law of $*$ over $\oplus$: For all a, b, $c \in S$, $a * (b \oplus c) =$
$a * b \oplus a * c$.
Look at the statement in reverse order; you have

$a * b \oplus a * c =$ _____.

▼

Compare your statements:

$a * (b \oplus c) = a * b \oplus a * c$

$a * b \oplus a * c = \underline{\hspace{2cm}}$

Notice the similarity to factoring.

$a * (b \oplus c)$

$a * (b \oplus c)$

1251   Since the distributive law for $*$ over $\oplus$ holds in S, then for all
$a, b, c \in S$, $a * (b \oplus c) = \underline{\hspace{2cm}}$.

$a * b \oplus a * c$

1252   Recall that in all of the earlier examples in this section, the identity
for addition did not have an inverse with respect to multiplication.
Now we have two identities in S:

z with respect to **(1)** $\underline{\hspace{1cm}}$ and

u with respect to **(2)** $\underline{\hspace{1cm}}$.

Let us see if there is a reason for what seems to be a discrepancy.
We have assumed that every $x \in S$ has an inverse with respect to $*$;
in particular, we assume that z has an inverse with respect to $*$,
indicated by **(3)** $\underline{\hspace{1cm}}$. *If* this were so, then $z * z^{-1} = z^{-1} * z =$
(4) $\underline{\hspace{1cm}}$.

---

(1) $\oplus$ **(2)** $*$ **(3)** z^{-1} **(4)** u

1253   A good question is whether z and u can be the same element; that
is, could we have one element which is the $\underline{\hspace{2cm}}$ with respect to
both operations? We will see on frame 1254.

---

identity

1254   Suppose $z = u$. Let $x \in S$. Consider the expression $x * (u \oplus u)$.
1. Since $u = z$ $x * (u \oplus u) = x * (z \oplus z)$
2. Since z is identity with respect to $\oplus$ $= x * z$
3. Since $z = u$ $= x * u$
                                                    $= x$

4. But if we use the distributive law of
   $*$ over $\oplus$, $x * (u \oplus u) = x * u \oplus x * u$
5. Since u is the identity with respect to $*$, $= x \oplus x$
Therefore the two answers from statements 1 and 5 must be equal,
so we have for all $x \in S$, $x \oplus x = x$. But only one element of S has

▼

this property. That is, $x \oplus$ _____ $= x$ has only one solution, namely,
_____ , so $x =$ _____ .

$z,$ $z,$ z

1255   We have reached the peculiar conclusion that if $u = z$, then for every
$x \in S$, $x = z$. S would contain only _____ (how many) element(s),
namely, z. We would have $z \oplus z = z$, $z * z =$ _____ , $z * (z \oplus z) =$
_____ , etc. This would not make a very interesting structure.

---

one, $z,$ z

1256   We found that, if $u = z$, then S contains only one element, namely, z.
To eliminate this trivial possibility, let us consider S with $u \neq z$.
Now we are sure that S contains at least _____ (how many) ele-
ments.

---

two

1257   Now we have a set S (with at least two elements) having two well-
defined binary operations, $\oplus$ and $*$, such that:
(1) S is a commutative group with respect to $\oplus$. (The identity with
respect to $\oplus$ is z and each $x \in S$ has an inverse with respect
to $\oplus$ indicated by _____.
(2) S is a commutative group with respect to $*$. (The identity element with respect to $*$ is u ($u \neq z$) and each $x \in S$ has an inverse with respect to $*$ indicated by _____.
(3)   For all a, b, $c \in S$, $a * (b \oplus c) =$ _____ .

---

(1) $\bar{x}$ (2) x^{-1} (3) $a * b \oplus a * c$

1258   The description given in frame 1257 would fit the examples we have
seen except for the one troublesome element which does not have an
inverse. For example, if S is the set of rational numbers, 0, the
identity with respect to addition, does not have a(n) _____ with
respect to multiplication.

---

inverse

1259   Similarly, the set $x + y\sqrt{2}$ with x and y rational is a commutative
group with respect to addition and is a commutative group with respect to multiplication except that $0 + 0\sqrt{2}$, the identity with respect

▼

to addition, does not have a(n) _____ with respect to multiplication.

---

inverse

1260   So, if we want our set S to be a structure having the same form as the examples which led us to construct S, we should simply eliminate z^{-1} from S and say: For every $x \neq z$, there exists an x^{-1} such that _____ . We would still wonder whether it would be possible to have a $z^{-1} \in S$. So we shall investigate.

$x * x^{-1} = x^{-1} * x = u$

1261   *First* recall that if G is a group with respect to a binary operation $\cdot$, the left-hand cancelation law holds; that is, if $x \cdot a = x \cdot b$, then _____. So, in S, since S is a group with respect to $\oplus$, if $x \oplus a = x \oplus b$, then _____ .

$a = b$
$a = b$

1262   Now we shall prove a theorem about S.
For all $a \in S$, $a * z = z$ (and $z * a = z$).
Proof:

$\begin{aligned} a * z \oplus z &= a * z & \text{(since } z \text{ is the identity with respect to } \oplus) \\ &= a * (z \oplus z) & \text{(since } z \oplus z = z) \\ &= a * z \oplus a * z & \text{(because of the distributive law)} \end{aligned}$

$\therefore a * z \oplus z = a * z \oplus a * z$

Therefore, using the cancelation law, we get $z = a * z$, and since $*$ is _____ , $a * z = z * a$, so $z * a = z$.

---

commutative

1263   So, in S, $a * z = z$ and _____ $= z$ for all $a \in S$. Just as in the system of real numbers, $x \cdot 0 = 0 \cdot x =$ _____ .

$z * a$
0

1264   Now we find the difficulty.
1. If z^{-1} exists, then $z * z^{-1} = u$. We just proved that for every $x \in S$, $z * x = z$, in particular
2. $z * z^{-1} = z$

▼

So we would have from statement 1, $z * z^{-1} = u$
and from statement 2, $z * z^{-1} = z$
Then we would have _____ , which is not true.

$u = z$

V. Proofs of Some Theorems of Fields

So, in S, we will *have* to make the qualification, *every $x \in S$ except z* has an inverse with respect to $*$.

If we did not exempt z, we would be back at the spot where $u = z$ and then, as we saw, every $x = z$ and S would have only one element. Since we decided to have $u \neq z$, then we find that z^{-1} cannot exist in S. This discussion should convince you that building a structure does not consist merely of deciding on a set of elements and some assumptions about relations and operations. The inconsistency we found in S was not too easy to see, and we found that a set having the properties we originally listed could not exist, unless we were willing to accept different answers when doing a problem in different ways.

We are now ready. The structure having the properties we have been discussing is called a *field*. We will indicate the set having these properties by F instead of S since the original properties given to S had to be modified.

The properties of a field are listed on Panel 12. *Read Panel 12 carefully.*

1265   Look at Panel 12. Notice that the properties listed contain the two qualifications we discussed previously.
(1) In M_2 we state that _____ $\neq$ _____ for, if not, F would contain only _____ (how many) element(s).
(2) In M_3 we state that _____ does not have an inverse with respect to $*$.

(1) $u \neq x$,   one   (2) z

1266   Look at Panel 12. Does the set of rational numbers with $\oplus$ representing ordinary addition and $*$ representing ordinary multiplication satisfy all of the field properties ?

yes

1267   The set of rational numbers satisfies the field properties in Panel 12 where $\oplus$ represents ordinary addition and $*$ represents ordinary multiplication. In the field of rational numbers, the element z of property A_2 is _____ .

0

1268   In the field of rational numbers, property A_3 states that for every $a \in F$ there exists an $\bar{a}$ such that $a \oplus \bar{a} = \bar{a} \oplus a = z$. In the field of rational numbers, z is 0. What is $\bar{5}$?

-5

1269   In the field of rational numbers what is the element u mentioned in property M_2?

$u = 1$

1270   In the field of rational numbers look at property M_3. M_3 says that for every $a \neq z$ there is an a^{-1} such that $a^{-1} * a = a * a^{-1} = u$. Since, in the field of rational numbers, z is _____ and $u =$ _____ , note that z^{-1} does not exist.

0,   1

1271   In the field of rational numbers $\left(\dfrac{1}{3}\right)^{-1}$ mentioned in property M_3 is _____ since _____ $\cdot \dfrac{1}{3} = \dfrac{1}{3} \cdot$ _____ $=$ _____ .

3,   3,   3,   1 (or u)

1272   The set S of numbers of the form $x + y\sqrt{2}$ where x and y are rational numbers also satisfies all the field properties of Panel 12 if $\oplus$ represents ordinary addition and $*$ represents ordinary multiplication. The element z of property A_2 is $0 + 0\sqrt{2}$. If $a = 3 - 2\sqrt{2}$, then $\bar{a} =$ _____ .

$-3 + 2\sqrt{2}$

COMMENT

There are many other examples of sets satisfying the field properties. We will consider the field in general, and using only the properties listed on Panel 12, see what we can prove about a field. Recall
the similar type of work we did with groups. Note that whatever we
can prove about a field can be applied to any set which we can identify as a field.

The theorems we prove about fields will be listed on Panel 13. Keep
Panels 12 and 13 in front of you. Remember, as soon as a theorem
has been proved, you may use it for subsequent work, but not before.
Note that some of the first theorems will simply be theorems about
groups which we proved in Part Three. We do them again for practice and to become familiar with the notation.

1273　As in the work with groups, we will allow the replacing of an element
by its equivalent rather than requiring the tedious application of E_3.
For example, prove: in a field F, $b * (b^{-1} * a) = a$.
1. $b * (b^{-1} * a) = (b * b^{-1}) * a$　　1. M_1
2. $b * (b^{-1} * a) = u * a$　　　　　　2. M_3
3. $b * (b^{-1} * a) = a$　　　　　　　3. _____
In step 2, we replaced the element $(b * b^{-1})$ of step 1 by its
_____(4)_____ u and gave the reason that $b * b^{-1} = u$. Similarly,
$u * a$ of step 2 is replaced by _____(5)_____ in step 3, the reason being
$u * a = a$.

(3) M_2　　**(4)** equivalent　　**(5)** a

1274　Look at Panel 12, note 3. B_1, roughly speaking, allows us to $\oplus$ the
same elements on the left side of both members of an equation.
For example, if $a = b$ and $x \in F$, then $x \oplus a = x \oplus b$.

We can prove that x could have appeared on the right of both members of the equation. In a field, if $a = b$, and $x \in F$, then
$a \oplus x = b \oplus x$.
Proof:
1. $a = b$　　　　　1. Hypothesis
2. $x \in F$　　　　　2. _____
3. $x \oplus a = x \oplus b$　　3. _____
4. $a \oplus x = b \oplus x$　　4. A_4

(2) Hypothesis　　**(3)** B_1

1275   Similarly, B_2 states that, if $a = b$ and $x \epsilon F$, then $x * a = x * b$. We can show that, if $a = b$ and $x \epsilon F$, then $a * x = b * x$.
Proof:
1. $a = b$, $x \epsilon F$ 1. _____
2. $x * a = x * b$ 2. B_2
3. $a * x = b * x$ 3. _____

(1)   Hypothesis   (3) M_4

1276   In a field, we need not worry nearly so much about order as in a group. This is true because in a field, both operations are commutative, while the operation in a group is not (except in special cases of _____ groups). For example, in a noncommutative group G, $a \cdot (b \cdot a^{-1})$ will not simplify, since we have no way of getting the a and a^{-1} together. But in a field F, $a * (b * a^{-1}) =$ _____ .

commutative, b (See frame 1277 for proof.)

1277   *Prove*: In a field, $a * (b * a^{-1}) = b$.
Proof:
1. $a * (b * a^{-1}) = a * (a^{-1} * b)$ 1. M_4
2. $= (a * a^{-1}) * b$ 2. M_1
3. $= u * b$ 3. _____
4. $\therefore a * (b * a^{-1}) = b$ 4. _____

(3) M_3 (4) M_2

1278   *Prove*: In a field F, $a \oplus (b \oplus \bar{a}) = b$.

Proof:
1. $a \oplus (b \oplus \bar{a}) = a \oplus (\bar{a} \oplus b)$ 1. A_4
2. $= (a \oplus \bar{a}) \oplus b$ 2. A_1
3. $= z \oplus b$ 3. A_3
4. $= b$ 4. A_2
You may have an acceptable proof which is different.

1279   On Panel 12, A_4, the commutative law for $\oplus$, says that for any $a, b \epsilon F$ $a \oplus b = b \oplus a$.

Now, since $\oplus$ is a binary operation in F, $(x \oplus y) \epsilon F$ so $(x \oplus y) \oplus z = z \oplus (x \oplus y)$ by A_4.

Similarly $(x \oplus y) * z = z * (x \oplus y)$ by _____ .

M_4

1280   Look at Panel 12. D is sometimes called the left-hand distributive
law of $*$ over $\oplus$ since a is on the left. The right-hand distributive
law of $*$ over $\oplus$ would look like this: _____ .

$(b \oplus c) * a = b * a \oplus c * a$ (or $a * b \oplus a * c$)
We will present the proof in frame 1281.

1281   *Theorem 1.* In a field F, $(b \oplus c) * a = b * a \oplus c * a$.
Proof:

1.	$(b \oplus c) \in F$	1.	C
2.	$(b \oplus c) * a = a * (b \oplus c)$	2.	M_4
3.	$\quad\quad = a * b \oplus a * c$	3.	____
	$\quad\quad = b * a \oplus c * a$	4.	____

(3) D (4) M_4

1282   Many students have trouble understanding a proof because they do
not realize the generality of the properties listed on Panel 12. For
example, A_4 states:

if $a, b \in F$, then $a \oplus b = b \oplus a$.

Note that a (or b) represents *any* element of F.
Some students, when confronted with an expression such as
$(x * y) \oplus w$ where $x, y, w \in F$, do not realize that A_4 can be used.
The difficulty is in not knowing that, since $*$ is a binary operation in
F, $(x * y)$ *is an element of* F, just as the a in A_4 is. $(x * y)$ is just
fancier. Therefore, using A_4, since $x * y$ and $w \in F$, then
$(x * y) \oplus w = w \oplus$ ____ .

$(x * y)$

1283   In the same vein, on Panel 12, A_3 states that, if $a \in F$, $a \oplus \bar{a} = z$.
Now, if $x, y \in F$, $(x \oplus y) \in F$, since $\oplus$ is a binary operation in F.
Therefore $(x \oplus y)$ is a fancy way of representing some element of F,
say r, and the inverse of $(x \oplus y)$ with respect to $\oplus$ would be written
$\overline{(x \oplus y)}$. Then, by A_3, $(x \oplus y) \oplus \overline{(x \oplus y)} =$ ____ .

z

•1284   *Prove*: In a field F, $a \oplus (b \oplus \bar{a}) = b$.
Note: Looking at the left member, we see that we would like to get a
and $\bar{a}$ together to produce z. The most obvious thing would be to use

▼

A_4 to rearrange the elements and then use A_1 to get a and $\bar{a}$ associated. You do the proof.

Two obvious proofs are:

1. $a \oplus (b + \bar{a}) = a \oplus (\bar{a} \oplus b)$	1. A_4
$= (a \oplus \bar{a}) \oplus b$	2. A_1
$= z \oplus b$	3. A_3
$= b$	4. A_2

1. $a \oplus (b \oplus \bar{a}) = (b \oplus \bar{a}) \oplus a$	1. A_4
$= b \oplus (\bar{a} \oplus a)$	2. A_1
$= b \oplus z$	3. A_3
$= b$	4. A_2

1285   *Prove*: In a field, $(a \oplus b) \oplus (\bar{a} \oplus \bar{b}) = z$.

Here again we would like to get a and $\bar{a}$ together and b and $\bar{b}$ together, so again we use A_1 and A_4. One method is as follows:

1. $(a \oplus b) \oplus (\bar{a} \oplus \bar{b}) = (a \oplus b) \oplus (\bar{b} \oplus \bar{a})$	1. ____
2. $= [(a \oplus b) \oplus \bar{b}] \oplus \bar{a}$	2. A_1
3. $= [a \oplus (b \oplus \bar{b})] + \bar{a}$	3. A_1
4. $= (a \oplus z) \oplus \bar{a}$	4. ____
5. $= a \oplus \bar{a}$	5. ____
6. $= z$	6. ____

(1) A_4 **(4)** A_3 **(5)** A_2 **(6)** A_3

1286   *Prove*: In a field, $(a * b) * (a^{-1} * b^{-1}) = u$.

Here again we obviously will use M_1 and M_4 to get a and a^{-1} together and b and b^{-1} together.

1. $(a * b) * (a^{-1} * b^{-1}) = (a * b) * (b^{-1} * a^{-1})$	1. M_4
2. $= [(a * b) * b^{-1}] * a^{-1}$	2. M_1
3. $= [a * (b * b^{-1})] * a^{-1}$	3. M_1
4. $= (a * u) * a^{-1}$	4. M_3
5. $= a * a^{-1}$	5. M_2
$= u$	6. M_3

•1287   *Prove*: In a field F, $(a * b) * b^{-1} = a$.

The most obvious proof:

1. $(a * b) * b^{-1} = a * (b * b^{-1})$	1. M_1
2. $= a * u$	2. M_3
3. $= a$	3. M_2

•1288 *Prove*: In a field F, $(a \oplus b) \oplus \bar{b} = a$.

One proof:
1. $(a \oplus b) \oplus \bar{b} = a \oplus (b \oplus \bar{b})$ 1. A_1
2. $\qquad\qquad = a \oplus z$ 2. A_3
3. $\qquad\qquad = a$ 3. A_2

1289 *Prove*: In a field F, $(a \oplus b) \oplus \bar{a} = b$.

1. $(a \oplus b) \ominus \bar{a} = (b \oplus a) \oplus \bar{a}$ 1. A_4
$\qquad\qquad = b \oplus (a \oplus \bar{a})$ 2. A_1
$\qquad\qquad = b \oplus z$ 3. A_3
$\qquad\qquad = b$ 4. A_2

1290 Again we stress the fact that some of the statements and theorems
in this section could be proved by using the theorems on groups from
Part Three. For example, we proved that if G is a group with re-
spect to a binary operation $\cdot$ and if a, b, $x \in G$ and $x \cdot a = x \cdot b$,
then $a = b$. Suppose we wish to prove: In a field F, if $x \oplus a = x \oplus b$,
then $a = b$. We need only note that F is a group with respect to $\oplus$,
so this problem is merely a direct application of the theorem on
_____ . Similarly, in a group G, if $a \cdot x = b$, then $x = a^{-1} \cdot b$,
when translated into the notation in F with respect to $\oplus$, becomes if
$a \oplus x = b$, then $x =$ ____ . (Be careful; we are using F as a group
with respect to $\oplus$.)

group, $\bar{a} \oplus b$

1291 Look at Panel 12. Read note 3. B_1 is the property which allows
"addition" of the same element of F to the left side of both members of an equation; i.e., if $a = b$, then $x \oplus a = x \oplus b$, or it might be
thought of as "substituting" b for a in $x \oplus a$ and getting $x \oplus b$. We
need not assume also that if $a = b$, then $a \oplus x = b \oplus x$ as we did for
a group. We can prove this using A_4 as follows:
1. $a = b$, $x \in F$ 1. Hypothesis
2. $x \oplus a = x \oplus b$ 2. ____
3. $a \oplus x = b \oplus x$ 3. A_4

(2) B_1

1292 Similarly: the proof of B_2 as applied to a field.
Prove: In a field F, if $a = b$ and $x \in F$,
    then $a * x = b * x$.

▼

Proof:
1. $a = b$, $x \in F$ 1. _____
2. $x * a = x * b$ 2. _____
3. $a * x = b * x$ 3. _____

---

(1) Hypothesis   **(2)** B_2 **(3)** M_4

1293 We would like to have more general cases of B_1 and B_2; that is, we would like to prove: In a field F, if $a = b$ and $c = d$, then $a \oplus c = b \oplus d$ (and similarly for $*$). It seems fairly obvious that to prove these, we need only use B_1 (or B_2) twice, that is, begin with $a = b$. We wish to prove something involving $a \oplus c$, so we use B_1 on $a = b$ and get _____ .

This proof will be completed in frame 1294.

$c \oplus a = c \oplus b$

1294 *Prove*: In a field F, if $a = b$ and $c = d$, then $a \oplus c = b \oplus d$.
Proof:
1. $a = b$ 1. Hypothesis
2. $c \oplus a = c \oplus b$ 2. B_1
3. $c = d$ 3. _____
4. $b \oplus c = b \oplus d$ 4. _____
5. $c \oplus b = b \oplus d$ 5. _____
6. $\therefore c \oplus a = b \oplus d$ 6. E_3 (using statements 2 and 5)
7. $a \oplus c = b \oplus d$ 7. _____

---

(3) Hypothesis   **(4)** B_1 **(5)** A_4 **(7)** A_4

1295 Similarly, *Theorem 2*. In a field F, if $a = b$ and $c = d$, then $a * c = b * d$.
Proof:
1. $a = b$ 1. Hypothesis
2. $c * a = c * b$ 2. _____
3. $c = d$ 3. Hypothesis
4. $b * c = b * d$ 4. _____
5. $c * b = b * d$ 5. M_4
6. $c * a = b * d$ 6. _____
7. $a * c = b * d$ 7. M_4

---

(2) B_2 **(4)** B_2 **(6)** E_3

1296   *Theorem 3* (law of cancelation for $\oplus$). In a field F, if $x \oplus a = x \oplus b$, then $a = b$.

    Proof:
1. $x \oplus a = x \oplus b$	1. Hypothesis
2. there exists $\bar{x} \in F$	2. A_3
3. $\bar{x} \oplus (x \oplus a) = \bar{x} \oplus (x \oplus b)$	3. B_1
4. $(\bar{x} \oplus x) \oplus a = (\bar{x} \oplus x) \oplus b$	4. A_1
5. $z \oplus a = z \oplus b$	5. A_3
6. $\therefore a = b$	6. A_2

1297   *Theorem 4.* In a field, $a * z = z$.
    Proof:
1. $(a * z) \oplus z = a * z$	1. A_2
2. $(a * z) \oplus z = a * (z \oplus z)$	2. A_2
3. $(a * z) \oplus z = (a * z) \oplus (a * z)$	3. _____
4. $\qquad\qquad z = a * z$	4. Theorem 3
5. $a * z = z$	5. E_2

(3)   Distributive law

1298   *Theorem 5.* If $a \oplus x = z$, then $x = \bar{a}$.
    Proof:
1. $a \oplus x = z$	1. Hypothesis
2. $a \oplus \bar{a} = z$	2. ____
3. $z = a \oplus \bar{a}$	3. E_2
4. $\therefore a \oplus x = a \oplus \bar{a}$	4. E_3
5. $x = a$	5. _____ .

(2) A_3 (5)   Theorem 3

1299   *Note*: Theorem 5 shows that for every $a \in F$, $\bar{a}$ is unique. There-fore, if we wish to show that some $x \in F$ is the inverse of y with re-spect to $\oplus$, we need only show that $y \oplus x = z$. Then, by Theorem _____ , $x = \bar{y}$.

5

1300   For example, in a field F $\overline{(\bar{a})} = a$. We want to prove that a is the in-verse of $\bar{a}$ with respect to $\oplus$, so we need only prove that $\bar{a} \oplus a = z$ and use Theorem 5.
    Proof:
1. $\bar{a} \oplus a = z$	1. A_3
2. $\therefore a = \overline{(\bar{a})}$	2. _____

(2)   Theorem 5

1301   *Theorem 6.* In a field, $\overline{(x * y)} = x * \bar{y}$. Again, to prove that $x * \bar{y}$ is
the inverse of $x * y$ with respect to $\oplus$, we need only show that
$(x * y) \oplus (x * \bar{y}) = z$ and use Theorem 5.
Proof:
1. $(x * y) \oplus (x * \bar{y}) = x * (y \oplus \bar{y})$ 1. ____
2. $(x * y) \oplus (x * \bar{y}) = x * z$ 2. ____
3. $(x * y) \oplus (x * \bar{y}) = z$ 3. _____
4. $\therefore x * \bar{y} = \overline{(x * y)}$ 4. _____

(1) D **(2)** A_3 **(3)** Theorem 4   **(4)** Theorem 5

1302   *Prove*: In a field F, $\overline{(x * y)} = \bar{x} * y$.
(Theorems 4 and 5 will help you.)

Proof:
1. $(x * y) \oplus (\bar{x} * y) = (x \oplus \bar{x}) * y$ 1. Theorem 1
2. $\qquad\qquad\qquad = z * y$ 2. A_3
3. $\qquad\qquad\qquad = z$ 3. Theorem 4
4. $\therefore \bar{x} * y = \overline{(x * y)}$ 4. Theorem 5

1303   *Time out*: Recall that one specific example of a field is the set of
real numbers with $\oplus$ representing $+$ and $*$ representing $\cdot$, $z = 0$,
and $\bar{a}$ is really $(-a)$. Look at the theorems we have proved.

For example, Theorem 4: if $a \,\epsilon\, F$, $a * z = z$ when applied to the
field of real numbers says that if a is any real number, $a \cdot 0 = $ ____ .

0

1304   Theorem 5 states: In a field F, if $a \oplus x = z$, then $x = \bar{a}$. Inter-
preting this in the field of real numbers, we have:
if $a + x = 0$, then $x = $ ____ .

$-a$

1305   We also proved: In a field, $\overline{(\bar{a})} = a$; thus we have proved in the field
of real numbers that $-(-a) = $ ____ .

a

1306   We also have proved that in a field, $\overline{x * y} = \bar{x} * y$. Rewrite this in the
field of real numbers.

$-(x \cdot y) = (-x) \cdot y$

COMMENT

Thus we have proved many of the properties of real numbers which you have accepted without proof until now. We could continue proving others. Also, note that these theorems can be applied to any set of elements having the properties listed on Panel 12.

1307   *Theorem 7.* (law of cancelation for $*$). In a field, if $x * a = x * b$ and $x \neq z$, then $a = b$.
Proof:

1. $x \neq z$	1. Hypothesis
2. $\therefore x^{-1} \in F$	2. M_3
3. $x * a = x * b$	3. Hypothesis
4. $x^{-1} * (x * a) = x^{-1} * (x * b)$	4. _____
5. $(x^{-1} * x) * a = (x^{-1} * x) * b$	5. _____
6. $u * a = u * b$	6. _____
7. $a = b$	7. _____

(4) B_2 (5) M_1 (6) M_3 (7) M_2

1308   *Theorem 8.* In a field, if $a * x = u$, where $a \neq z$, then $x = a^{-1}$.
Proof:

1. $a * x = u$	1. Hypothesis
2. $a^{-1} \in F$	2. M_3
3. $a^{-1} * (a * x) = a^{-1} * u$	3. _____
4. $(a^{-1} * a) * x = a^{-1} * u$	4. _____
5. $u * x = a^{-1} * u$	5. _____
6. $x = a^{-1}$	6. _____

(3) B_2 (4) M_1 (5) M_3 (6) M_2

1309   Theorem 8 proves that the inverse of any $a \in F$ with respect to $*$ is unique. Thus, if we wish to prove that some $x = y^{-1}$, we need only show that $y * x = u$. Then, by Theorem 8, $x =$ _____ .

---

y^{-1}

1310   For example, prove that in a field, if $x \neq z$, $(x^{-1})^{-1} = x$. (That is, the inverse with respect to $*$ of x inverse is x. The proof is quite simple.)

---

1. $x \neq z$	1. Hypothesis
2. $x * x^{-1} = u$	2. M_3
3. $x^{-1} * x = u$	3. M_4
4. $\therefore x = (x^{-1})^{-1}$	4. Theorem 8

1311   *Theorem 9.* If $x * y = z$ and $x \neq z$, then $y = z$.
        Proof:

1. $x * y = z$ 1. Hypothesis
2. $x \neq z$ 2. Hypothesis
3. $\therefore x^{-1} \epsilon F$ 3. M_3
4. $x^{-1} * (x * y) = x^{-1} * z$ 4. B_2
5. $(x^{-1} * x) * y = x^{-1} * z$ 5. ____
6. $u * y = x^{-1} * z$ 6. ____
7. $y = x^{-1} * z$ 7. ____
8. $y = z$ 8. ____

   (5) M_1 (6) M_3 (7) M_2 (8) Theorem 5

1312   As a result of Theorem 9, in a field F, if $x * y = z$, then either $x = z$
        or $y = z$. In the field of real numbers where $*$ represents ordinary
        multiplication and z is 0, this becomes the very important theorem:
        if $x \cdot y = 0$, then either ____ or ____ .

   $x = 0$, $y = 0$

1313   *Theorem 10.* In a field, $\bar{u} * \bar{u} = u$.
        Proof:

1. $\bar{u} * (z) = z$ 1. Theorem 3
2. $\bar{u} * (u \oplus \bar{u}) = z$ 2. A_3
3. $\bar{u} * u \oplus \bar{u} * \bar{u} = z$ 3. ____
4. $\bar{u} \oplus \bar{u} * \bar{u} = z$ 4. ____
5. $u \oplus (\bar{u} \oplus \bar{u} * \bar{u}) = u \oplus z$ 5. ____
6. $(u \oplus \bar{u}) \oplus \bar{u} \oplus \bar{u} = u \oplus z$ 6. A_1
7. $z \oplus \bar{u} * \bar{u} = u \oplus z$ 7. A_3
8. $z \oplus \bar{u} * \bar{u} = z \oplus u$ 8. A_4
9. $\therefore \bar{u} * \bar{u} = u$ 9. Theorem 3 or A_2

   (3) D (4) M_2 (5) B_1

1314   In the field of real numbers where $*$ represents ordinary multipli-
        cation, u is 1, $\bar{x}$ is $-x$, Theorem 10 becomes _____ , another
        rule you have accepted as true and used previously.

   $(-1)(-1) = 1$

1315   *Theorem 11.* In a field, $a * \bar{u} = \bar{a}$.
        Proof:

1. $a \oplus a * \bar{u} = a * u \oplus a * \bar{u}$ 1. M_2
2. $a \oplus a * \bar{u} = a * (u \oplus \bar{u})$ 2. D
3. $a \oplus a * \bar{u} = a * z$ 3. ____

▼

4. $a \oplus a * \bar{u} = z$ 4. _____

5. $\therefore a * \bar{u} = \bar{a}$ 5. _____

---

(3) A_3 (4) Theorem 3   (5) Theorem 5

1316   Rewriting Theorem 11 in the field of real numbers, we get

_____ .

---

in the field of real numbers $a \cdot (-1) = -a$

1317   *Theorem 12.* In a field, $\bar{x} * \bar{y} = x * y$.

Proof:

1. $\bar{x} = x * \bar{u}, \; \bar{y} = y * \bar{u}$ 1. Theorem 11

2. $\bar{x} * \bar{y} = (x * \bar{u}) * (y * \bar{u})$ 2. Theorem 2

3. $\bar{x} * \bar{y} = (x * \bar{u}) * (\bar{u} * y)$ 3. ____

4. $\bar{x} * \bar{y} = x * (\bar{u} * \bar{u}) * y$ 4. ____

5. $\bar{x} * \bar{y} = x * u * y$ 5. _____

6. $\bar{x} * \bar{y} = x * y$ 6. ____

---

(3) M_4 (4) M_1 (5) Theorem 10   (6) M_2

1318   Rewrite Theorem 12 in the field of real numbers.

$(-x) \cdot (-y) = x \cdot y$

1319   We want to prove: In a field F, $a * x \oplus b = z$ with $a \neq z$ has a unique solution, namely, $x = a^{-1} * \bar{b}$.

Recall that to prove this statement we must prove two things:

1. If $a * x \oplus b = z$ and $a \neq z$, then $x = a^{-1} * \bar{b}$. Thus, if there is a solution to the equation, this solution must be $a^{-1} * \bar{b}$.

2. $x = a^{-1} * \bar{b}$ is a solution; that is, if $x = a^{-1} * \bar{b}$, then _____ .

$a * x \oplus b = z$

1320   *Theorem 13.* In a field, $a * x \oplus b = z$ with $a \neq z$ has a unique solu- unique solution, $x = a^{-1} * \bar{b}$.

Prove (part A): If $a * x \oplus b = z$ and $a \neq z$, then $x = a^{-1} * \bar{b}$.

Proof:

1. $a * x \oplus b = z$ 1. Hypothesis

2. $b \oplus a * x = z$ 2. ____

3. $\bar{b} \in F$ 3. ____

4. $\bar{b} \oplus (b \oplus a * x) = \bar{b} \oplus z$ 4. ____

5. $(\bar{b} \oplus b) \oplus a * x = \bar{b} \oplus z$ 5. ____

▼

6. $z \oplus a * x = \bar{b} \oplus z$ 6. ____
7. $a * x = \bar{b}$ 7. ____
8. $a \neq z$ 8. Hypothesis
9. $a^{-1} \epsilon F$ 9. ____
10. $a^{-1} * (a * x) = a^{-1} * \bar{b}$ 10. ____
11. $(a^{-1} * a) * x = a^{-1} * \bar{b}$ 11. ____
12. $u * x = a^{-1} * \bar{b}$ 12. ____
13. $x = a^{-1} * \bar{b}$ 13. ____

(2) A_4 (3) A_3 (4) B_1 (5) A_1 (6) A_3 (7) A_2
(9) M_3 (10) B_2 (11) M_1 (12) M_3 (13) M_2
So we have proved: In a field F, if there is a solution to $a * x \oplus b = z$, where $a \neq z$, this solution must be $x = a^{-1} * \bar{b}$.

1321   *Theorem 13.* In a field F, $a * x \oplus b = z$ with $a \neq z$ has a unique solution, $x = a^{-1} * \bar{b}$.
Prove (part B): If $a \neq z$ and $x = a^{-1} * \bar{b}$, then $a * x \oplus b = z$.
Proof:

1. $x = a^{-1} * \bar{b}$ 1. Hypothesis
2. $a * x = a * (a^{-1} * \bar{b})$ 2. ____
3. $a * x = (a * a^{-1}) * \bar{b}$ 3. ____
4. $a * x = u * \bar{b}$ 4. ____
5. $a * x = \bar{b}$ 5. ____
6. $b \oplus a * x = b \oplus \bar{b}$ 6. ____
7. $a * x \oplus b = b \oplus \bar{b}$ 7. ____
8. $a * x \oplus b = z$ 8. ____

Therefore $x = a^{-1} * \bar{b}$ is a solution to $a * x \oplus b = z$.

(2) B_2 (3) M_1 (4) M_3 (5) M_2
(6) B_1 (7) A_4 (8) A_3

VI. Review Test for Part Four   (Answers on page 318)

1 *Prove*: In a field, $(a * b) * (a^{-1} * b^{-1}) = u$.

2 Name the conditions under which a binary relation R in a set S is an equivalence relation.

3 Let S be the set of permutations of degree 5 with respect to permutation multiplication. The identity element with respect to multiplication is $\begin{pmatrix} 1 & 2 & 3 & 4 & 5 \\ 1 & 2 & 3 & 4 & 5 \end{pmatrix}$. Find the inverse of $\begin{pmatrix} 1 & 2 & 3 & 4 & 5 \\ 3 & 1 & 2 & 5 & 4 \end{pmatrix}$.

4 State the requirements for a set N to be a field.

5 If S is to be a commutative group with respect to $*$, then the commutative law for $*$ must hold; that is, for all $a, b \in S$ _____ , *and* the associative law for $*$ must hold; that is, for all $a, b, c \in S$ _____ .

6 The binary operation multiplication ($\cdot$) of numbers is distributive over addition ($+$) of numbers. Symbolically, this fact can be stated as follows: If x, y, z are numbers, _____ .

7 In a field F where $\cdot$ is the symbol for multiplication and $+$ is the symbol for addition, prove:

$$\overline{(x \cdot y)} = (y) \cdot (\bar{x})$$

8 Let N be a *field*, having equivalence relation "$=$," two binary operations $+$ and $\cdot$, identity element 0, and inverse $-x$ with respect to $+$; identity element 1 and inverse x^{-1} with respect to $\cdot$. *Prove*: If $x + y = x + z$, then $y = z$.

9 Let S be a set of rational numbers. Define two binary operations in S as follows:
$$a \oplus b = a^2 + b^2$$
$$a * b = ab + 4a^2 + 4b^2$$

Is S a field? Prove it.

10 Let S be the set of rational numbers. Define two binary operation in S as follows:
$$a \oplus b = a + b + 5$$
$$a * b = ab + 3a + 3b + 3$$

(1) Prove that $\oplus$ is commutative.
(2) Prove that $*$ is commutative.

Appendix A   AN ARBITRARY EQUIV-
ALENCE RELATION

An example of a binary operation which is not well defined with respect to an equivalence relation.

A1   Let $S = \{(1,1), (1,2), (2,1), (2,2)\}$, and let $(a,b) * (c,d)$ be associated with (a,c). Part of the multiplication table is given below:

*	(1,1)	(1,2)	(2,1)	(2,2)
(1,1)	(1,1)	(1,1)	(1,2)	(1,2)
(1,2)				
(2,1)				
(2,2)				

Complete the table. Is $*$ a binary operation in S?

Answer on Panel 5
yes

A2   Look at Panel 5. A binary relation is introduced in S as follows: $(a,b)\ R\ (c,d)$ if and only if $ad = bc$. For example, $(1,1)\ R\ (2,2)$ since $1 \cdot 2 = 2 \cdot 1$; but $(1,1)\ R\!\!\!/\ (1,2)$ since $1 \cdot 2 \neq 1 \cdot 1$. What property of R is proved in item 1 of Panel 5?

---

reflexive

A3   What property of R is proved in item 2 of Panel 5?

---

symmetric

A4   What property of R is proved in item 3 of Panel 5?

---

transitive

303

A5 Since, in Panel 5, R is reflexive, symmetric, and transitive, R is a(n) _____ .

equivalence relation

A6 Find the equivalence classes of S for the equivalence relation R.

$S_1 = \{(1,1),\ (2,2)\},\ \ S_2 = \{(1,2)\},\ \ S_3 = \{(2,1)\}$

A7 So by definition of R, $(1,1)\ R\ (2,2)$; or using our symbol for equivalence relation, $(1,1) \approx (2,2)$; that is, $(1,1)$ is equivalent to $(2,2)$. Now look at the multiplication table:

$(1,1) * (2,1) = (1,2)$
$(2,2) * (2,1) = (2,2)$

but $(1,2)$ is not equivalent to $(2,2)$.

No answer is required.

Appendix B   ELEMENTARY SET THEORY

This appendix is provided for reference and review for those who have forgotten some of the elementary results from a study of set theory. It includes only those concepts and results of set theory which are requisite for this program and it makes no attempt to be rigorous.

I. Sets, Elements, Membership

A collection of objects of any sort will be called a *set*. For example, we may consider the set of former presidents of the United States, or the set of integers from 1 through 10, or the set of solutions of the equation $x^2 + 3x - 2 = 0$. Each of these examples is a *finite set*. The set of all real numbers, the set of all points on a given line, the set of even integers are examples of *infinite sets*.

Each of the objects which makes up a given set is called an *element* of that set or a *member* of that set. For example, 4 is an element (or member) of the set of even integers; George Washington is an element of the set of former presidents of the United States; 2 is *not* an element of the set of solutions of the equation $x^2 + 3x - 2 = 0$.

Given any specific set A, it is assumed that, for any given object x, *exactly one* of the following conditions is true:

1. x is an element of the set A.
2. x is not an element of the set A.

This fundamental relationship of *membership* or *belonging* between objects and sets is denoted by the symbol ϵ. If S is a set and x is a member of S, we write $x \epsilon S$ (read "x is a member of the set S," or "x is an element of the set S," or "x belongs to the set S").

If x is not an element of the set S, we write $x \notin S$ (read "x is not an element of the set S," or "x is not a member of the set S," or "x does not belong to the set S"). For example, let N be the set of positive integers (natural numbers). Then $15 \epsilon N$, $\pi \notin N$.

II. Equality of Sets

Two sets are equal if and only if they have the same elements. Thus, if every element of a set A is also an element of a set B *and* if every element of B is also an element of A, we say that sets A and B are equal and write $A = B$. Note that to prove $A = B$, we must show that if $x \in A$, then $x \in B$, *and* if $x \in B$, then $x \in A$. Also, to prove $A \neq B$, we must exhibit an x which is an element of one of the sets but is not an element of the other. A set, then, is completely determined by its members.

III. Designating Sets

We will often describe a set by enclosing within braces the names of its members separated by commas. For example, $\{1, 2, 3\}$ denotes the set whose members are the first three positive integers. Note that, by definition of equality of sets,

$$\{1, 2, 3\} = \{1, 3, 2\}$$

since the *order* in which the members appear is of *no importance,* and

$$\{1, 2, 3\} = \{1, 2, 2, 3\}$$

since an object is either an element of a set or it is not, and we do not count a member of a set more than once.

This method of describing a set is called the "roster" notation and is convenient for finite sets having a small number of elements.

For infinite sets or finite sets having a large number of elements, a notation (sometimes called "set-builder" notation), described as follows, is used. A rule is constructed which can be used to determine whether or not any given object is a member of the set or not. For example, a rule determining the set of positive integers might be: "An object is an element of the set if and only if the object is an integer and the object is greater than zero." Then, replacing the words "the object" by some symbol, say x, we obtain a formula in x, "x is an integer and $x > 0$." Now we designate the set by:

$$\{x \mid x \text{ is an integer and } x > 0\}$$

read "The set of all x such that x is an integer and $x > 0$." In general, then, given a formula in x, denoted by $f(x)$, we denote the set determined by that formula by $\{x \mid f(x)\}$, read "the set of all x such that $f(x)$." (Note that the vertical bar is read "such that.")

Note that the choice of symbol x is arbitrary and that for a given formula $f(x)$,

$$\{x \mid f(x)\} = \{y \mid f(y)\}$$

and the same set can be defined by more than one formula in x. For example,

$$\{x \mid 0 < x < 5\} = \{x \mid x > 0 \text{ and } x^2 < 25\}$$

This notation can be used for finite or infinite sets.

Examples:

$\{x \mid x^2 = 4\} = \{2, -2\}$
$\{x \mid x \text{ is an integer and } 5 < x < 10\} = \{6, 7, 8, 9, 10\}$
$\{x \mid x > 0\} = \text{the set of positive real numbers}$
$\{x \mid x \geq 5 \text{ and } x \leq 5\} = \{5\}$

Note that $\{5\}$ *is a set* having exactly one member and is not the same thing as the member, that is, $\{5\} \neq 5$.

$$\{x \mid x + 2 = 2\} = \{0\}$$

IV. The Empty Set

It is evidently possible that, for some formulas in x, the sets so defined will be found to have no members. For example, $\{x \mid x > 3 \text{ and } x < 2\}$ obviously has no members. Such a set is called an empty set. By definition of equality of sets, there is only one set having no members, so we refer to it as *the* empty set and denote it by ϕ.

V. Inclusion; Subsets

Let A and B be sets. A is *included* in B, or A is a *subset* of B if and only if every element of A is an element of B. In this case, we write $A \subset B$, and read "A is included in B" or "A is a subset of B." For example, if $S = \{a, b, c\}$ and $T = \{a, b, c, d, e\}$, then $S \subset T$ since every element of S is an element of T. We have immediately the following:

1. For any set A, $A \subset A$, since every member of any set is a member of itself.
2. For any set A, $\phi \subset A$, since every member of the empty set is a member of A. (There certainly are no members of ϕ which are not in A.) Hence, the empty set is a subset of any set.
3. If $A \subset B$ and $B \subset C$, then $A \subset C$. For, if every member of A is a member of B and every member of B is a member of C, then every member of A is a member of C.
4. $A \subset B$ and $B \subset A$ if and only if $A = B$. This is simply a different formulation of the definition of equality of sets.

Examples:

1. Let A be the set of integers and B be the set of even integers. Then $A \subset B$.
2. Let $A = \{1, 2, 3\}$. There are 8 subsets of A:
   $\{1, 2, 3\}, \{1, 2\}, \{1, 3\}, \{2, 3\}, \{1\}, \{2\}, \{3\}$, and ϕ

Note: If $S \subset T$, we sometimes say that T includes S or T contains S, and write $T \supset S$. We also call T a *superset* of A. Also if $S \subset T$ and $S \neq T$, we sometimes say that S is a *proper subset* of T or that S is properly contained in T. Thus, in the last example, there are 7 proper subsets of A (namely, the last seven listed). The first subset $\{1, 2, 3\}$ is also a subset of A and would correctly be written $\{1, 2, 3\} \subseteq A$. This symbol is used if and only if every element of a subset is also an element of the superset *and* every element of the superset is an element of the subset.

VI. Operations on Sets

Let A and B be sets. The *intersection* of A and B, written $A \cap B$ and read "A intersect B," is the set of all objects which are members of both A and of B. Symbolically,

$$A \cap B = \{x \mid x \in A \text{ and } x \in B\}$$

Examples:

1. Let $A = \{1, 2, 3, 4\}$ and $B = \{2, 4, 6, 8\}$. Then $A \cap B = \{2, 4\}$.
2. Let $A = \{1, 2, 3\}$ and $B = \{1, 2, 3, 4, 5\}$. Then $A \cap B = \{1, 2, 3\}$.
3. Let $A = \{1, 2, 3\}$ and $B = \{5, 10, 15\}$. Then $A \cap B = \phi$.

Two sets, S and T, are called *mutually exclusive* sets or *disjoint* sets if and only if $S \cap T = \phi$.

For example, if A is the set of even integers and B is the set of odd integers, then $A \cap B = \phi$, so A and B are disjoint sets.

Let A and B be sets. The *union* of A and B, written $A \cup B$ and read "A union B," is the set of all objects which are members of A or of B (or both). Symbolically,

$$A \cup B = \{x \mid x \in A \text{ or } x \in B\}$$

The word "or" is used here in the inclusive sense; that is, it is used in the sense of "and/or."

Examples:

1. Let $A = \{1, 2, 3\}$ and $B = \{2, 4, 6\}$. Then $A \cup B = \{1, 2, 3, 4, 6\}$.
2. Let $A = \{1, 2, 3\}$ and $B = \{1, 2, 3, 4, 5\}$. Then $A \cup B = \{1, 2, 3, 4, 5\}$.
3. Let $A = \{1, 2, 3\}$ and $B = \{5, 10, 15\}$. Then $A \cup B = \{1, 2, 3, 5, 10, 15\}$.
4. Let A be the set of even integers and B be the set of odd integers. Then $A \cup B$ is the set of all integers.

In any particular discussion, all sets being considered may be subsets of some set U which is called the universal set for that discussion. For example, in any problem from elementary algebra, the universal set would probably be the set of real numbers. Then, if A is any set, the *complement* of A, denoted by A', and read "A complement," is the set of all members of U which are *not* members of A. Symbolically,

$$A' = \{x \mid x \in U \text{ and } x \notin A\}$$

Examples:

1. Suppose U is the set of real numbers and $A = \{x \mid x < 3\}$. Then $A' = \{x \mid x \geq 3\}$.
2. Suppose $U = \{1, 2, 3, 4, 5, 6, 7, 8, 9, 10\}$ and $A = \{2, 4, 6\}$. Then $A'\{1, 3, 5, 7, 8, 9, 10\}$.

VII. Some Important Properties of the Operations on Sets (Without Proofs)

1. $A \cup B = B \cup A$ commutativity of union
2. $A \cap B = B \cap A$ commutativity of intersection
3. $A \cup (B \cup C) = (A \cup B) \cup C$ associativity of union
4. $A \cap (B \cap C) = (A \cap B) \cap C$ associativity of intersection
5. $A \cap (B \cup C) = (A \cap B) \cup (A \cap C)$ distributive law of intersection over union
6. $A \cup (B \cap C) = (A \cup B) \cap (A \cup C)$ distributive law of union over intersection
7. $(A \cup B)' = A' \cap B'$ ⎫
8. $(A \cap B)' = A' \cup B'$ ⎬   De Morgan's laws

Answers to Test Questions

Self-test I (Page 14)

1 ordered pair

2 first coordinate,   second coordinate

3 $a = c$ and $b = d$
   If you missed any one of problems 1 to 3, you should review frames
   1 to 20.

4 **(1)** cartesian (or cross) product of S and T
   (2) $\{(x,y) \mid x \in S$ and $y \in T\}$
   If you missed this problem, review frames 41 to 48.

5 $S \times T = \{(a,1), (a,2), (a,3), (b,1), (b,2), (b,3)\}$

6 $A \times A = \{(1,1), (1,2), (2,1), (2,2)\}$
   If you missed either of problems 5 and 6, review frames 39 to 42.

Self-test II (Page 35)

1 **(1)** $\{(0,0), (0,1), (0,2), (1,0), (1,1), (1,2), (2,0), (2,1), (2,2)\}$
   (2) $\{(0,0), (0,1), (0,2), (1,1), (1,2), (2,2)\}$
   (3) binary relation in S
   If you missed **(1)**, review frames 26 through 31.
   If you missed **(2)**, review frames 68 through 81.
   If you missed **(3)**, review frames 95 through 99.

2 A binary relation in $S \times T$ is a subset of $S \times T$ (or R is a binary
   relation in $S \times T$ if R is a subset of $S \times T$).

   If your answer is not correct, review frames 95 through 99.
3 $x \, R \, y$, read x is related to y.
   If your answer is not correct, review frames 149 through 152.

Self-test III (Page 50)

1 ordered pair,   first coordinate,   second coordinate
   If your answer is not correct, review frames 5 to 13.

2 If (a,b) and (c,d) are ordered pairs, then $(a,b) = (c,d)$ if and only if
   $a = c$ and $b = d$.
   If your answer is not correct, review frames 15 to 21.

3 **(1)** the cartesian (cross) product of $S \times S$
(2) $S \times S = \{(x,y) \mid x \in S \text{ and } y \in S\}$
If your answer is not correct, review frames 44 to 47.

4 $S \times T = \{(1,a), (1,b), (1,c), (2,a), (2,b), (2,c)\}$
If your answer is not correct, review frames 26 to 31.

5 R is a subset of $S \times S$
If your answer is not correct, review frames 85 to 97.

6 A binary relation R in a set S is reflexive if and only if $(x,x) \in R$
for every $x \in S$
If your answer is not correct, review frames 177 to 181.

7 Yes, $x \leq x$ for every $x \in S$.
If your answer is not correct, review frames 184 to 187.

8 No, $b \in S$, but $(b,b) \notin R$.

Review Test, Part One   (Page 88)

1 $S \times S$ (or cross or cartesian product of S and S, or R_2).

2 (d,a)

3 ordered pair

4 no

5 first coordinate,   second coordinate

6 R is a subset of $S \times S$

7 binary relation in S

8 **(1)** $T \times T = \{(x,y) \mid x \in T \text{ and } y \in T\}$
(2) the cartesian (or cross) product of T and T

9 $(x,x) \in R$ for every $x \in S$

10 R_2, R_6

11 whenever $(x,y) \in R$, then $(y,x) \in R$

12 whenever $(x,y) \in R$ and $(y,z) \in R$, then $(x,z) \in R$

13 R_1, R_2, R_4, R_5, R_6

14 An equivalence relation is a binary relation which is reflexive, symmetric, and transitive.

15   R_2, R_6

16   partition,   equivalence class

17   $S_1 = \{a\}$, $S_2 = \{b,\ e\}$, $S_3 = \{c,\ d\}$

18   $\{a,\ b,\ c,\ d,\ e\}$

19   **(1)**   yes
    (2)   There are two equivalence classes. S_1 is the set of negative integers and S_2 is the set of positive integers.

20   **(1)**   yes
    (2)   There are two: S_1 is the set of even integers and S_2 is the set of odd integers.

21   $S_1 = \{0,\ 4,\ 8\}$, $S_2 = \{1,\ 5,\ 9\}$, $S_3 = \{2,\ 6,\ 10\}$, $S_4 = \{3,\ 7\}$

22   **(1)** S **(2)** $x\ R\ y$ [or $x \approx y$, or $(x,y) \in R$]
    (3) $x\ R\!\!\!/\ y$ [or $x \not\approx y$, or $(x,y) \notin R$]

23   $(a,a),\ (d,d),\ (a,d),\ (d,a),\ (b,b),\ (c,c),\ (b,c),\ (c,b),\ (e,e)$

24   $(0,0),\ (2,2),\ (0,2),\ (2,0),\ (1,1),\ (3,3)$

25   ordered pair

26   first coordinate,   second coordinate

27   $a = c$ and $b = d$

28   **(1)** $\{(x,y)\ |\ x \in S$ and $y \in S\}$
    (2)   the cartesian product of S and S

29   $\{(a,a),\ (a,b),\ (a,c),\ (b,a),\ (b,b),\ (b,c),\ (c,a),\ (c,b),\ (c,c)\}$

30   binary relation

31   $\{a,\ 2,\ 1,\ b,\ 5\}$,   binary relation

32   $(x,x) \in R$ for every $x \in S$

33   whenever $(x,y) \in R$, then $(y,x) \in R$

34   whenever $(x,y) \in R$ and $(y,z) \in R$, then $(x,z) \in R$

35   No, $(1,2) \in R$ and $(2,4) \in R$, but $(1,4) \notin R$

36   An equivalence relation is a binary relation which is reflexive, symmetric, and transitive.

37   **(1)**   yes   **(2)**   yes   **(3)**   yes   **(4)**   yes

38 (1) yes
    (2) yes
    (3) No, because $(0,1) \epsilon R$ and $(1,3) \epsilon R$, but $(0,3) \notin R$ [or $(3,1) \epsilon R$ and $(1,0) \epsilon R$, but $(3,0) \notin R$].
    (4) no

39 $S_1 = \{a, c\}$, $S_2 = \{b\}$

40 $R = \{(1,1), (1,3), (2,2), (3,1), (3,3), (4,4)\}$

Self-test IV (Page 113)

1 (1) $\{x \mid$ there is a y for which $(x,y) \epsilon R\}$
  (2) $\{y \mid$ there is an x for which $(x,y) \epsilon R\}$
  If your answer is not correct, review frames 448 to 460.

2 dom $R = S$
  If your answer is not correct, review frames 461 to 469.

3 dom $R = S$ (or R is a binary relation from S into T), ran $R = T$
  If your answer is not correct, review frames 475 to 483.

4 dom $R = S$ (or R is a binary relation from S into T) and for each $x \epsilon S$ there is exactly one $y \epsilon T$ such that $(x,y) \epsilon R$
  If your answer is not correct, review frames 488 to 502.

5 ran $\alpha = T$
  If your answer is not correct, review frames 503 to 508.

6 $(x,y) \epsilon f$,   the image of x under (the function) f,
  $f(x)$ [or $(x)f$]
  If your answer is not correct, review frames 511 to 521.

Self-test V (Page 154)

1 mapping (or function) from $S \times S$ into S
  If your answer is not correct, review frames 589 to 597.

2 $x * y = y * x$ for all x, $y \epsilon S$
  If your answer is not correct, review frames 623 to 632.

3 $(x * y) * z = x * (y * z)$ for all x, y, $z \epsilon S$
  If your answer is not correct, review frames 659 to 664.

4 $e * x = x * e = x$ for all $x \epsilon S$ (or $e * x = x$ and $x * e = x$ for all $x \epsilon S$)
  If your answer is not correct, review frames 685 to 689.

5 (1) is   (2) is   (3) is   (4) yes,   0

6 (1) yes   (2) yes   (3) yes   (4) yes,   1

7 no   For example, (3,2) has no image under ÷ in the set of integers.

8 no   For example, (2,0) has no image under ÷ in the set of rational
numbers. Division by zero is not defined.

9 (1) yes   Under +, the sum of two negative integers is a unique
negative integer.
 (2) no   Note: $0 \notin S$.

10 (1) yes   The union of any two subsets of S is a unique subset of S.
 (2) yes $A \cup B = B \cup A$, for any sets A, B
 (3) yes $(A \cup B) \cup C = A \cup (B \cup C)$, for any sets A, B, C
 (4) yes, ϕ $A \cup \phi = A$ and $\phi \cup A = A$, for any set A

Review Test, Part Two   (Page 163)

1 $N * P = \begin{pmatrix} a & b \\ a & a \end{pmatrix}$ or $N * P = N$

2 (1) You can make a table or you can simply check every pair without
making the table.

*	M	N	P	Q
M	M	N	P	Q
N	N	M	P	Q
P	P	Q	P	Q
Q	Q	P	P	Q

 (2) You can show only one example, such as $N * Q \neq Q * N$ or
$P * N \neq N * P$

3 (1) yes, M
 (2) M has M as its inverse, N has N as its inverse

4 (1) yes   (2) yes   (3) yes,   0 (zero)
 (4) yes (the inverse of any integers, x, is $-x$)

5 no
For example, $B \cdot C \neq C \cdot B$ since $B \cdot C = D$ and $C \cdot B = E$.
Other examples could be used also.

6 (1) yes   (2) yes, A (3) yes

7 (1) yes   (2) yes

8 (1) yes, ϕ

(2) No, none have inverses except ϕ, whose inverse is ϕ.

9 Since $e * x = x * e = x$ when e is the identity element, $e * e_1 = e_1 * e$. Now $e * e_1 = e_1$, but since e_1 is an identity element, $e * e_1 = e$. Therefore, $e_1 = e$.

10 (1) $a * b = 5 \cdot a \cdot b$
$b * a = 5 \cdot b \cdot a$
But in multiplication, $5 \cdot a \cdot b = 5 \cdot b \cdot a$
$\therefore a * b = b * a$

(2) $(a * b) * c = (5 \cdot a \cdot b) * c$
$= 5(5ab) \cdot c$
$= 25abc$
$a * (b * c) = a * (5 \cdot b \cdot c)$
$= 5 \cdot a \cdot (5bc)$
$= 25abc$
$\therefore (a * b) * c = a * (b * c)$

(3) $\frac{1}{5} * a = 5\left(\frac{1}{5} \cdot a\right)$
Also
$a * \frac{1}{5} = 5\left(a \cdot \frac{1}{5}\right) = a$
$\therefore \frac{1}{5}$ is identity element

(4) $\frac{1}{15} * \frac{3}{5}$ = identity element
$= \frac{1}{5}$
$\frac{1}{15} * \frac{3}{5} = 5\left(\frac{1}{15} \cdot \frac{3}{5}\right)$
$\therefore \frac{1}{15}$ is inverse of $\frac{3}{5}$

Self-test VI   (Page 198)

1 binary relation in $S \times T$

2 a binary relation from S into T

3 a function (or mapping) from S into T

4 image, $f(x)$ [or $(x)f$]

5 (1) S (2) $y \in T$ (3) is   (4) 4

6 function from S *onto* T

Review Test, Part Three   (Page 249)

1 Proof:

1. $a * x = b$	1. Hypothesis
2. There exists $a^{-1} \in G$	2. G_3
3. $a^{-1} * (a * x) = a^{-1} * b$	3. B_1
4. $(a^{-1} * a) * x = a$	4. G_1
5. $e * x = a^{-1} * b$	5. Definition 2
6. $x = a^{-1} * b$	6. Definition 1

Second part: Now to prove that if $x = a^{-1} * b$, then $a * x = b$ to show that $x = a^{-1} * b$ is the solution:

7. if $x = a^{-1} * b$, then $a * x = a * (a^{-1} * b)$	7. B_1
8. $a * x = (a * a^{-1}) * b$	8. G_1
9. $a * x = e * b$	9. Definition 2
10. $a * x = b$	10. Definition 1

2 Proof: We need only to show that $(a * b) * (b^{-1} * a^{-1}) = e$ where e is the identity element.

1. $(a * b) * (b^{-1} * a^{-1}) = a * (b * b^{-1}) * a^{-1}$	1. G_1
2. $\quad = a * e * a^{-1}$	2. Definition 2
3. $\quad = a * a^{-1}$	3. Definition 1
4. $\therefore (a * b) * (b^{-1} * a^{-1}) = e$	4. Definition 2
5. $\therefore (a * b)^{-1} = b^{-1} * a^{-1}$	5. Definition 2

3 Proof: To show that $-$ is not a commutative operation in T, we need exhibit only one instance where $R - S \neq S - R$. Set $R = A$, $S = B$; then
$$A - B = \{0, 1\} - \{0\}$$
$$= \{1\}$$
$$= C$$
and $\quad B - A = \{0\} - \{0, 1\}$
$$= \phi$$
$$= D$$
But $C \neq D$
$$\therefore A - B \neq B - A$$

4 Proof:

1. $x * a = x * b$	1. Hypothesis
2. There exists $x^{-1} \in G$	2. G_3
3. $x^{-1} * (x * a) = x^{-1} * (x * b)$	3. B_1
4. $(x^{-1} * x) * a = (x^{-1} * x) * b$	4. G_1
5. $e * a = e * b$	5. Definition 2
6. $a = b$	6. Definition 1

5 (1)   yes   (2)   6, since $6 \cdot x = x \cdot 6 = x$
    (3) 7^{-1} is 5 since $7 \cdot 5 = 5 \cdot 7 = 6$

6 (1)   yes

(2)   No, since not all integers in N are images of some integer.

Example: N α N

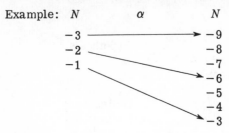

(3)   yes

7 (1) β and γ (2) $\beta^{-1} = \beta$

8 S α^{-1} S S $\alpha \cdot \alpha^{-1}$ S

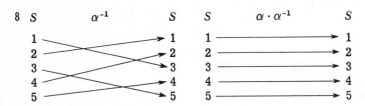

9 (1)   7   (2)   3
(3)   Multiplication of transformations is not a commutative binary operation.

10 (1)   yes,   no   (2)   no
(3)   No, since $(3)\alpha^{-1} = d$ and $(3)\alpha^{-1} = c$
         $(1)\alpha^{-1} = b$ and $(1)\alpha^{-1} = a$

Review Test, Part Four   (Page 302)

1 1. $(a * b) * (a^{-1} * b^{-1}) = (a * b) * (b^{-1} * a^{-1})$ 1. M_4
  2. $= [(a * b) * b^{-1}] * a^{-1}$ 2. M_1
  3. $= [a * (b * b^{-1})] * a^{-1}$ 3. M_1
  4. $= [a * u] * a^{-1}$ 4. M_3
  5. $= a * a^{-1}$ 5. M_2
  6. $= u$ 6. M_3

2 if and only if R is reflexive, symmetric, and transitive

3 $\begin{pmatrix} 1 & 2 & 3 & 4 & 5 \\ 2 & 3 & 1 & 5 & 4 \end{pmatrix}$

4 1. Has an equivalence relation and two well-defined operations $*$
     and $\oplus$.
  2. Has associative and commutative property under $\oplus$.
  3. Has identity element and inverses under $\oplus$.
  4. Has associative and commutative properties under $*$.

5. Has identity element and inverses (for all nonzero elements) under $*$.
6. Distributive law of $*$ over $\oplus$.

5 $a * b = b * a$
$a * (b * c) = (a * b) * c$

6 $x \cdot (y + z) = x \cdot y + x \cdot z$

7 1. $(x \cdot y) + (\bar{x} \cdot y) = (x + \bar{x}) \cdot y$ 1. Theorem 1
  2. $= 0 \cdot y$ 2. A_3
                     $= 0$ Theorem 4
  3. $\therefore (\bar{x} \cdot y) = \overline{x \cdot y}$ 3. Theorem 5
or
  1. $x + \bar{x} = 0$ 1. A_3
  2. $(x + \bar{x}) \cdot y = 0 \cdot y$ 2. B_2 and M_4
  3. $x \cdot y + \bar{x} \cdot y = 0$ 3. Theorem 1 and Theorem 4
  4. $\overline{x \cdot y} + (x \cdot y + \bar{x} \cdot y) = \overline{x \cdot y} + 0$ 4. B_1
  5. $(\overline{x \cdot y} + x \cdot y) + \bar{x} \cdot y = \overline{x \cdot y}$ 5. A_1 and A_2
  6. $0 + \bar{x} \cdot y = \overline{x \cdot y}$ 6. A_3
  7. $\bar{x} \cdot y = \overline{x \cdot y}$ 7. A_2

8 1. $x + y = x + z$ 1. Hypothesis
  2. There exists $\bar{x} \in F$ 2. A_3
  3. $\bar{x} + (x + y) = \bar{x} + (x + z)$ 3. B_1
  4. $(\bar{x} + x) + y = (\bar{x} + x) + z$ 4. A_1
  5. $0 + y = 0 + z$ 5. A_3
  6. $y = z$ 6. A_2

9 No, the associative property does not hold; for example:

$a \oplus (b \oplus c) = a \oplus (b^2 + c^2)$
$\qquad\qquad = a^2 + [b^2 + c^2]^2$

but

$(a \oplus b) \oplus c = (a^2 + b^2) \oplus c$
$\qquad\qquad = (a^2 + b^2)^2 + c^2$

A similar example could be given for the associative property under $*$.

10 (1) $a \oplus b = a + b + 5$
           $= b + a + 5$ commutative property of $+$
      $b \oplus a = b + a + 5$
      $\therefore a \oplus b = b + a$
  (2) $a * b = ab + 3a + 3b + 3$
         $b * a = ba + 3b + 3a + 3$ definition
              $= ab + 3b + 3a + 3$ commutative property of $\cdot$
              $= ab + 3a + 3b + 3$ commutative property of $+$

Algebra review, 860-868
Associative binary operations, 656-
    664, 667-672, 674, 680, 684,
    739, 1100-1102, 1104, 1167,
    1170
  definition, 660

Binary operations on a set, 581-622,
    1089-1092
  definition, 580
Binary relations, general, 74-161
  definition, 95
  from S into T, 465-473, 476-
    478, 487-489
  definition, 466
  from S onto T, 476-486
  definition, 475

Cartesian (cross) products, 28-33,
    36-37
  definition, 42
Codomain, 924-926
  definition, 923
Commutative binary operations,
    623-655, 665, 666, 672, 673,
    675-679, 683, 738, 1093-
    1099, 1103, 1221, 1222
  definition, 629
Commutative groups, 1072, 1128,
    1129, 1135-1137, 1148, 1189
  definition, 1071
Complement, **309**

DeMorgan laws, **309**
Distributive laws, 1192-1197, 1247-
    1251, 1280, 1281
  definition, 1193
Domain of a relation, 448-464
  definition, 454

Element, **305**
Empty set, **307**
Equality of sets, **306**

Equivalence classes, 418-447
  definition, 425
Equivalence relations, 361-402, 803-
    807, 1086-1088, 1223, **303**,
    304
  definition, 363

Fields, 1265-1272
  panels 12 and 13
  definition, **288**
Functions (mappings), one-to-one,
    956-974
  definition, 957
  pictorial representations, 874-
    895
  reversible, 984-1018
    definition, 983
  from S into T, 489-524, 911, 912,
    929-942
    definition, 494
  from S onto T, 503-509, 512,
    514, 515, 928-940, 943-
    953
    definition, 508

Groups, 768-798, 1127, 1131-1135
  definition, 773
  panels 10 and 11

Identity (unit) elements, 685-709,
    740-742, 1105-1115, 1198-
    1210, 1213, 1220, 1227-
    1232, 1237
  definition, 686
Images, 514-524, 897-905, 913-922
  definition, 516
Intersection, **308**
Inverse element, 710-743, 1116-
    1125, 1202-1208, 1211-
    1214, 1220, 1236, 1237
  definition, 713

Member, **305**
Mutually exclusive sets, **308**

Ordered pairs, 5-26

Partition of a set, 403-417
    definition, 408
Permutation multiplication, 541-
    579
Permutations of degree N, 525-541
    definition, 527
    panels 6 and 7
Proofs, fields, 1265-1321
    groups, 809-858, 869-873
Proper subset, 308

Range of a relation, 448-463
    definition, 455
Reflexive property, 163-241, 253,
        263, 267-270, 272-275,
        277-282, 284, 289-291,
        294-300, 322, 339-352,
        361, 362, 1074-1077
    definition, 177
Roster, 306

Sets, 1, 2, 6, 9, 24, 25, 34, 35, 305
Subsets, 3, 4, 90, 91, 307, 308
    panels 1-4
Superset, 308
Symmetric property, 242-252, 254-
        283, 285-300, 321, 339-
        349, 353-355, 361, 362,
        1078-1081
    definition, 249

Transformation groups, 1024-1070
Transformations, 1020-1023
    definition, 1019
Transitive property, 301-320, 323-
        349, 356-362, 1082-1085
    definition, 306

Union, 308, 309

Well-defined binary operations,
        807, 808, 1126

Panel 1

Let $S = \{a, b, c\}$ and $T = \{1, 2\}$.
$S \times T = \{(a,1), (a,2), (b,1), (b,2), (c,1), (c,2)\}$
A graphical representation of $S \times T$ is as follows:

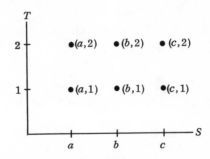

Any subset of $S \times T$ is a binary relation in $S \times T$. There are 2^6 or 64 distinct relations possible. *Among* them are the following:

$R_1 = \phi$
$R_2 = \{(a,2)\}$
$R_3 = \{(a,1), (b,2)\}$
$R_4 = \{(a,1), (a,2), (c,1)\}$
$R_5 = \{(a,1), (b,1), (c,1)\}$
$R_6 = \{(b,2)\}$
$R_7 = \{(a,1), (b,2), (c,1), (c,2)\}$
$R_8 = \{(a,1), (a,2), (b,1), (b,2), (c,1), (c,2)\} = S \times T$
$R_9 = \{(a,1), (b,2), (c,1), (b,2)\}$

Panel 2

Let $S = \{a, b, c\}$.

$S \times S = \{(a,a),\ (a,b),\ (a,c),\ (b,a),\ (b,b),\ (b,c),\ (c,a),\ (c,b),\ (c,c)\}$

Graphically:

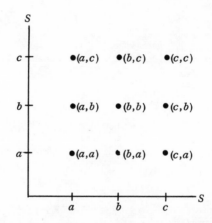

Any subset of $S \times S$ is a binary relation in S. There are 2^9 distinct relations in this case. Among them are the following:

$R_1 = \{(b,c),\ (c,b),\ (b,b),\ (c,c)\}$

$R_2 = \{(a,a),\ (a,b),\ (a,c),\ (b,b),\ (b,c),\ (c,c)\}$

$R_3 = \{(a,a),\ (a,b),\ (b,b),\ (b,a),\ (c,c)\}$

$R_4 = \{(a,a),\ (a,c),\ (b,b),\ (c,b),\ (c,c)\}$

$R_5 = \{(a,b),\ (b,a)\}$

$R_6 = \{(a,b),\ (b,c),\ (a,c)\}$

$R_7 = \{(a,a),\ (a,b),\ (b,b),\ (b,a),\ (b,c),\ (c,c),\ (c,b)\}$

$R_8 = \{(a,b),\ (b,c),\ (c,c)\}$

Panel 3

Let $S = \{1, 2\}$. Then $S \times S = \{(1,1), (1,2), (2,1), (2,2)\}$.
Any subset of $S \times S$ is a binary relation in S. There are sixteen distinct subsets of $S \times S$ in this case.

$R_1 = \phi$
$R_2 = \{(1,1)\}$
$R_3 = \{(1,2)\}$
$R_4 = \{(2,1)\}$
$R_5 = \{(2,2)\}$
$R_6 = \{(1,1), (1,2)\}$
$R_7 = \{(1,1), (2,1)\}$
$R_8 = \{(1,1), (2,2)\}$
$R_9 = \{(1,2), (2,1)\}$
$R_{10} = \{(1,2), (2,2)\}$
$R_{11} = \{(2,1), (2,2)\}$
$R_{12} = \{(1,1), (1,2), (2,1)\}$
$R_{13} = \{(1,1), (1,2), (2,2)\}$
$R_{14} = \{(1,1), (2,1), (2,2)\}$
$R_{15} = \{(1,2), (2,1), (2,2)\}$
$R_{16} = \{(1,1), (1,2), (2,1), (2,2)\}$

Panel 4

Let $S = \{a, b, c, d, e\}$
Some of the binary relations in S are:

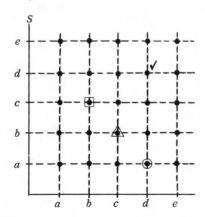

$R_1 = \phi$
$R_2 = S \times S$
$R_3 = \{(b,c), (c,b), (d,a), (d,d)\}$
$R_4 = \{(a,a), (c,d)\}$
$R_5 = \{(a,a), (a,d), (d,a), (d,d)\}$
$R_6 = \{(a,a), (b,b), (b,e), (c,c), (c,d), (d,c), (d,d), (e,b), (e,e)\}$
$R_7 = \{(a,b), (b,b), (c,a), (d,e), (e,a)\}$

Panel 5

Let $S = \{(1,1), (1,2), (2,1), (2,2)\}$.

*	(1,1)	(1,2)	(2,1)	(2,2)
(1,1)	(1,1)	(1,1)	(1,2)	(1,2)
(1,2)	(1,1)	(1,1)	(1,2)	(1,2)
(2,1)	(2,1)	(2,1)	(2,2)	(2,2)
(2,2)	(2,1)	(2,1)	(2,2)	(2,2)

Suppose (a,b) R (c,d) if and only if $ad = bc$.

1. If $(a,b) \in S$, (a,b) R (a,b) since $ab = ba$.
2. If (a,b) R (c,d), then $ad = bc$

$$\therefore bc = ad$$
$$cb = da$$

$$\therefore (c,d)\ R\ (a,b)$$

3. If (a,b) R (c,d) and (c,d) R (e,f), then $ac = bd$ and $cf = de$.
   Therefore, $(ad)f = (bc)f$, $b(cf) = b(de)$
   $$adf = bde,\quad af = be$$

   $$\therefore (a,b)\ R\ (e,f)$$

Panel 6

Let $S = \{1, 2, 3, 4\}$. The twenty-four permutations are:

$$R_1 = \begin{pmatrix} 1 & 2 & 3 & 4 \\ 1 & 2 & 3 & 4 \end{pmatrix} \qquad R_2 = \begin{pmatrix} 1 & 2 & 3 & 4 \\ 1 & 2 & 4 & 3 \end{pmatrix} \qquad R_3 = \begin{pmatrix} 1 & 2 & 3 & 4 \\ 1 & 3 & 2 & 4 \end{pmatrix}$$

$$R_4 = \begin{pmatrix} 1 & 2 & 3 & 4 \\ 1 & 3 & 4 & 2 \end{pmatrix} \qquad R_5 = \begin{pmatrix} 1 & 2 & 3 & 4 \\ 1 & 4 & 2 & 3 \end{pmatrix} \qquad R_6 = \begin{pmatrix} 1 & 2 & 3 & 4 \\ 1 & 4 & 3 & 2 \end{pmatrix}$$

$$R_7 = \begin{pmatrix} 1 & 2 & 3 & 4 \\ 2 & 1 & 3 & 4 \end{pmatrix} \qquad R_8 = \begin{pmatrix} 1 & 2 & 3 & 4 \\ 2 & 1 & 4 & 3 \end{pmatrix} \qquad R_9 = \begin{pmatrix} 1 & 2 & 3 & 4 \\ 2 & 3 & 1 & 4 \end{pmatrix}$$

$$R_{10} = \begin{pmatrix} 1 & 2 & 3 & 4 \\ 2 & 3 & 4 & 1 \end{pmatrix} \qquad R_{11} = \begin{pmatrix} 1 & 2 & 3 & 4 \\ 2 & 4 & 1 & 3 \end{pmatrix} \qquad R_{12} = \begin{pmatrix} 1 & 2 & 3 & 4 \\ 2 & 4 & 3 & 1 \end{pmatrix}$$

$$R_{13} = \begin{pmatrix} 1 & 2 & 3 & 4 \\ 3 & 1 & 2 & 4 \end{pmatrix} \qquad R_{14} = \begin{pmatrix} 1 & 2 & 3 & 4 \\ 3 & 1 & 4 & 2 \end{pmatrix} \qquad R_{15} = \begin{pmatrix} 1 & 2 & 3 & 4 \\ 3 & 2 & 1 & 4 \end{pmatrix}$$

$$R_{16} = \begin{pmatrix} 1 & 2 & 3 & 4 \\ 3 & 2 & 4 & 1 \end{pmatrix} \qquad R_{17} = \begin{pmatrix} 1 & 2 & 3 & 4 \\ 3 & 4 & 1 & 2 \end{pmatrix} \qquad R_{18} = \begin{pmatrix} 1 & 2 & 3 & 4 \\ 3 & 4 & 2 & 1 \end{pmatrix}$$

$$R_{19} = \begin{pmatrix} 1 & 2 & 3 & 4 \\ 4 & 1 & 2 & 3 \end{pmatrix} \qquad R_{20} = \begin{pmatrix} 1 & 2 & 3 & 4 \\ 4 & 1 & 3 & 2 \end{pmatrix} \qquad R_{21} = \begin{pmatrix} 1 & 2 & 3 & 4 \\ 4 & 2 & 1 & 3 \end{pmatrix}$$

$$R_{22} = \begin{pmatrix} 1 & 2 & 3 & 4 \\ 4 & 2 & 3 & 1 \end{pmatrix} \qquad R_{23} = \begin{pmatrix} 1 & 2 & 3 & 4 \\ 4 & 3 & 1 & 2 \end{pmatrix} \qquad R_{24} = \begin{pmatrix} 1 & 2 & 3 & 4 \\ 4 & 3 & 2 & 1 \end{pmatrix}$$

Panel 7

Let $S = \{1, 2, 3\}$.
The six permutations on S are:

$$a = \begin{pmatrix} 1 & 2 & 3 \\ 1 & 2 & 3 \end{pmatrix} \quad b = \begin{pmatrix} 1 & 2 & 3 \\ 2 & 3 & 1 \end{pmatrix} \quad c = \begin{pmatrix} 1 & 2 & 3 \\ 3 & 1 & 2 \end{pmatrix} \quad d = \begin{pmatrix} 1 & 2 & 3 \\ 1 & 3 & 2 \end{pmatrix}$$

$$e = \begin{pmatrix} 1 & 2 & 3 \\ 3 & 2 & 1 \end{pmatrix} \quad f = \begin{pmatrix} 1 & 2 & 3 \\ 2 & 1 & 3 \end{pmatrix}$$

	a	b	c	d	e	f
a	a	b	c	d	e	f
b	b	c	a	e	f	d
c	c	a	b	f	d	e
d	d	f	e	a	c	b
e	e	d	f	b	a	c
f	f	e	d	c	b	a

Panel 8

Given the equilateral triangle:

Let $R_0 =$ a counterclockwise rotation through $0°$
$\quad R_1 =$ a counterclockwise rotation through $120°$
$\quad R_2 =$ a counterclockwise rotation through $240°$
$\quad F_1 =$ a flip about altitude through the upper vertex
$\quad F_2 =$ a flip about altitude through the lower left vertex
$\quad F_3 =$ a flip about altitude through the lower right vertex

Then after:

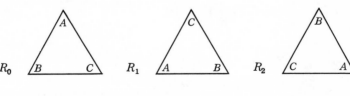

Panel 9

·	R_0	R_1	R_2	F_1	F_2	F_3
R_0	R_0	R_1	R_2	F_1	F_2	F_3
R_1	R_1	R_2	R_0	F_2	F_3	F_1
R_2	R_2	R_0	R_1	F_3	F_1	F_2
F_1	F_1	F_3	F_2	R_0	R_2	R_1
F_2	F_2	F_1	F_3	R_1	R_0	R_2
F_3	F_3	F_2	F_1	R_2	R_1	R_0

Panel 10

Let G be a set having an equivalence relation ($=$) and a well-defined binary operation ($*$) such that:

G_1:   For all $x, y, z \in G$, $(x * y) * z = x * (y * z)$ (associativity)
G_2:   There exists an identity element $e \in G$ with respect to $*$
G_3:   Every $x \in G$ has an inverse $x^{-1} \in G$ with respect to $*$
Then G is a group with respect to $*$.

Note 1: An equivalence relation (indicated by $=$) on a set S has the following 3 properties:
E_1:   For all $x \in G$, $x = x$ (reflexive property)
E_2:   If $x = y$, then $y = x$ (symmetric property)
E_3:   If $x = y$ and $y = z$, then $x = z$ (transitive property)
Note 2: Given a set S having an equivalence relation ($=$), a binary operation $*$ on S is *well-defined with respect to the equivalence relation* means that if $x = y$, then, for all $a \in G$,
B_1: $a * x = a * y$
B_2: $x * a = y * a$
Notice, the order is important. Operate both times on the left or both times on the right.

Definition 1: Given a binary operation $*$ in a set S, an *identity* element e is an element such that for all $x \in S$, $e * x = x * e = x$.
Definition 2: Given a set S having a binary operation $*$ and an identity element e an inverse of an element $x \in S$ is an element of S, say x^{-1} such that $x * x^{-1} = x^{-1} * x = e$.

Panel 11

Theorem 1: In a group if $a = b$ and $c = d$, then $a * c = b * d$.

Theorem 2: In a group if $x * y = x * z$, then $y = z$ (left cancelation law).

Theorem 3: In a group if $y * x = z * x$, then $y = z$ (right cancelation law).

Theorem 4: In a group if $a = b$, then $a^{-1} = b^{-1}$.

Theorem 5: In a group $a * x = b$ has a unique solution, namely, $x = a^{-1} * b$.

Theorem 6: In a group $y * a = b$ has a unique solution, namely, $y = b * a^{-1}$.

Panel 12

A field F is a set of elements having an equivalence relation and two well-defined binary operations $\oplus$ and $*$ such that if $a, b, c \in F$,

(under $\oplus$ *F is a commutative group)*	*(under $*$, except for z,* *F is a commutative group)*
Associativity A_1: $a \oplus (b \oplus c) = (a \oplus b) \oplus c$	M_1: $a * (b * c) = (a * b) * c$
Identity element A_2: there exists $z \in F$ such that for all $a \in F$ $a \oplus z = z \oplus a = a$	M_2: there exists $u \in F$ $(u \neq z)$ such that for all $a \in F$ $a * u = u * a = a$
Inverse A_3: for every a there exists $\bar{a} \in F$ such that $a \oplus \bar{a} = \bar{a} \oplus a = z$	M_3: for every $a \neq z$ there exists $a^{-1} \in F$ such that $a * a^{-1} = a^{-1} * a = u$
Commutativity A_4: $a \oplus b = b \oplus a$	M_4: $a * b = b * a$
Distributive law of $*$ over $\oplus$	D: $a * (b \oplus c) = a * b \oplus a * c$

Note 1: Since $=$ is an equivalence relation, we also have for all
$a, b, c \in F$:
E_1: $a = a$
E_2: if $a = b$, then $b = a$
E_3: if $a = b$ and $b = c$, then $a = c$

Note 2: C: Since $\oplus$ and $*$ are binary operations in F, then $a \oplus b$ and $a * b$ are elements of F.

Note 3: Since $\oplus$ and $*$ are well-defined, we have
B_1: if $a = b$ and $x \in F$, then $x \oplus a = x \oplus b$
B_2: if $a = b$ and $x \in F$, then $x * a = x * b$

Panel 13

In a field, F:

Theorem 1: $(b \oplus c) * a = b * a \oplus c * a$

Theorem 2: If $a = b$ and $c = d$, then $a * c = b * d$

Theorem 3: If $x \oplus a = x \oplus b$, then $a = b$ (law of cancelation for $\oplus$)

Theorem 4: If $a \in F$, $a * z = z$

Theorem 5: If $a \oplus x = z$, then $x = \bar{a}$

Theorem 6: $(\overline{x * y}) = x * \bar{y}$

Theorem 7: If $x * a = x * b$ and $x \neq z$, then $a = b$ (law of cancelation for $*$)

Theorem 8: If $a * x = u$, where $a \neq z$, then $x = a^{-1}$

Theorem 9: If $x * y = z$ and $x \neq z$, then $y = z$

Theorem 10: $\bar{u} * \bar{u} = u$

Theorem 11: $a * \bar{u} = \bar{a}$

Theorem 12: $\bar{x} * \bar{y} = x * y$

Theorem 13: In a field F, $a * x \oplus b = z$ with $a \neq z$ has a unique solution, $x = a^{-1} * \bar{b}$